Riverside Edition

THE

COMPLETE WORKS OF NATHANIEL HAWTHORNE, WITH INTRODUCTORY NOTES BY GEORGE PARSONS LATHROP

AND ILLUSTRATED WITH

Etchings by Blum, Church, Dielman, Gifford, Shirlaw, and Turner

IN THIRTEEN VOLUMES

VOLUME IV.

PANDORA.

A WONDER–BOOK, TANGLEWOOD TALES, AND GRANDFATHER'S CHAIR

BY

NATHANIEL HAWTHORNE

BOSTON AND NEW YORK
HOUGHTON, MIFFLIN AND COMPANY
The Riverside Press, Cambridge

CONTENTS.

---◆---

A WONDER-BOOK FOR GIRLS AND BOYS.

A WONDER–BOOK

FOR GIRLS AND BOYS

INTRODUCTORY NOTE.

THE WONDER–BOOK.

Even from the data to be obtained by a perusal of his works, the general reader will be likely to infer that Hawthorne took a vital interest in child-life; and in his published Note-Books are found many brief memoranda which indicate his disposition to write for children. After he married and had begun to rear a family of his own, this interest of his in the earliest developments of mind and character became, naturally, much more active. He was accustomed to observe his children very closely. There are private manuscripts still extant, which present exact records of what his young son and elder daughter said or did, from hour to hour; the father seating himself in their play-room and patiently noting all that passed.

To this habit of watchful and sympathetic scrutiny we may attribute in part the remarkable felicity, the fortunate ease of adaptation to the immature understanding, and the skilful appeal to fresh imaginations, which characterize his stories for the young. Natural tact and insight prompted, faithful study from the real assisted, these productions.

While still living at Lenox, and soon after publishing "The House of the Seven Gables," he sketched as follows, in a letter to Mr. James T. Fields, May 23,

1851, his plan for the work which this note accompanies : —

"I mean to write, within six weeks or two months next ensuing, a book of stories made up of classical myths.   The subjects are : The Story of Midas, with his Golden Touch, Pandora's Box, The Adventure of Hercules in quest of the Golden Apples, Bellerophon and the Chimæra, Baucis and Philemon, Perseus and Medusa ; these, I think, will be enough to make up a volume.   As a framework, I shall have a young college-student telling these stories to his cousins and brothers and sisters, during his vacations, sometimes at the fireside, sometimes in the woods and dells.   Unless I greatly mistake, these old fictions will work up admirably for the purpose ; and I shall aim at substituting a tone in some degree Gothic or romantic, or any such tone as may best please myself, instead of the classic coldness which is as repellant as the touch of marble."

With such precision as to time did he carry out this scheme, that on the 15th of July he wrote the Preface to the completed volume.   It was unusual, however, for him to work with such rapidity, or indeed to write at all in the summer season ; and this exertion, coming so soon after his work upon the romance, may have had something to do with increasing a languor which he had already begun to feel, and inducing him to remove from Lenox in the autumn.   While he remained in Berkshire he had more or less literary companionship, which is alluded to in the Note-Books and also in the closing chapter of the "Wonder-Book," where he likewise refers thus to himself : —

"'Have we not an author for our next neighbor?' asked Primrose.   'That silent man, who lives in the old red house near Tanglewood Avenue, and whom we sometimes meet, with two children at his side, in the woods or at the lake. I think I have heard of his having written a poem, or a romance, or an arithmetic, or a school-history, or something of that kind.' "

The manuscript of the " Wonder-Book " is the only one of Hawthorne's completed books which, in its original form, is owned by any member of his family. The book was written on thin blue paper of rather large size, and on both sides of the pages. Scarcely a correction or an erasure occurs, from the beginning to the end; and wherever an alteration was made, the after-thought was evidently so swift that the author did not stop to blot, for the word first written is merely smeared into illegibility and another substituted for it. It appears to be certain that, although Hawthorne meditated long over what he intended to do and came rather slowly to the point of publication, yet when the actual task of writing was begun it proceeded rapidly and with very little correction; and in most cases probably very little re-drafting was done. His private correspondence exhibits the same easy flow of composition, in sentences of notable finish; offering a marked contrast, for example, to the habit of the historian Motley, who even in his letters expunged words on every page.

The " Wonder-Book " proved to be a financial as well as literary success, and was presently translated and published in Germany.

G. P. L.

PREFACE.

THE author has long been of opinion that many of the classical myths were capable of being rendered into very capital reading for children. In the little volume here offered to the public, he has worked up half a dozen of them, with this end in view. A great freedom of treatment was necessary to his plan ; but it will be observed by every one who attempts to render these legends malleable in his intellectual furnace, that they are marvellously independent of all temporary modes and circumstances. They remain essentially the same, after changes that would affect the identity of almost anything else.

He does not, therefore, plead guilty to a sacrilege, in having sometimes shaped anew, as his fancy dictated, the forms that have been hallowed by an antiquity of two or three thousand years. No epoch of time can claim a copyright in these immortal fables. They seem never to have been made ; and certainly, so long as man exists, they can never perish ; but, by their indestructibility itself, they are legitimate subjects for every age to clothe with its own garniture of manners and sentiment, and to imbue with its own morality. In the present version they may have lost much of their classical aspect (or, at all events, the author has not been careful to preserve it), and have, perhaps, assumed a Gothic or romantic guise.

In performing this pleasant task, — for it has been really a task fit for hot weather, and one of the most agreeable, of a literary kind, which he ever undertook, — the author has not always thought it necessary to write downward, in order to meet the comprehension of children. He has generally suffered the theme to soar, whenever such was its tendency, and when he himself was buoyant enough to follow without an effort. Children possess an unestimated sensibility to whatever is deep or high, in imagination or feeling, so long as it is simple, likewise. It is only the artificial and the complex that bewilder them.

LENOX, *July* 15, 1851.

THE GORGON'S HEAD.

TANGLEWOOD PORCH.

INTRODUCTORY TO "THE GORGON'S HEAD."

BENEATH the porch of the country-seat called Tanglewood, one fine autumnal morning, was assembled a merry party of little folks, with a tall youth in the midst of them. They had planned a nutting expedition, and were impatiently waiting for the mists to roll up the hill-slopes, and for the sun to pour the warmth of the Indian summer over the fields and pastures, and into the nooks of the many-colored woods. There was a prospect of as fine a day as ever gladdened the aspect of this beautiful and comfortable world. As yet, however, the morning mist filled up the whole length and breadth of the valley, above which, on a gently sloping eminence, the mansion stood.

This body of white vapor extended to within less than a hundred yards of the house. It completely hid everything beyond that distance, except a few ruddy or yellow tree-tops, which here and there emerged, and were glorified by the early sunshine, as was likewise the broad surface of the mist. Four or five miles off to the southward rose the summit of Monument Mountain, and seemed to be floating on a cloud. Some fif-

teen miles farther away, in the same direction, appeared the loftier Dome of Taconic, looking blue and
indistinct, and hardly so substantial as the vapory sea
that almost rolled over it. The nearer hills, which
bordered the valley, were half submerged, and were
specked with little cloud-wreaths all the way to their
tops. On the whole, there was so much cloud, and so
little solid earth, that it had the effect of a vision.

The children above-mentioned, being as full of life
as they could hold, kept overflowing from the porch of
Tanglewood, and scampering along the gravel-walk, or
rushing across the dewy herbage of the lawn. I can
hardly tell how many of these small people there were ;
not less then nine or ten, however, nor more than a
dozen, of all sorts, sizes, and ages, whether girls or
boys. They were brothers, sisters, and cousins, together with a few of their young acquaintances, who
had been invited by Mr. and Mrs. Pringle to spend
some of this delightful weather with their own children, at Tanglewood. I am afraid to tell you their
names, or even to give them any names which other
children have ever been called by ; because, to my certain knowledge, authors sometimes get themselves into
great trouble by accidentally giving the names of real
persons to the characters in their books. For this reason, I mean to call them Primrose, Periwinkle, Sweet
Fern, Dandelion, Blue Eye, Clover, Huckleberry, Cowslip, Squash-Blossom, Milkweed, Plantain, and Buttercup ; although, to be sure, such titles might better
suit a group of fairies than a company of earthly children.

It is not to be supposed that these little folks were
to be permitted by their careful fathers and mothers,
uncles, aunts, or grandparents, to stray abroad into

the woods and fields, without the guardianship of some particularly grave and elderly person. Oh no, indeed! In the first sentence of my book, you will recollect that I spoke of a tall youth, standing in the midst of the children. His name — (and I shall let you know his real name, because he considers it a great honor to have told the stories that are here to be printed) — his name was Eustace Bright. He was a student at Williams College, and had reached, I think, at this period, the venerable age of eighteen years; so that he felt quite like a grandfather towards Periwinkle, Dandelion, Huckleberry, Squash-Blossom, Milkweed, and the rest, who were only half or a third as venerable as he. A trouble in his eyesight (such as many students think it necessary to have, nowadays, in order to prove their diligence at their books) had kept him from college a week or two after the beginning of the term. But, for my part, I have seldom met with a pair of eyes that looked as if they could see farther or better than those of Eustace Bright.

This learned student was slender, and rather pale, as all Yankee students are; but yet of a healthy aspect, and as light and active as if he had wings to his shoes. By the by, being much addicted to wading through streamlets and across meadows, he had put on cowhide boots for the expedition. He wore a linen blouse, a cloth cap, and a pair of green spectacles, which he had assumed, probably, less for the preservation of his eyes than for the dignity that they imparted to his countenance. In either case, however, he might as well have let them alone; for Huckleberry, a mischievous little elf, crept behind Eustace as he sat on the steps of the porch, snatched the spectacles from his nose, and clapped them on her own; and as the stu-

dent forgot to take them back, they fell off into the
grass, and lay there till the next spring.

Now, Eustace Bright, you must know, had won great
fame among the children, as a narrator of wonderful
stories; and though he sometimes pretended to be an-
noyed, when they teased him for more, and more, and
always for more, yet I really doubt whether he liked
anything quite so well as to tell them. You might
have seen his eyes twinkle, therefore, when Clover,
Sweet Fern, Cowslip, Buttercup, and most of their
playmates, besought him to relate one of his stories,
while they were waiting for the mist to clear up.

"Yes, Cousin Eustace," said Primrose, who was a
bright girl of twelve, with laughing eyes, and a nose
that turned up a little, " the morning is certainly the
best time for the stories with which you so often tire
out our patience. We shall be in less danger of hurt-
ing your feelings, by falling asleep at the most interesting points, — as little Cowslip and I did last
night! "

"Naughty Primrose," cried Cowslip, a child of six
years old; "I did not fall asleep, and I only shut my
eyes, so as to see a picture of what Cousin Eustace was
telling about. His stories are good to hear at night,
because we can dream about them asleep; and good in
the morning, too, because then we can dream about
them awake. So I hope he will tell us one this very
minute."

"Thank you, my little Cowslip," said Eustace;
" certainly you shall have the best story I can think
of, if it were only for defending me so well from that
naughty Primrose. But, children, I have already told
you so many fairy tales, that I doubt whether there is
a single one which you have not heard at least twice

over. I am afraid you will fall asleep in reality, if I repeat any of them again."

" No, no, no ! " cried Blue Eye, Periwinkle, Plantain, and half a dozen others. " We like a story all the better for having heard it two or three times before."

And it is a truth, as regards children, that a story seems often to deepen its mark in their interest, not merely by two or three, but by numberless repetitions. But Eustace Bright, in the exuberance of his resources, scorned to avail himself of an advantage which an older story-teller would have been glad to grasp at.

" It would be a great pity," said he, " if a man of my learning (to say nothing of original fancy) could not find a new story every day, year in and year out, for children such as you. I will tell you one of the nursery tales that were made for the amusement of our great old grandmother, the Earth, when she was a child in frock and pinafore. There are a hundred such ; and it is a wonder to me that they have not long ago been put into picture-books for little girls and boys. But, instead of that, old gray - bearded grandsires pore over them in musty volumes of Greek, and puzzle themselves with trying to find out when, and how, and for what they were made."

" Well, well, well, well, Cousin Eustace ! " cried all the children at once ; " talk no more about your stories, but begin."

" Sit down, then, every soul of you," said Eustace Bright, " and be all as still as so many mice. At the slightest interruption, whether from great, naughty Primrose, little Dandelion, or any other, I shall bite the story short off between my teeth, and swallow the

untold part. But, in the first place, do any of you
know what a Gorgon is?"

" I do," said Primrose.

" Then hold your tongue!" rejoined Eustace, who
had rather she would have known nothing about the
matter. " Hold all your tongues, and I shall tell you
a sweet pretty story of a Gorgon's head."

And so he did, as you may begin to read on the
next page. Working up his sophomorical erudition
with a good deal of tact, and incurring great obliga-
tions to Professor Anthon, he, nevertheless, disre-
garded all classical authorities, whenever the vagrant
audacity of his imagination impelled him to do so.

THE GORGON'S HEAD.

PERSEUS was the son of Danaë, who was the daughter of a king. And when Perseus was a very little boy, some wicked people put his mother and himself into a chest, and set them afloat upon the sea. The wind blew freshly, and drove the chest away from the shore, and the uneasy billows, tossed it up and down; while Danaë clasped her child closely to her bosom, and dreaded that some big wave would dash its foamy crest over them both. The chest sailed on, however, and neither sank nor was upset; until, when night was coming, it floated so near an island that it got entangled in a fisherman's nets, and was drawn out high and dry upon the sand. The island was called Seriphus, and it was reigned over by King Polydectes, who happened to be the fisherman's brother.

This fisherman, I am glad to tell you, was an exceedingly humane and upright man. He showed great kindness to Danaë and her little boy; and continued to befriend them, until Perseus had grown to be a handsome youth, very strong and active, and skilful in the use of arms. Long before this time, King Polydectes had seen the two strangers — the mother and her child — who had come to his dominions in a floating chest. As he was not good and kind, like his brother the fisherman, but extremely wicked, he resolved to send Perseus on a dangerous enterprise, in which he would probably be killed, and then to do some great mischief to Danaë herself. So this bad-hearted king spent a long while in considering what was the most dangerous thing that a young man could possibly undertake to perform. At last, having hit upon an enterprise that promised to turn out as fatally as he desired, he sent for the youthful Perseus.

The young man came to the palace, and found the king sitting upon his throne.

"Perseus," said King Polydectes, smiling craftily upon him, "you are grown up a fine young man. You and your good mother have received a great deal of kindness from myself, as well as from my worthy brother the fisherman, and I suppose you would not be sorry to repay some of it."

"Please your Majesty," answered Perseus, "I would willingly risk my life to do so."

"Well, then," continued the king, still with a cunning smile on his lips, "I have a little adventure to propose to you; and, as you are a brave and enterprising youth, you will doubtless look upon it as a great piece of good luck to have so rare an opportunity of distinguishing yourself. You must know, my good Perseus, I think of getting married to the beautiful Princess Hippodamia; and it is customary, on these occasions, to make the bride a present of some far-fetched and elegant curiosity. I have been a little perplexed, I must honestly confess, where to obtain anything likely to please a princess of her exquisite taste. But, this morning, I flatter myself, I have thought of precisely the article."

"And can I assist your Majesty in obtaining it?" cried Perseus, eagerly.

"You can, if you are as brave a youth as I believe you to be," replied King Polydectes, with the utmost

graciousness of manner. "The bridal gift which I
have set my heart on presenting to the beautiful Hippodamia is the head of the Gorgon Medusa with the
snaky locks; and I depend on you, my dear Perseus,
to bring it to me. So, as I am anxious to settle affairs
with the princess, the sooner you go in quest of the
Gorgon, the better I shall be pleased."

"I will set out to-morrow morning," answered
Perseus.

"Pray do so, my gallant youth," rejoined the king.
"And, Perseus, in cutting off the Gorgon's head, be
careful to make a clean stroke, so as not to injure its
appearance. You must bring it home in the very best
condition, in order to suit the exquisite taste of the
beautiful Princess Hippodamia."

Perseus left the palace, but was scarcely out of
hearing before Polydectes burst into a laugh; being
greatly amused, wicked king that he was, to find how
readily the young man fell into the snare. The news
quickly spread abroad that Perseus had undertaken to
cut off the head of Medusa with the snaky locks.
Everybody was rejoiced; for most of the inhabitants
of the island were as wicked as the king himself, and
would have liked nothing better than to see some
enormous mischief happen to Danaë and her son.
The only good man in this unfortunate island of Seriphus appears to have been the fisherman. As Perseus
walked along, therefore, the people pointed after him,
and made mouths, and winked to one another, and
ridiculed him as loudly as they dared.

"Ho, ho!" cried they; "Medusa's snakes will sting
him soundly!"

Now, there were three Gorgons alive at that period;
and they were the most strange and terrible monsters

that had ever been since the world was made, or that
have been seen in after days, or that are likely to be
seen in all time to come. I hardly know what sort of
creature or hobgoblin to call them. They were three
sisters, and seem to have borne some distant resemblance to women, but were really a very frightful and
mischievous species of dragon. It is, indeed, difficult
to imagine what hideous beings these three sisters
were. Why, instead of locks of hair, if you can believe me, they had each of them a hundred enormous
snakes growing on their heads, all alive, twisting,
wriggling, curling, and thrusting out their venomous
tongues, with forked stings at the end! The teeth
of the Gorgons were terribly long tusks; their hands
were made of brass; and their bodies were all over
scales, which, if not iron, were something as hard and
impenetrable. They had wings, too, and exceedingly
splendid ones, I can assure you; for every feather in
them was pure, bright, glittering, burnished gold, and
they looked very dazzlingly, no doubt, when the Gorgons were flying about in the sunshine.

But when people happened to catch a glimpse of
their glittering brightness, aloft in the air, they seldom stopped to gaze, but ran and hid themselves as
speedily as they could. You will think, perhaps, that
they were afraid of being stung by the serpents that
served the Gorgons instead of hair, — or of having
their heads bitten off by their ugly tusks, — or of being torn all to pieces by their brazen claws. Well, to
be sure, these were some of the dangers, but by no
means the greatest, nor the most difficult to avoid.
For the worst thing about these abominable Gorgons
was, that, if once a poor mortal fixed his eyes full
upon one of their faces, he was certain, that very in-

stant to be changed from warm flesh and blood into cold and lifeless stone !

Thus, as you will easily perceive, it was a very dangerous adventure that the wicked King Polydectes had contrived for this innocent young man. Perseus himself, when he had thought over the matter, could not help seeing that he had very little chance of coming safely through it, and that he was far more likely to become a stone image than to bring back the head of Medusa with the snaky locks. For, not to speak of other difficulties, there was one which it would have puzzled an older man than Perseus to get over. Not only must he fight with and slay this golden-winged, iron-scaled, long-tusked, brazen-clawed, snaky-haired monster, but he must do it with his eyes shut, or, at least, without so much as a glance at the enemy with whom he was contending. Else, while his arm was lifted to strike, he would stiffen into stone, and stand with that uplifted arm for centuries, until time, and the wind and weather, should crumble him quite away. This would be a very sad thing to befall a young man who wanted to perform a great many brave deeds, and to enjoy a great deal of happiness, in this bright and beautiful world.

So disconsolate did these thoughts make him, that Perseus could not bear to tell his mother what he had undertaken to do. He therefore took his shield, girded on his sword, and crossed over from the island to the mainland, where he sat down in a solitary place, and hardly refrained from shedding tears.

But, while he was in this sorrowful mood, he heard a voice close beside him.

" Perseus," said the voice, " why are you sad ? "

He lifted his head from his hands, in which he had

hidden it, and, behold! all alone as Perseus had supposed himself to be, there was a stranger in the solitary place. It was a brisk, intelligent, and remarkably shrewd-looking young man, with a cloak over his shoulders, an odd sort of cap on his head, a strangely twisted staff in his hand, and a short and very crooked sword hanging by his side. He was exceedingly light and active in his figure, like a person much accustomed to gymnastic exercises, and well able to leap or run. Above all, the stranger had such a cheerful, knowing, and helpful aspect (though it was certainly a little mischievous, into the bargain), that Perseus could not help feeling his spirits grow livelier as he gazed at him. Besides, being really a courageous youth, he felt greatly ashamed that anybody should have found him with tears in his eyes, like a timid little school-boy, when, after all, there might be no occasion for despair. So Perseus wiped his eyes, and answered the stranger pretty briskly, putting on as brave a look as he could.

"I am not so very sad," said he, "only thoughtful about an adventure that I have undertaken."

"Oho!" answered the stranger. "Well, tell me all about it, and possibly I may be of service to you. I have helped a good many young men through adventures that looked difficult enough beforehand. Perhaps you may have heard of me. I have more names than one; but the name of Quicksilver suits me as well as any other. Tell me what the trouble is, and we will talk the matter over, and see what can be done."

The stranger's words and manner put Perseus into quite a different mood from his former one. He resolved to tell Quicksilver all his difficulties, since he could not easily be worse off than he already was, and, very possibly, his new friend might give him some advice that would turn out well in the end. So he let the stranger know, in few words, precisely what the case was, — how that King Polydectes wanted the head of Medusa with the snaky locks as a bridal gift for the beautiful Princess Hippodamia, and how that he had undertaken to get it for him, but was afraid of being turned into stone.

" And that would be a great pity," said Quicksilver, with his mischievous smile. " You would make a very handsome marble statue, it is true, and it would be a considerable number of centuries before you crumbled away; but, on the whole, one would rather be a young man for a few years, than a stone image for a great many."

"Oh, far rather!" exclaimed Perseus, with the tears again standing in his eyes. " And, besides, what would my dear mother do, if her beloved son were turned into a stone ? "

" Well, well, let us hope that the affair will not turn out so very badly," replied Quicksilver, in an encouraging tone. " I am the very person to help you, if anybody can. My sister and myself will do our utmost to bring you safe through the adventure, ugly as it now looks."

" Your sister ? " repeated Perseus.

" Yes, my sister," said the stranger. " She is very wise, I promise you ; and as for myself, I generally have all my wits about me, such as they are. If you show yourself bold and cautious, and follow our advice, you need not fear being a stone image yet awhile. But, first of all, you must polish your shield, till you can see your face in it as distinctly as in a mirror."

This seemed to Perseus rather an odd beginning of the adventure ; for he thought it of far more consequence that the shield should be strong enough to defend him from the Gorgon's brazen claws, than that it should be bright enough to show him the reflection of his face.   However, concluding that Quicksilver knew better than himself, he immediately set to work, and scrubbed the shield with so much diligence and good-will, that it very quickly shone like the moon at harvest-time.   Quicksilver looked at it with a smile, and nodded his approbation.   Then, taking off his own short and crooked sword, he girded it about Perseus, instead of the one which he had before worn.

"No sword but mine will answer your purpose," observed he; "the blade has a most excellent temper, and will cut through iron and brass as easily as through the slenderest twig.   And now we will set out.   The next thing is to find the Three Gray Women, who will tell us where to find the Nymphs."

"The Three Gray Women!" cried Perseus, to whom this seemed only a new difficulty in the path of his adventure; "pray who may the Three Gray Women be?   I never heard of them before."

"They are three very strange old ladies," said Quicksilver, laughing.   "They have but one eye among them, and only one tooth.   Moreover, you must find them out by starlight, or in the dusk of the evening; for they never show themselves by the light either of the sun or moon."

"But," said Perseus, "why should I waste my time with these Three Gray Women?   Would it not be better to set out at once in search of the terrible Gorgons?"

"No, no," answered his friend.   "There are other things to be done, before you can find your way to the Gorgons.   There is nothing for it but to hunt up these old ladies; and when we meet with them, you may be sure that the Gorgons are not a great way off. Come, let us be stirring!"

Perseus, by this time, felt so much confidence in his companion's sagacity, that he made no more objections, and professed himself ready to begin the adventure immediately. They accordingly set out, and walked at a pretty brisk pace; so brisk, indeed, that Perseus found it rather difficult to keep up with his nimble friend Quicksilver. To say the truth, he had a singular idea that Quicksilver was furnished with a pair of winged shoes, which, of course, helped him along marvellously. And then, too, when Perseus looked sideways at him, out of the corner of his eye, he seemed to see wings on the side of his head; although, if he turned a full gaze, there were no such things to be perceived, but only an odd kind of cap. But, at all events, the twisted staff was evidently a great convenience to Quicksilver, and enabled him to proceed so fast, that Perseus, though a remarkably active young man, began to be out of breath.

"Here!" cried Quicksilver, at last, — for he knew well enough, rogue that he was, how hard Perseus found it to keep pace with him, — "take you the staff, for you need it a great deal more than I. Are there no better walkers than yourself in the island of Seriphus?"

"I could walk pretty well," said Perseus, glancing slyly at his companion's feet, "if I had only a pair of winged shoes."

"We must see about getting you a pair," answered Quicksilver.

But the staff helped Perseus along so bravely, that he no longer felt the slightest weariness. In fact, the

stick seemed to be alive in his hand, and to lend some
of its life to Perseus. He and Quicksilver now walked
onward at their ease, talking very sociably together;
and Quicksilver told so many pleasant stories about
his former adventures, and how well his wits had served
him on various occasions, that Perseus began to think
him a very wonderful person. He evidently knew the
world; and nobody is so charming to a young man as
a friend who has that kind of knowledge. Perseus
listened the more eagerly, in the hope of brightening
his own wits by what he heard.

At last, he happened to recollect that Quicksilver
had spoken of a sister, who was to lend her assistance
in the adventure which they were now bound upon.

"Where is she?" he inquired. "Shall we not
meet her soon?"

"All at the proper time," said his companion.
"But this sister of mine, you must understand, is
quite a different sort of character from myself. She
is very grave and prudent, seldom smiles, never
laughs, and makes it a rule not to utter a word unless she has something particularly profound to say.
Neither will she listen to any but the wisest conversation."

"Dear me!" ejaculated Perseus; "I shall be afraid
to say a syllable."

"She is a very accomplished person, I assure you,"
continued Quicksilver, "and has all the arts and
sciences at her fingers' ends. In short, she is so im-
moderately wise, that many people call her wisdom
personified. But, to tell you the truth, she has hardly
vivacity enough for my taste; and I think you would
scarcely find her so pleasant a travelling companion
as myself. She has her good points, nevertheless:

and you will find the benefit of them, in your encounter with the Gorgons."

By this time it had grown quite dusk. They were
now come to a very wild and desert place, overgrown
with shaggy bushes, and so silent and solitary that
nobody seemed ever to have dwelt or journeyed there.
All was waste and desolate, in the gray twilight,
which grew every moment more obscure. Perseus
looked about him, rather disconsolately, and asked
Quicksilver whether they had a great deal farther
to go.

"Hist! hist!" whispered his companion. "Make
no noise! This is just the time and place to meet the
Three Gray Women. Be careful that they do not see
you before you see them; for, though they have but a
single eye among the three, it is as sharp-sighted as
half a dozen common eyes."

"But what must I do," asked Perseus, "when we
meet them?"

Quicksilver explained to Perseus how the Three
Gray Women managed with their one eye. They
were in the habit, it seems, of changing it from one to
another, as if it had been a pair of spectacles, or —
which would have suited them better — a quizzing-
glass. When one of the three had kept the eye a
certain time, she took it out of the socket and passed
it to one of her sisters, whose turn it might happen to
be, and who immediately clapped it into her own
head, and enjoyed a peep at the visible world. Thus
it will easily be understood that only one of the Three
Gray Women could see, while the other two were in
utter darkness; and, moreover, at the instant when
the eye was passing from hand to hand, neither of the
poor old ladies was able to see a wink. I have heard

of a great many strange things, in my day, and have witnessed not a few; but none, it seems to me, that can compare with the oddity of these Three Gray Women, all peeping through a single eye.

So thought Perseus, likewise, and was so astonished that he almost fancied his companion was joking with him, and that there were no such old women in the world.

"You will soon find whether I tell the truth or no," observed Quicksilver. "Hark! hush! hist! hist! There they come, now!"

Perseus looked earnestly through the dusk of the evening, and there, sure enough, at no great distance off, he descried the Three Gray Women. The light being so faint, he could not well make out what sort of figures they were; only he discovered that they had long gray hair; and, as they came nearer, he saw that two of them had but the empty socket of an eye, in the middle of their foreheads. But, in the middle of the third sister's forehead, there was a very large, bright, and piercing eye, which sparkled like a great diamond in a ring; and so penetrating did it seem to be, that Perseus could not help thinking it must possess the gift of seeing in the darkest midnight just as perfectly as at noonday. The sight of three persons' eyes was melted and collected into that single one.

Thus the three old dames got along about as comfortably, upon the whole, as if they could all see at once. She who chanced to have the eye in her forehead led the other two by the hands, peeping sharply about her, all the while; insomuch that Perseus dreaded lest she should see right through the thick clump of bushes behind which he and Quicksilver had hidden themselves. My stars! it was positively terrible to be within reach of so very sharp an eye!

But, before they reached the clump of bushes, one of the Three Gray Women spoke.

"Sister! Sister Scarecrow!" cried she, "you have had the eye long enough. It is my turn now!"

"Let me keep it a moment longer, Sister Nightmare," answered Scarecrow. "I thought I had a glimpse of something behind that thick bush."

"Well, and what of that?" retorted Nightmare, peevishly. "Can't I see into a thick bush as easily as yourself? The eye is mine as well as yours; and I know the use of it as well as you, or may be a little better. I insist upon taking a peep immediately!"

But here the third sister, whose name was Shake-joint, began to complain, and said that it was her turn to have the eye, and that Scarecrow and Nightmare wanted to keep it all to themselves. To end the dispute, old Dame Scarecrow took the eye out of her forehead, and held it forth in her hand.

"Take it, one of you," cried she, "and quit this foolish quarrelling. For my part, I shall be glad of a little thick darkness. Take it quickly, however, or I must clap it into my own head again!"

Accordingly, both Nightmare and Shakejoint put out their hands, groping eagerly to snatch the eye out of the hand of Scarecrow. But, being both alike blind, they could not easily find where Scarecrow's hand was; and Scarecrow, being now just as much in the dark as Shakejoint and Nightmare, could not at once meet either of their hands, in order to put the eye into it. Thus (as you will see, with half an eye, my wise little auditors), these good old dames had fallen into a strange perplexity. For, though the eye shone and glistened like a star, as Scarecrow held it out, yet the Gray Women caught not the least glimpse of its light, and were all three in utter darkness, from too impatient a desire to see.

Quicksilver was so much tickled at beholding Shake-joint and Nightmare both groping for the eye, and each finding fault with Scarecrow and one another, that he could scarcely help laughing aloud.

"Now is your time!" he whispered to Perseus. "Quick, quick! before they can clap the eye into either of their heads. Rush out upon the old ladies, and snatch it from Scarecrow's hand!"

In an instant, while the Three Gray Women were still scolding each other, Perseus leaped from behind the clump of bushes, and made himself master of the prize. The marvellous eye, as he held it in his hand, shone very brightly, and seemed to look up into his face with a knowing air, and an expression as if it would have winked, had it been provided with a pair of eyelids for that purpose. But the Gray Women knew nothing of what had happened; and, each supposing that one of her sisters was in possession of the eye, they began their quarrel anew. At last, as Perseus did not wish to put these respectable dames to greater inconvenience than was really necessary, he thought it right to explain the matter.

"My good ladies," said he, "pray do not be angry with one another. If anybody is in fault, it is myself; for I have the honor to hold your very brilliant and excellent eye in my own hand!"

"You! you have our eye! And who are you?" screamed the Three Gray Women, all in a breath; for they were terribly frightened, of course, at hearing a strange voice, and discovering that their eyesight had got into the hands of they could not guess whom. "Oh, what shall we do, sisters? what shall we do? We are all in the dark! Give us our eye! Give us our one, precious, solitary eye! You have two of your own! Give us our eye!"

"Tell them," whispered Quicksilver to Perseus, "that they shall have back the eye as soon as they direct you where to find the Nymphs who have the flying slippers, the magic wallet, and the helmet of darkness."

"My dear, good, admirable old ladies," said Perseus, addressing the Gray Women, "there is no occasion for putting yourselves into such a fright. I am by no means a bad young man. You shall have back your eye, safe and sound, and as bright as ever, the moment you tell me where to find the Nymphs."

"The Nymphs! Goodness me! sisters, what Nymphs does he mean?" screamed Scarecrow. "There are a great many Nymphs, people say; some that go a hunting in the woods, and some that live inside of trees, and some that have a comfortable home in fountains of water. We know nothing at all about them. We are three unfortunate old souls, that go wandering about in the dusk, and never had but one eye amongst us, and that one you have stolen away. Oh, give it back, good stranger! — whoever you are, give it back!"

All this while the Three Gray Women were groping with their outstretched hands, and trying their utmost to get hold of Perseus. But he took good care to keep out of their reach.

"My respectable dames," said he, — for his mother had taught him always to use the greatest civility, — "I hold your eye fast in my hand, and shall keep it safely for you, until you please to tell me where to find these Nymphs. The Nymphs, I mean, who keep the enchanted wallet, the flying slippers, and the what is it? — the helmet of invisibility."

"Mercy on us, sisters! what is the young man talking about?" exclaimed Scarecrow, Nightmare, and Shakejoint, one to another, with great appearance of astonishment. "A pair of flying slippers, quoth he! His heels would quickly fly higher than his head, if he were silly enough to put them on. And a helmet of invisibility! How could a helmet make him invisible, unless it were big enough for him to hide under it? And an enchanted wallet! What sort of a contrivance may that be, I wonder? No, no, good stranger! we can tell you nothing of these marvellous things. You have two eyes of your own, and we have but a single one amongst us three. You can find out such wonders better than three blind old creatures, like us."

Perseus, hearing them talk in this way, began really to think that the Gray Women knew nothing of the matter; and, as it grieved him to have put them to so much trouble, he was just on the point of restoring their eye and asking pardon for his rudeness in snatching it away. But Quicksilver caught his hand.

"Don't let them make a fool of you!" said he. "These Three Gray Women are the only persons in the world that can tell you where to find the Nymphs; and, unless you get that information, you will never succeed in cutting off the head of Medusa with the snaky locks. Keep fast hold of the eye, and all will go well."

As it turned out, Quicksilver was in the right. There are but few things that people prize so much as they do their eyesight; and the Gray Women valued their single eye as highly as if it had been half a dozen, which was the number they ought to have had. Finding that there was no other way of recovering it,

they at last told Perseus what he wanted to know. No
sooner had they done so, than he immediately, and
with the utmost respect, clapped the eye into the vacant socket in one of their foreheads, thanked them
for their kindness, and bade them farewell. Before
the young man was out of hearing, however, they had
got into a new dispute, because he happened to have
given the eye to Scarecrow, who had already taken her
turn of it when their trouble with Perseus commenced.

It is greatly to be feared that the Three Gray
Women were very much in the habit of disturbing
their mutual harmony by bickerings of this sort;
which was the more pity, as they could not conveniently do without one another, and were evidently intended to be inseparable companions. As a general
rule, I would advise all people, whether sisters or
brothers, old or young, who chance to have but one
eye amongst them, to cultivate forbearance, and not
all insist upon peeping through it at once.

Quicksilver and Perseus, in the mean time, were
making the best of their way in quest of the Nymphs.
The old dames had given them such particular directions, that they were not long in finding them out.
They proved to be very different persons from Nightmare, Shakejoint, and Scarecrow; for, instead of being old, they were young and beautiful; and instead
of one eye amongst the sisterhood, each Nymph had
two exceedingly bright eyes of her own, with which
she looked very kindly at Perseus. They seemed to
be acquainted with Quicksilver; and, when he told
them the adventure which Perseus had undertaken,
they made no difficulty about giving him the valuable
articles that were in their custody. In the first place,
they brought out what appeared to be a small purse,

made of deer skin, and curiously embroidered, and bade him be sure and keep it safe. This was the magic wallet. The Nymphs next produced a pair of shoes, or slippers, or sandals, with a nice little pair of wings at the heel of each.

"Put them on, Perseus," said Quicksilver. "You will find yourself as light-heeled as you can desire for the remainder of our journey."

So Perseus proceeded to put one of the slippers on, while he laid the other on the ground by his side. Unexpectedly, however, this other slipper spread its wings, fluttered up off the ground, and would probably have flown away, if Quicksilver had not made a leap, and luckily caught it in the air.

"Be more careful," said he, as he gave it back to Perseus. "It would frighten the birds, up aloft, if they should see a flying slipper amongst them."

When Perseus had got on both of these wonderful slippers, he was altogether too buoyant to tread on earth. Making a step or two, lo and behold! upward he popped into the air, high above the heads of Quicksilver and the Nymphs, and found it very difficult to clamber down again. Winged slippers, and all such high-flying contrivances, are seldom quite easy to manage until one grows a little accustomed to them. Quicksilver laughed at his companion's involuntary activity, and told him that he must not be in so desperate a hurry, but must wait for the invisible helmet.

The good-natured Nymphs had the helmet, with its dark tuft of waving plumes, all in readiness to put upon his head. And now there happened about as wonderful an incident as anything that I have yet told you. The instant before the helmet was put on, there stood Perseus, a beautiful young man, with golden ringlets and rosy cheeks, the crooked sword by his side, and the brightly polished shield upon his arm, — a figure that seemed all made up of courage, sprightliness, and glorious light. But when the helmet had descended over his white brow, there was no longer any Perseus to be seen! Nothing but empty air! Even the helmet, that covered him with its invisibility, had vanished!

"Where are you, Perseus?" asked Quicksilver.

"Why, here, to be sure!" answered Perseus, very quietly, although his voice seemed to come out of the transparent atmosphere. "Just where I was a moment ago. Don't you see me?"

"No, indeed!" answered his friend. "You are hidden under the helmet. But, if I cannot see you, neither can the Gorgons. Follow me, therefore, and we will try your dexterity in using the winged slippers."

With these words, Quicksilver's cap spread its wings, as if his head were about to fly away from his shoulders; but his whole figure rose lightly into the air, and Perseus followed. By the time they had ascended a few hundred feet, the young man began to feel what a delightful thing it was to leave the dull earth so far beneath him, and to be able to flit about like a bird.

It was now deep night. Perseus looked upward, and saw the round, bright, silvery moon, and thought that he should desire nothing better than to soar up thither, and spend his life there. Then he looked downward again, and saw the earth, with its seas and lakes, and the silver courses of its rivers, and its snowy mountain-peaks, and the breadth of its fields, and the dark cluster of its woods, and its cities of

white marble ; and, with the moonshine sleeping over
the whole scene, it was as beautiful as the moon or
any star could be.   And, among other objects, he saw
the island of Seriphus, where his dear mother was.
Sometimes he and Quicksilver approached a cloud,
that, at a distance, looked as if it were made of fleecy
silver; although, when they plunged into it, they
found themselves chilled and moistened with gray
mist.   So swift was their flight, however, that, in an
instant, they emerged from the cloud into the moonlight again.   Once, a high-soaring eagle flew right
against the invisible Perseus.   The bravest sights were
the meteors, that gleamed suddenly out, as if a bonfire
had been kindled in the sky, and made the moonshine
pale for as much as a hundred miles around them.

As the two companions flew onward, Perseus fancied
that he could hear the rustle of a garment close by his
side ; and it was on the side opposite to the one where
he beheld Quicksilver, yet only Quicksilver was visible.

" Whose garment is this," inquired Perseus, " that
keeps rustling close beside me in the breeze ? "

" Oh, it is my sister's ! " answered Quicksilver.
" She is coming along with us, as I told you she
would.   We could do nothing without the help of my
sister.   You have no idea how wise she is.   She has
such eyes, too !   Why, she can see you, at this moment, just as distinctly as if you were not invisible ;
and I 'll venture to say, she will be the first to discover the Gorgons."

By this time, in their swift voyage through the air,
they had come within sight of the great ocean, and
were soon flying over it.   Far beneath them, the
waves tossed themselves tumultuously in mid-sea, or
rolled a white surf-line upon the long beaches, or

foamed against the rocky cliffs, with a roar that was
thunderous, in the lower world; although it became a
gentle murmur, like the voice of a baby half asleep,
before it reached the ears of Perseus. Just then a
voice spoke in the air close by him. It seemed to be
a woman's voice, and was melodious, though not exactly what might be called sweet, but grave and mild.

"Perseus," said the voice, "there are the Gorgons."

"Where?" exclaimed Perseus. "I cannot see
them."

"On the shore of that island beneath you," replied
the voice. "A pebble, dropped from your hand, would
strike in the midst of them."

"I told you she would be the first to discover them,"
said Quicksilver to Perseus. "And there they are!"

Straight downward, two or three thousand feet below him, Perseus perceived a small island, with the sea
breaking into white foam all around its rocky shore,
except on one side, where there was a beach of snowy
sand. He descended towards it, and, looking earnestly
at a cluster or heap of brightness, at the foot of a precipice of black rocks, behold, there were the terrible
Gorgons! They lay fast asleep, soothed by the thunder of the sea; for it required a tumult that would
have deafened everybody else to lull such fierce creatures into slumber. The moonlight glistened on their
steely scales, and on their golden wings, which drooped
idly over the sand. Their brazen claws, horrible to
look at, were thrust out, and clutched the wave-beaten
fragments of rock, while the sleeping Gorgons dreamed
of tearing some poor mortal all to pieces. The snakes
that served them instead of hair seemed likewise to be
asleep; although, now and then, one would writhe,
and lift its head, and thrust out its forked tongue,

emitting a drowsy hiss, and then let itself subside among its sister snakes.

The Gorgons were more like an awful, gigantic kind of insect,—immense, golden-winged beetles, or dragon-flies, or things of that sort, — at once ugly and beautiful, — than like anything else; only that they were a thousand and a million times as big. And, with all this, there was something partly human about them, too. Luckily for Perseus, their faces were completely hidden from him by the posture in which they lay; for, had he but looked one instant at them, he would have fallen heavily out of the air, an image of senseless stone.

"Now," whispered Quicksilver, as he hovered by the side of Perseus, — "now is your time to do the deed! Be quick; for, if one of the Gorgons should awake, you are too late!"

"Which shall I strike at?" asked Perseus, drawing his sword and descending a little lower. "They all three look alike. All three have snaky locks. Which of the three is Medusa?"

It must be understood that Medusa was the only one of these dragon-monsters whose head Perseus could possibly cut off. As for the other two, let him have the sharpest sword that ever was forged, and he might have hacked away by the hour together, without doing them the least harm.

"Be cautious," said the calm voice which had before spoken to him. "One of the Gorgons is stirring in her sleep, and is just about to turn over. That is Medusa. Do not look at her! The sight would turn you to stone! Look at the reflection of her face and figure in the bright mirror of your shield."

Perseus now understood Quicksilver's motive for so

earnestly exhorting him to polish his shield. In its surface he could safely look at the reflection of the Gorgon's face. And there it was, — that terrible countenance, — mirrored in the brightness of the shield, with the moonlight falling over it, and displaying all its horror. The snakes, whose venomous natures could not altogether sleep, kept twisting themselves over the forehead. It was the fiercest and most horrible face that ever was seen or imagined, and yet with a strange, fearful, and savage kind of beauty in it. The eyes were closed, and the Gorgon was still in a deep slumber; but there was an unquiet expression disturbing her features, as if the monster was troubled with an ugly dream. She gnashed her white tusks, and dug into the sand with her brazen claws.

The snakes, too, seemed to feel Medusa's dream, and to be made more restless by it. They twined themselves into tumultuous knots, writhed fiercely, and uplifted a hundred hissing heads, without opening their eyes.

"Now, now!" whispered Quicksilver, who was growing impatient. "Make a dash at the monster!"

"But be calm," said the grave, melodious voice, at the young man's side. "Look in your shield, as you fly downward, and take care that you do not miss your first stroke."

Perseus flew cautiously downward, still keeping his eyes on Medusa's face, as reflected in his shield. The nearer he came, the more terrible did the snaky visage and metallic body of the monster grow. At last, when he found himself hovering over her within arm's length, Perseus uplifted his sword, while, at the same instant, each separate snake upon the Gorgon's head stretched threateningly upward, and Medusa unclosed her eyes.

But she awoke too late. The sword was sharp; the stroke fell like a lightning-flash; and the head of the wicked Medusa tumbled from her body!

"Admirably done!" cried Quicksilver. "Make haste, and clap the head into your magic wallet."

To the astonishment of Perseus, the small, embroidered wallet, which he had hung about his neck, and which had hitherto been no bigger than a purse, grew all at once large enough to contain Medusa's head. As quick as thought, he snatched it up, with the snakes still writhing upon it, and thrust it in.

"Your task is done," said the calm voice. "Now fly; for the other Gorgons will do their utmost to take vengeance for Medusa's death."

It was, indeed, necessary to take flight; for Perseus had not done the deed so quietly but that the clash of his sword, and the hissing of the snakes, and the thump of Medusa's head as it tumbled upon the sea-beaten sand, awoke the other two monsters. There they sat, for an instant, sleepily rubbing their eyes with their brazen fingers, while all the snakes on their heads reared themselves on end with surprise, and with venomous malice against they knew not what. But when the Gorgons saw the scaly carcass of Medusa, headless, and her golden wings all ruffled, and half spread out on the sand, it was really awful to hear what yells and screeches they set up. And then the snakes! They sent forth a hundred-fold hiss, with one consent, and Medusa's snakes answered them out of the magic wallet.

No sooner were the Gorgons broad awake than they hurtled upward into the air, brandishing their brass talons, gnashing their horrible tusks, and flapping their huge wings so wildly, that some of the golden feathers were shaken out, and floated down upon the shore. And there, perhaps, those very feathers lie scattered, till this day. Up rose the Gorgons, as I tell you, staring horribly about, in hopes of turning somebody to stone. Had Perseus looked them in the face, or had he fallen into their clutches, his poor mother would never have kissed her boy again! But he took good care to turn his eyes another way; and, as he wore the helmet of invisibility, the Gorgons knew not in what direction to follow him; nor did he fail to make the best use of the winged slippers, by soaring upward a perpendicular mile or so. At that height, when the screams of those abominable creatures sounded faintly beneath him, he made a straight course for the island of Seriphus, in order to carry Medusa's head to King Polydectes.

I have no time to tell you of several marvellous things that befell Perseus, on his way homeward; such as his killing a hideous sea-monster, just as it was on the point of devouring a beautiful maiden; nor how he changed an enormous giant into a mountain of stone, merely by showing him the head of the Gorgon. If you doubt this latter story, you may make a voyage to Africa, some day or other, and see the very mountain, which is still known by the ancient giant's name.

Finally, our brave Perseus arrived at the island, where he expected to see his dear mother. But, during his absence, the wicked king had treated Danaë so very ill that she was compelled to make her escape, and had taken refuge in a temple, where some good old priests were extremely kind to her. These praiseworthy priests, and the kind-hearted fisherman, who had first shown hospitality to Danaë and little Perseus when he found them afloat in the chest, seem to have been the only persons on the island who cared about doing right. All the rest of the people, as well as King Polydectes himself, were remarkably ill-behaved, and deserved no better destiny than that which was now to happen.

Not finding his mother at home, Perseus went straight to the palace, and was immediately ushered into the presence of the king. Polydectes was by no means rejoiced to see him; for he had felt almost certain, in his own evil mind, that the Gorgons would have torn the poor young man to pieces, and have eaten him up, out of the way. However, seeing him safely returned, he put the best face he could upon the matter and asked Perseus how he had succeeded.

"Have you performed your promise?" inquired he. "Have you brought me the head of Medusa with the snaky locks? If not, young man, it will cost you dear; for I must have a bridal present for the beautiful Princess Hippodamia, and there is nothing else that she would admire so much."

"Yes, please your Majesty," answered Perseus, in a quiet way, as if it were no very wonderful deed for such a young man as he to perform. "I have brought you the Gorgon's head, snaky locks and all!"

"Indeed! Pray let me see it," quoth King Polydectes. "It must be a very curious spectacle, if all that travellers tell about it be true!"

"Your Majesty is in the right," replied Perseus. "It is really an object that will be pretty certain to fix the regards of all who look at it. And, if your Majesty think fit, I would suggest that a holiday be proclaimed, and that all your Majesty's subjects be summoned to behold this wonderful curiosity. Few of them, I imagine, have seen a Gorgon's head before, and perhaps never may again ! "

The king well knew that his subjects were an idle set of reprobates, and very fond of sight-seeing, as idle persons usually are. So he took the young man's advice, and sent out heralds and messengers, in all directions, to blow the trumpet at the street-corners, and in the market-places, and wherever two roads met, and summon everybody to court. Thither, accordingly, came a great multitude of good-for-nothing vagabonds, all of whom, out of pure love of mischief, would have been glad if Perseus had met with some ill-hap in his encounter with the Gorgons. If there were any better people in the island (as I really hope there may have been, although the story tells nothing about any such), they stayed quietly at home, minding their business, and taking care of their little children. Most of the inhabitants, at all events, ran as fast as they could to the palace, and shoved, and pushed, and elbowed one another, in their eagerness to get near a balcony, on which Perseus showed himself, holding the embroidered wallet in his hand.

On a platform, within full view of the balcony, sat the mighty King Polydectes, amid his evil counsellors, and with his flattering courtiers in a semicircle round about him. Monarch, counsellors, courtiers, and subjects, all gazed eagerly towards Perseus.

" Show us the head ! Show us the head ! " shouted the people ; and there was a fierceness in their cry as if they would tear Perseus to pieces, unless he should satisfy them with what he had to show. " Show us the head of Medusa with the snaky locks ! "

A feeling of sorrow and pity came over the youthful Perseus.

"O King Polydectes," cried he, "and ye many people, I am very loath to show you the Gorgon's head!"

"Ah, the villain and coward!" yelled the people, more fiercely than before. "He is making game of us! He has no Gorgon's head! Show us the head, if you have it, or we will take your own head for a football!"

The evil counsellors whispered bad advice in the king's ear; the courtiers murmured, with one consent, that Perseus had shown disrespect to their royal lord and master; and the great King Polydectes himself waved his hand, and ordered him, with the stern, deep voice of authority, on his peril, to produce the head.

"Show me the Gorgon's head, or I will cut off your own!"

And Perseus sighed.

"This instant," repeated Polydectes, "or you die!"

"Behold it, then!" cried Perseus, in a voice like the blast of a trumpet.

And, suddenly holding up the head, not an eyelid had time to wink before the wicked King Polydectes, his evil counsellors, and all his fierce subjects were no longer anything but the mere images of a monarch and his people. They were all fixed, forever, in the look and attitude of that moment! At the first glimpse of the terrible head of Medusa, they whitened into marble! And Perseus thrust the head back into his wallet, and went to tell his dear mother that she need no longer be afraid of the wicked King Polydectes.

TANGLEWOOD PORCH.

AFTER THE STORY.

" Was not that a very fine story ? " asked Eustace.

" Oh yes, yes ! " cried Cowslip, clapping her hands. " And those funny old women, with only one eye amongst them ! I never heard of anything so strange."

" As to their one tooth, which they shifted about," observed Primrose, " there was nothing so very wonderful in that. I suppose it was a false tooth. But think of your turning Mercury into Quicksilver, and talking about his sister ! You are too ridiculous ! "

" And was she not his sister ? " asked Eustace Bright. " If I had thought of it sooner, I would have described her as a maiden lady, who kept a pet owl ! "

" Well, at any rate," said Primrose, " your story seems to have driven away the mist."

And, indeed, while the tale was going forward, the vapors had been quite exhaled from the landscape. A scene was now disclosed which the spectators might almost fancy as having been created since they had last looked in the direction where it lay. About half a mile distant, in the lap of the valley, now appeared a beautiful lake, which reflected a perfect image of its own wooded banks, and of the summits of the more distant hills. It gleamed in glassy tranquillity, without the trace of a winged breeze on any part of its

bosom.   Beyond its farther shore was Monument
Mountain, in a recumbent position, stretching almost
across the valley.   Eustace Bright compared it to a
huge, headless sphinx, wrapped in a Persian shawl;
and, indeed, so rich and diversified was the autumnal
foliage of its woods, that the simile of the shawl was
by no means too high-colored for the reality.   In the
lower ground, between Tanglewood and the lake, the
clumps of trees and borders of woodland were chiefly
golden-leaved or dusky brown, as having suffered more
from frost than the foliage on the hill-sides.

Over all this scene there was a genial sunshine, intermingled with a slight haze, which made it unspeak-
ably soft and tender.   Oh, what a day of Indian summer was it going to be!   The children snatched their
baskets, and set forth, with hop, skip, and jump, and
all sorts of frisks and gambols; while Cousin Eustace
proved his fitness to preside over the party, by outdo-
ing all their antics, and performing several new capers,
which none of them could ever hope to imitate.   Behind went a good old dog, whose name was Ben.   He
was one of the most respectable and kind-hearted of
quadrupeds, and probably felt it to be his duty not to
trust the children away from their parents without
some better guardian than this feather-brained Eustace Bright.

THE GOLDEN TOUCH.

SHADOW BROOK.

INTRODUCTORY TO "THE GOLDEN TOUCH."

AT noon, our juvenile party assembled in a dell, through the depths of which ran a little brook. The dell was narrow, and its steep sides, from the margin of the stream upward, were thickly set with trees, chiefly walnuts and chestnuts, among which grew a few oaks and maples. In the summer time, the shade of so many clustering branches, meeting and intermingling across the rivulet, was deep enough to produce a noontide twilight. Hence came the name of Shadow Brook. But now, ever since autumn had crept into this secluded place, all the dark verdure was changed to gold, so that it really kindled up the dell, instead of shading it. The bright yellow leaves, even had it been a cloudy day, would have seemed to keep the sunlight among them; and enough of them had fallen to strew all the bed and margin of the brook with sunlight, too. Thus the shady nook, where summer had cooled herself, was now the sunniest spot anywhere to be found.

The little brook ran along over its pathway of gold, here pausing to form a pool, in which minnows were darting to and fro; and then it hurried onward at a swifter pace, as if in haste to reach the lake; and, forgetting to look whither it went, it tumbled over the root of a tree, which stretched quite across its current. You would have laughed to hear how noisily it babbled about this accident. And even after it had run onward, the brook still kept talking to itself, as if it were in a maze. It was wonder-smitten, I suppose, at finding its dark dell so illuminated, and at hearing the prattle and merriment of so many children. So it stole away as quickly as it could, and hid itself in the lake.

In the dell of Shadow Brook, Eustace Bright and his little friends had eaten their dinner. They had brought plenty of good things from Tanglewood, in their baskets, and had spread them out on the stumps of trees, and on mossy trunks, and had feasted merrily, and made a very nice dinner indeed. After it was over, nobody felt like stirring.

"We will rest ourselves here," said several of the children, "while Cousin Eustace tells us another of his pretty stories."

Cousin Eustace had a good right to be tired, as well as the children, for he had performed great feats on that memorable forenoon. Dandelion, Clover, Cowslip, and Buttercup were almost persuaded that he had winged slippers, like those which the Nymphs gave Perseus; so often had the student shown himself at the tiptop of a nut-tree, when only a moment before he had been standing on the ground. And then, what showers of walnuts had he sent rattling down upon their heads, for their busy little hands to gather into the baskets! In short, he had been as active as a squirrel or a monkey, and now, flinging himself down on the yellow leaves, seemed inclined to take a little rest.

But children have no mercy nor consideration for anybody's weariness; and if you had but a single breath left, they would ask you to spend it in telling them a story.

" Cousin Eustace," said Cowslip, " that was a very nice story of the Gorgon's Head. Do you think you could tell us another as good ? "

" Yes, child," said Eustace, pulling the brim of his cap over his eyes, as if preparing for a nap. " I can tell you a dozen, as good or better, if I choose."

" O Primrose and Periwinkle, do you hear what he says ? " cried Cowslip, dancing with delight. " Cousin Eustace is going to tell us a dozen better stories than that about the Gorgon's Head ! "

" I did not promise you even one, you foolish little Cowslip ! " said Eustace, half pettishly. " However, I suppose you must have it. This is the consequence of having earned a reputation ! I wish I were a great deal duller than I am, or that I had never shown half the bright qualities with which nature has endowed me ; and then I might have my nap out, in peace and comfort ! "

But Cousin Eustace, as I think I have hinted before, was as fond of telling his stories as the children of hearing them. His mind was in a free and happy state, and took delight in its own activity, and scarcely required any external impulse to set it at work.

How different is this spontaneous play of the intellect from the trained diligence of maturer years, when toil has perhaps grown easy by long habit, and the day's work may have become essential to the day's comfort, although the rest of the matter has bubbled away ! This remark, however, is not meant for the children to hear.

Without further solicitation, Eustace Bright proceeded to tell the following really splendid story. It had come into his mind as he lay looking upward into the depths of a tree, and observing how the touch of Autumn had transmuted every one of its green leaves into what resembled the purest gold. And this change, which we have all of us witnessed, is as wonderful as anything that Eustace told about in the story of Midas.

THE GOLDEN TOUCH.

ONCE upon a time, there lived a very rich man, and a king besides, whose name was Midas; and he had a little daughter, whom nobody but myself ever heard of, and whose name I either never knew, or have entirely forgotten. So, because I love odd names for little girls, I choose to call her Marygold.

This King Midas was fonder of gold than of anything else in the world. He valued his royal crown chiefly because it was composed of that precious metal. If he loved anything better, or half so well, it was the one little maiden who played so merrily around her father's footstool. But the more Midas loved his daughter, the more did he desire and seek for wealth. He thought, foolish man! that the best thing he could possibly do for this dear child would be to bequeath her the immensest pile of yellow, glistening coin, that had ever been heaped together since the world was made. Thus, he gave all his thoughts and all his time to this one purpose. If ever he happened to gaze for an instant at the gold-tinted clouds of sunset, he wished that they were real gold, and that they could be squeezed safely into his strong box. When little Marygold ran to meet him, with a bunch of buttercups and dandelions, he used to say, " Poh, poh, child ! If these flowers were as golden as they look, they would be worth the plucking ! "

And yet, in his earlier days, before he was so entirely possessed of this insane desire for riches, King

Midas had shown a great taste for flowers. He had
planted a garden, in which grew the biggest and beautifullest and sweetest roses that any mortal ever saw
or smelt. These roses were still growing in the garden, as large, as lovely, and as fragrant, as when
Midas used to pass whole hours in gazing at them,
and inhaling their perfume. But now, if he looked
at them at all, it was only to calculate how much the
garden would be worth if each of the innumerable rose-
petals were a thin plate of gold. And though he once
was fond of music (in spite of an idle story about his
ears, which were said to resemble those of an ass), the
only music for poor Midas, now, was the chink of one
coin against another.

At length (as people always grow more and more
foolish, unless they take care to grow wiser and wiser),
Midas had got to be so exceedingly unreasonable, that
he could scarcely bear to see or touch any object that
was not gold. He made it his custom, therefore, to
pass a large portion of every day in a dark and dreary
apartment, under ground, at the basement of his palace. It was here that he kept his wealth. To this
dismal hole — for it was little better than a dungeon — Midas betook himself, whenever he wanted
to be particularly happy. Here, after carefully lock-
ing the door, he would take a bag of gold coin, or a
gold cup as big as a washbowl, or a heavy golden
bar, or a peck-measure of gold-dust, and bring them
from the obscure corners of the room into the one
bright and narrow sunbeam that fell from the dun-
geon-like window. He valued the sunbeam for no
other reason but that his treasure would not shine
without its help. And then would he reckon over the
coins in the bag; toss up the bar, and catch it as it

came down ; sift the gold-dust through his fingers ;
look at the funny image of his own face, as reflected
in the burnished circumference of the cup ; and whisper to himself, " O Midas, rich King Midas, what a
happy man art thou ! " But it was laughable to see
how the image of his face kept grinning at him, out
of the polished surface of the cup. It seemed to be
aware of his foolish behavior, and to have a naughty
inclination to make fun of him.

Midas called himself a happy man, but felt that he
was not yet quite so happy as he might be. The very
tiptop of enjoyment would never be reached, unless
the whole world were to become his treasure-room, and
be filled with yellow metal which should be all his
own.

Now, I need hardly remind such wise little people
as you are, that in the old, old times, when King Midas was alive, a great many things came to pass,
which we should consider wonderful if they were to
happen in our own day and country. And, on the
other hand, a great many things take place nowadays,
which seem not only wonderful to us, but at which the
people of old times would have stared their eyes out.
On the whole, I regard our own times as the strangest
of the two ; but, however that may be, I must go on
with my story.

Midas was enjoying himself in his treasure-room,
one day, as usual, when he perceived a shadow fall
over the heaps of gold ; and, looking suddenly up,
what should he behold but the figure of a stranger,
standing in the bright and narrow sunbeam ! It
was a young man, with a cheerful and ruddy face.
Whether it was that the imagination of King Midas
threw a yellow tinge over everything, or whatever the

cause might be, he could not help fancying that the smile with which the stranger regarded him had a kind of golden radiance in it. Certainly, although his figure intercepted the sunshine, there was now a brighter gleam upon all the piled-up treasures than before. Even the remotest corners had their share of it, and were lighted up, when the stranger smiled, as with tips of flame and sparkles of fire.

As Midas knew that he had carefully turned the key in the lock, and that no mortal strength could possibly break into his treasure-room, he, of course, concluded that his visitor must be something more than mortal. It is no matter about telling you who he was. In those days, when the earth was comparatively a new affair, it was supposed to be often the resort of beings endowed with supernatural power, and who used to interest themselves in the joys and sorrows of men, women, and children, half playfully and half seriously. Midas had met such beings before now, and was not sorry to meet one of them again. The stranger's aspect, indeed, was so good-humored and kindly, if not beneficent, that it would have been unreasonable to suspect him of intending any mischief. It was far more probable that he came to do Midas a favor. And what could that favor be, unless to multiply his heaps of treasure?

The stranger gazed about the room; and when his lustrous smile had glistened upon all the golden objects that were there, he turned again to Midas.

"You are a wealthy man, friend Midas!" he observed. "I doubt whether any other four walls, on earth, contain so much gold as you have contrived to pile up in this room."

"I have done pretty well, — pretty well," answered

Midas, in a discontented tone. "But, after all, it is but a trifle, when you consider that it has taken me my whole life to get it together. If one could live a thousand years, he might have time to grow rich!"

"What!" exclaimed the stranger. "Then you are not satisfied?"

Midas shook his head.

"And pray what would satisfy you?" asked the stranger. "Merely for the curiosity of the thing, I should be glad to know."

Midas paused and meditated. He felt a presentiment that this stranger, with such a golden lustre in his good-humored smile, had come hither with both the power and the purpose of gratifying his utmost wishes. Now, therefore, was the fortunate moment, when he had but to speak, and obtain whatever possible, or seemingly impossible thing, it might come into his head to ask. So he thought, and thought, and thought, and heaped up one golden mountain upon another, in his imagination, without being able to imagine them big enough. At last, a bright idea occurred to King Midas. It seemed really as bright as the glistening metal which he loved so much.

Raising his head, he looked the lustrous stranger in the face.

"Well, Midas," observed his visitor, "I see that you have at length hit upon something that will satisfy you. Tell me your wish."

"It is only this," replied Midas. "I am weary of collecting my treasures with so much trouble, and beholding the heap so diminutive, after I have done my best. I wish everything that I touch to be changed to gold!"

The stranger's smile grew so very broad, that it

seemed to fill the room like an outburst of the sun, gleaming into a shadowy dell, where the yellow autumnal leaves — for so looked the lumps and particles of gold — lie strewn in the glow of light.

"The Golden Touch!" exclaimed he. "You certainly deserve credit, friend Midas, for striking out so brilliant a conception. But are you quite sure that this will satisfy you?"

"How could it fail?" said Midas.

"And will you never regret the possession of it?"

"What could induce me?" asked Midas. "I ask nothing else, to render me perfectly happy."

"Be it as you wish, then," replied the stranger, waving his hand in token of farewell. "To-morrow, at sunrise, you will find yourself gifted with the Golden Touch."

The figure of the stranger then became exceedingly bright, and Midas involuntarily closed his eyes. On opening them again, he beheld only one yellow sunbeam in the room, and, all around him, the glistening of the precious metal which he had spent his life in hoarding up.

Whether Midas slept as usual that night, the story does not say. Asleep or awake, however, his mind was probably in the state of a child's, to whom a beautiful new plaything has been promised in the morning. At any rate, day had hardly peeped over the hills, when King Midas was broad awake, and, stretching his arms out of bed, began to touch the objects that were within reach. He was anxious to prove whether the Golden Touch had really come, according to the stranger's promise. So he laid his finger on a chair by the bedside, and on various other things, but was grievously disappointed to perceive that they remained

of exactly the same substance as before. Indeed, he
felt very much afraid that he had only dreamed about
the lustrous stranger, or else that the latter had been
making game of him. And what a miserable affair
would it be, if, after all his hopes, Midas must content
himself with what little gold he could scrape together
by ordinary means, instead of creating it by a touch!

All this while, it was only the gray of the morning,
with but a streak of brightness along the edge of the
sky, where Midas could not see it. He lay in a very
disconsolate mood, regretting the downfall of his
hopes, and kept growing sadder and sadder, until the
earliest sunbeam shone through the window, and
gilded the ceiling over his head. It seemed to Midas
that this bright yellow sunbeam was reflected in rather
a singular way on the white covering of the bed.
Looking more closely, what was his astonishment and
delight, when he found that this linen fabric had
been transmuted to what seemed a woven texture of
the purest and brightest gold! The Golden Touch
had come to him with the first sunbeam!

Midas started up, in a kind of joyful frenzy, and
ran about the room, grasping at everything that happened to be in his way. He seized one of the bed-
posts, and it became immediately a fluted golden
pillar. He pulled aside a window-curtain, in order to
admit a clear spectacle of the wonders which he was
performing; and the tassel grew heavy in his hand,
—a mass of gold. He took up a book from the table.
At his first touch, it assumed the appearance of such a
splendidly bound and gilt-edged volume as one often
meets with, nowadays; but, on running his fingers
through the leaves, behold! it was a bundle of thin
golden plates, in which all the wisdom of the book

had grown illegible. He hurriedly put on his clothes, and was enraptured to see himself in a magnificent suit of gold cloth, which retained its flexibility and softness, although it burdened him a little with its weight. He drew out his handkerchief, which little Marygold had hemmed for him. That was likewise gold, with the dear child's neat and pretty stitches running all along the border, in gold thread!

Somehow or other, this last transformation did not quite please King Midas. He would rather that his little daughter's handiwork should have remained just the same as when she climbed his knee and put it into his hand.

But it was not worth while to vex himself about a trifle. Midas now took his spectacles from his pocket, and put them on his nose, in order that he might see more distinctly what he was about. In those days, spectacles for common people had not been invented, but were already worn by kings; else, how could Midas have had any? To his great perplexity, however, excellent as the glasses were, he discovered that he could not possibly see through them. But this was the most natural thing in the world; for, on taking them off, the transparent crystals turned out to be plates of yellow metal, and, of course, were worthless as spectacles, though valuable as gold. It struck Midas as rather inconvenient that, with all his wealth, he could never again be rich enough to own a pair of serviceable spectacles.

"It is no great matter, nevertheless," said he to himself, very philosophically. "We cannot expect any great good, without its being accompanied with some small inconvenience. The Golden Touch is worth the sacrifice of a pair of spectacles, at least, if not of one's very eyesight. My own eyes will serve for ordinary purposes, and little Marygold will soon be old enough to read to me."

Wise King Midas was so exalted by his good fortune, that the palace seemed not sufficiently spacious to contain him. He therefore went down stairs, and smiled, on observing that the balustrade of the staircase became a bar of burnished gold, as his hand passed over it, in his descent. He lifted the door-latch (it was brass only a moment ago, but golden when his fingers quitted it), and emerged into the garden. Here, as it happened, he found a great number of beautiful roses in full bloom, and others in all the stages of lovely bud and blossom. Very delicious was their fragrance in the morning breeze. Their delicate blush was one of the fairest sights in the world; so gentle, so modest, and so full of sweet tranquillity, did these roses seem to be.

But Midas knew a way to make them far more precious, according to his way of thinking, than roses had ever been before. So he took great pains in going from bush to bush, and exercised his magic touch most indefatigably; until every individual flower and bud, and even the worms at the heart of some of them, were changed to gold. By the time this good work was completed, King Midas was summoned to breakfast; and as the morning air had given him an excellent appetite, he made haste back to the palace.

What was usually a king's breakfast in the days of Midas, I really do not know, and cannot stop now to investigate. To the best of my belief, however, on this particular morning, the breakfast consisted of hot cakes, some nice little brook trout, roasted potatoes, fresh boiled eggs, and coffee, for King Midas himself, and a bowl of bread and milk for his daughter Marygold. At all events, this is a breakfast fit to set before a king; and, whether he had it or not, King Midas could not have had a better.

Little Marygold had not yet made her appearance. Her father ordered her to be called, and, seating himself at table, awaited the child's coming, in order to begin his own breakfast. To do Midas justice, he really loved his daughter, and loved her so much the more this morning, on account of the good fortune which had befallen him. It was not a great while before he heard her coming along the passageway crying bitterly. This circumstance surprised him, because Marygold was one of the cheerfullest little people whom you would see in a summer's day, and hardly shed a thimbleful of tears in a twelvemonth. When Midas heard her sobs, he determined to put little Marygold into better spirits, by an agreeable surprise; so, leaning across the table, he touched his daughter's bowl (which was a China one, with pretty figures all around it), and transmuted it to gleaming gold.

Meanwhile, Marygold slowly and disconsolately opened the door, and showed herself with her apron at her eyes, still sobbing as if her heart would break.

" How now, my little lady ! " cried Midas. " Pray what is the matter with you, this bright morning? "

Marygold, without taking the apron from her eyes, held out her hand, in which was one of the roses which Midas had so recently transmuted.

" Beautiful ! " exclaimed her father. " And what is there in this magnificent golden rose to make you cry ? "

" Ah, dear father ! " answered the child, as well as

her sobs would let her; "it is not beautiful, but the ugliest flower that ever grew! As soon as I was dressed I ran into the garden to gather some roses for you; because I know you like them, and like them the better when gathered by your little daughter. But, oh dear, dear me! What do you think has happened? Such a misfortune! All the beautiful roses, that smelled so sweetly and had so many lovely blushes, are blighted and spoilt! They are grown quite yellow, as you see this one, and have no longer any fragrance! What can have been the matter with them?"

"Poh, my dear little girl, — pray don't cry about it!" said Midas, who was ashamed to confess that he himself had wrought the change which so greatly afflicted her. "Sit down and eat your bread and milk! You will find it easy enough to exchange a golden rose like that (which will last hundreds of years) for an ordinary one which would wither in a day."

"I don't care for such roses as this!" cried Marygold, tossing it contemptuously away. "It has no smell, and the hard petals prick my nose!"

The child now sat down to table, but was so occupied with her grief for the blighted roses that she did not even notice the wonderful transmutation of her China bowl. Perhaps this was all the better; for Marygold was accustomed to take pleasure in looking at the queer figures, and strange trees and houses, that were painted on the circumference of the bowl; and these ornaments were now entirely lost in the yellow hue of the metal.

Midas, meanwhile, had poured out a cup of coffee, and, as a matter of course, the coffee-pot, whatever metal it may have been when he took it up, was gold when he set it down. He thought to himself, that it

was rather an extravagant style of splendor, in a king
of his simple habits, to breakfast off a service of gold,
and began to be puzzled with the difficulty of keeping
his treasures safe. The cupboard and the kitchen
would no longer be a secure place of deposit for articles so valuable as golden bowls and coffee-pots.

Amid these thoughts, he lifted a spoonful of coffee
to his lips, and, sipping it, was astonished to perceive
that, the instant his lips touched the liquid, it became
molten gold, and, the next moment, hardened into a
lump!

"Ha!" exclaimed Midas, rather aghast.

"What is the matter, father?" asked little Marygold, gazing at him, with the tears still standing in her
eyes.

"Nothing, child, nothing!" said Midas. "Eat your
milk, before it gets quite cold."

He took one of the nice little trouts on his plate,
and, by way of experiment, touched its tail with his
finger. To his horror, it was immediately transmuted
from an admirably fried brook-trout into a gold-fish,
though not one of those gold-fishes which people often
keep in glass globes, as ornaments for the parlor.
No; but it was really a metallic fish, and looked as if
it had been very cunningly made by the nicest gold-
smith in the world. Its little bones were now golden
wires; its fins and tail were thin plates of gold; and
there were the marks of the fork in it, and all the delicate, frothy appearance of a nicely fried fish, exactly
imitated in metal. A very pretty piece of work, as
you may suppose; only King Midas, just at that moment, would much rather have had a real trout in his
dish than this elaborate and valuable imitation of one.

"I don't quite see," thought he to himself, "how I
am to get any breakfast!"

He took one of the smoking-hot cakes, and had scarcely broken it, when, to his cruel mortification, though, a moment before, it had been of the whitest wheat, it assumed the yellow hue of Indian meal. To say the truth, if it had really been a hot Indian cake, Midas would have prized it a good deal more than he now did, when its solidity and increased weight made him too bitterly sensible that it was gold. Almost in despair, he helped himself to a boiled egg, which immediately underwent a change similar to those of the trout and the cake. The egg, indeed, might have been mistaken for one of those which the famous goose, in the story-book, was in the habit of laying; but King Midas was the only goose that had had anything to do with the matter.

"Well, this is a quandary!" thought he, leaning back in his chair, and looking quite enviously at little Marygold, who was now eating her bread and milk with great satisfaction. "Such a costly breakfast before me, and nothing that can be eaten!"

Hoping that, by dint of great dispatch, he might avoid what he now felt to be a considerable inconvenience, King Midas next snatched a hot potato, and attempted to cram it into his mouth, and swallow it in a hurry. But the Golden Touch was too nimble for him. He found his mouth full, not of mealy potato, but of solid metal, which so burnt his tongue that he roared aloud, and, jumping up from the table, began to dance and stamp about the room, both with pain and affright.

"Father, dear father!" cried little Marygold, who was a very affectionate child, "pray what is the matter? Have you burnt your mouth?"

"Ah, dear child," groaned Midas, dolefully, "I don't know what is to become of your poor father!"

And, truly, my dear little folks, did you ever hear of such a pitiable case in all your lives? Here was literally the richest breakfast that could be set before a king, and its very richness made it absolutely good for nothing. The poorest laborer, sitting down to his crust of bread and cup of water, was far better off than King Midas, whose delicate food was really worth its weight in gold. And what was to be done? Already, at breakfast, Midas was excessively hungry. Would he be less so by dinner-time? And how ravenous would be his appetite for supper, which must undoubtedly consist of the same sort of indigestible dishes as those now before him! How many days, think you, would he survive a continuance of this rich fare?

These reflections so troubled wise King Midas, that he began to doubt whether, after all, riches are the one desirable thing in the world, or even the most desirable. But this was only a passing thought. So fascinated was Midas with the glitter of the yellow metal, that he would still have refused to give up the Golden Touch for so paltry a consideration as a breakfast. Just imagine what a price for one meal's victuals! It would have been the same as paying millions and millions of money (and as many millions more as would take forever to reckon up) for some fried trout, an egg, a potato, a hot cake, and a cup of coffee!

"It would be quite too dear," thought Midas.

Nevertheless, so great was his hunger, and the perplexity of his situation, that he again groaned aloud, and very grievously too. Our pretty Marygold could endure it no longer. She sat, a moment, gazing at her father, and trying, with all the might of her little wits, to find out what was the matter with him. Then, with a sweet and sorrowful impulse to comfort him, she started from her chair, and, running to Midas, threw her arms affectionately about his knees. He bent down and kissed her. He felt that his little daughter's love was worth a thousand times more than he had gained by the Golden Touch.

"My precious, precious Marygold!" cried he.

But Marygold made no answer.

Alas, what had he done? How fatal was the gift which the stranger bestowed! The moment the lips of Midas touched Marygold's forehead, a change had taken place. Her sweet, rosy face, so full of affection as it had been, assumed a glittering yellow color, with yellow tear-drops congealing on her cheeks. Her beautiful brown ringlets took the same tint. Her soft and tender little form grew hard and inflexible within her father's encircling arms. Oh, terrible misfortune! The victim of his insatiable desire for wealth, little Marygold was a human child no longer, but a golden statue!

Yes, there she was, with the questioning look of love, grief, and pity, hardened into her face. It was the prettiest and most woful sight that ever mortal saw. All the features and tokens of Marygold were there; even the beloved little dimple remained in her golden chin. But, the more perfect was the resemblance, the greater was the father's agony at beholding this golden image, which was all that was left him of a daughter. It had been a favorite phrase of Midas, whenever he felt particularly fond of the child, to say that she was worth her weight in gold. And now the phrase had become literally true. And now, at last, when it was too late, he felt how infinitely a warm and tender heart, that loved him, exceeded in value all the wealth that could be piled up betwixt the earth and sky!

It would be too sad a story, if I were to tell you how Midas, in the fulness of all his gratified desires, began to wring his hands and bemoan himself; and how he could neither bear to look at Marygold, nor yet to look away from her. Except when his eyes were fixed on the image, he could not possibly believe that she was changed to gold. But, stealing another glance, there was the precious little figure, with a yellow tear-drop on its yellow cheek, and a look so piteous and tender, that it seemed as if that very expression must needs soften the gold, and make it flesh again. This, however, could not be. So Midas had only to wring his hands, and to wish that he were the poorest man in the wide world, if the loss of all his wealth might bring back the faintest rose-color to his dear child's face.

While he was in this tumult of despair, he suddenly beheld a stranger standing near the door. Midas bent down his head, without speaking; for he recognized the same figure which had appeared to him, the day before, in the treasure-room, and had bestowed on him this disastrous faculty of the Golden Touch. The stranger's countenance still wore a smile, which seemed to shed a yellow lustre all about the room, and gleamed on little Marygold's image, and on the other objects that had been transmuted by the touch of Midas.

" Well, friend Midas," said the stranger, " pray how do you succeed with the Golden Touch ? "

Midas shook his head.

" I am very miserable," said he.

" Very miserable, indeed ! " exclaimed the stranger. " And how happens that ? Have I not faithfully kept my promise with you ? Have you not everything that your heart desired ? "

"Gold is not everything," answered Midas. "And I have lost all that my heart really cared for."

"Ah! So you have made a discovery, since yesterday?" observed the stranger. "Let us see, then. Which of these two things do you think is really worth the most, — the gift of the Golden Touch, or one cup of clear cold water?"

"O blessed water!" exclaimed Midas. "It will never moisten my parched throat again!"

"The Golden Touch," continued the stranger, "or a crust of bread?"

"A piece of bread," answered Midas, "is worth all the gold on earth!"

"The Golden Touch," asked the stranger, "or your own little Marygold, warm, soft, and loving as she was an hour ago?"

"Oh my child, my dear child!" cried poor Midas, wringing his hands. "I would not have given that one small dimple in her chin for the power of changing this whole big earth into a solid lump of gold!"

"You are wiser than you were, King Midas!" said the stranger, looking seriously at him. "Your own heart, I perceive, has not been entirely changed from flesh to gold. Were it so, your case would indeed be desperate. But you appear to be still capable of understanding that the commonest things, such as lie within everybody's grasp, are more valuable than the riches which so many mortals sigh and struggle after. Tell me, now, do you sincerely desire to rid yourself of this Golden Touch?"

"It is hateful to me!" replied Midas.

A fly settled on his nose, but immediately fell to the floor; for it, too, had become gold. Midas shuddered.

"Go, then," said the stranger, "and plunge into the

river that glides past the bottom of your garden. Take likewise a vase of the same water, and sprinkle it over any object that you may desire to change back again from gold into its former substance. If you do this in earnestness and sincerity, it may possibly repair the mischief which your avarice has occasioned."

King Midas bowed low; and when he lifted his head, the lustrous stranger had vanished.

You will easily believe that Midas lost no time in snatching up a great earthen pitcher (but, alas me! it was no longer earthen after he touched it), and hastening to the river-side. As he scampered along, and forced his way through the shrubbery, it was positively marvellous to see how the foliage turned yellow behind him, as if the autumn had been there, and nowhere else. On reaching the river's brink, he plunged headlong in, without waiting so much as to pull off his shoes.

" Poof! poof! poof!" snorted King Midas, as his head emerged out of the water. " Well ; this is really a refreshing bath, and I think it must have quite washed away the Golden Touch. And now for filling my pitcher! "

As he dipped the pitcher into the water, it gladdened his very heart to see it change from gold into the same good, honest earthen vessel which it had been before he touched it. He was conscious, also, of a change within himself. A cold, hard, and heavy weight seemed to have gone out of his bosom. No doubt, his heart had been gradually losing its human substance, and transmuting itself into insensible metal, but had now softened back again into flesh. Perceiving a violet, that grew on the bank of the river, Midas touched it with his finger, and was overjoyed to find that the delicate flower retained its purple hue, instead of undergoing a yellow blight. The curse of the Golden Touch had, therefore, really been removed from him.

King Midas hastened back to the palace; and, I suppose, the servants knew not what to make of it when they saw their royal master so carefully bringing home an earthen pitcher of water. But that water, which was to undo all the mischief that his folly had wrought, was more precious to Midas than an ocean of molten gold could have been. The first thing he did, as you need hardly be told, was to sprinkle it by handfuls over the golden figure of little Marygold.

No sooner did it fall on her than you would have laughed to see how the rosy color came back to the dear child's cheek! and how she began to sneeze and sputter! — and how astonished she was to find herself dripping wet, and her father still throwing more water over her!

" Pray do not, dear father ! " cried she. " See how you have wet my nice frock, which I put on only this morning ! "

For Marygold did not know that she had been a little golden statue ; nor could she remember anything that had happened since the moment when she ran with outstretched arms to comfort poor King Midas.

Her father did not think it necessary to tell his beloved child how very foolish he had been, but contented himself with showing how much wiser he had now grown. For this purpose, he led little Marygold into the garden, where he sprinkled all the remainder of the water over the rose-bushes, and with such good effect that above five thousand roses recovered their beautiful bloom. There were two circumstances, however, which, as long as he lived, used to put King Midas in mind of the Golden Touch. One was, that the sands of the river sparkled like gold; the other, that little Marygold's hair had now a golden tinge, which he had never observed in it before she had been transmuted by the effect of his kiss. This change of hue was really an improvement, and made Marygold's hair richer than in her babyhood.

When King Midas had grown quite an old man, and used to trot Marygold's children on his knee, he was fond of telling them this marvellous story, pretty much as I have now told it to you. And then would he stroke their glossy ringlets, and tell them that their hair, likewise, had a rich shade of gold, which they had inherited from their mother.

"And to tell you the truth, my precious little folks," quoth King Midas, diligently trotting the children all the while, " ever since that morning, I have hated the very sight of all other gold, save this!"

SHADOW BROOK.

AFTER THE STORY.

" WELL, children," inquired Eustace, who was very fond of eliciting a definite opinion from his auditors, " did you ever, in all your lives, listen to a better story than this of ' The Golden Touch ' ? "

" Why, as to the story of King Midas," said saucy Primrose, " it was a famous one thousands of years before Mr. Eustace Bright came into the world, and will continue to be so as long after he quits it. But some people have what we may call ' The Leaden Touch,' and make everything dull and heavy that they lay their fingers upon."

" You are a smart child, Primrose, to be not yet in your teens," said Eustace, taken rather aback by the piquancy of her criticism. " But you well know, in your naughty little heart, that I have burnished the old gold of Midas all over anew, and have made it shine as it never shone before. And then that figure of Marygold ! Do you perceive no nice workmanship in that ? And how finely I have brought out and deepened the moral ! What say you, Sweet Fern, Dandelion, Clover, Periwinkle ? Would any of you, after hearing this story, be so foolish as to desire the faculty of changing things to gold ? "

" I should like," said Periwinkle, a girl of ten, " to have the power of turning everything to gold with my right forefinger : but, with my left forefinger, I should want the power of changing it back again, if the first change did not please me. And I know what I would do, this very afternoon!"

"Pray tell me," said Eustace.

"Why," answered Periwinkle, "I would touch every one of these golden leaves on the trees with my left forefinger, and make them all green again; so that we might have the summer back at once, with no ugly winter in the mean time."

"O Periwinkle!" cried Eustace Bright, "there you are wrong, and would do a great deal of mischief. Were I Midas, I would make nothing else but just such golden days as these over and over again, all the year throughout. My best thoughts always come a little too late. Why did not I tell you how old King Midas came to America, and changed the dusky autumn, such as it is in other countries, into the burnished beauty which it here puts on? He gilded the leaves of the great volume of Nature."

"Cousin Eustace," said Sweet Fern, a good little boy, who was always making particular inquiries about the precise height of giants and the littleness of fairies, "how big was Marygold, and how much did she weigh after she was turned to gold?"

"She was about as tall as you are," replied Eustace, "and, as gold is very heavy, she weighed at least two thousand pounds, and might have been coined into thirty or forty thousand gold dollars. I wish Primrose were worth half as much. Come, little people, let us clamber out of the dell, and look about us."

They did so. The sun was now an hour or two beyond its noontide mark, and filled the great hollow of the valley with its western radiance, so that it seemed to be brimming with mellow light, and to spill it over the surrounding hill-sides, like golden wine out of a bowl. It was such a day that you could not help saying of it, " There never was such a day before ! " although yesterday was just such a day, and to-morrow will be just such another. Ah, but there are very few of them in a twelvemonth's circle! It is a remarkable peculiarity of these October days, that each of them seems to occupy a great deal of space, although the sun rises rather tardily at that season of the year, and goes to bed, as little children ought, at sober six o'clock, or even earlier. We cannot, therefore, call the days long; but they appear, somehow or other, to make up for their shortness by their breadth; and when the cool night comes, we are conscious of having enjoyed a big armful of life, since morning.

"Come, children, come ! " cried Eustace Bright. " More nuts, more nuts, more nuts ! Fill all your baskets; and, at Christmas time, I will crack them for you, and tell you beautiful stories ! "

So away they went; all of them in excellent spirits, except little Dandelion, who, I am sorry to tell you, had been sitting on a chestnut-bur, and was stuck as full as a pincushion of its prickles. Dear me, how uncomfortably he must have felt !

THE PARADISE OF CHILDREN.

TANGLEWOOD PLAY-ROOM.

INTRODUCTORY TO "THE PARADISE OF CHILDREN."

THE golden days of October passed away, as so many other Octobers have, and brown November likewise, and the greater part of chill December, too. At last came merry Christmas, and Eustace Bright along with it, making it all the merrier by his presence. And, the day after his arrival from college, there came a mighty snow-storm. Up to this time, the winter had held back, and had given us a good many mild days, which were like smiles upon its wrinkled visage. The grass had kept itself green, in sheltered places, such as the nooks of southern hill-slopes, and along the lee of the stone fences. It was but a week or two ago, and since the beginning of the month, that the children had found a dandelion in bloom, on the margin of Shadow Brook, where it glides out of the dell.

But no more green grass and dandelions now. This was such a snow-storm! Twenty miles of it might have been visible at once, between the windows of Tanglewood and the dome of Taconic, had it been possible to see so far among the eddying drifts that whitened all the atmosphere. It seemed as if the hills were giants, and were flinging monstrous handfuls of snow at one another, in their enormous sport.

So thick were the fluttering snow-flakes, that even the trees, midway down the valley, were hidden by them the greater part of the time. Sometimes, it is true, the little prisoners of Tanglewood could discern a dim outline of Monument Mountain, and the smooth whiteness of the frozen lake at its base, and the black or gray tracts of woodland in the nearer landscape. But these were merely peeps through the tempest.

Nevertheless, the children rejoiced greatly in the snow-storm. They had already made acquaintance with it, by tumbling heels over head into its highest drifts, and flinging snow at one another, as we have just fancied the Berkshire mountains to be doing. And now they had come back to their spacious play-room, which was as big as the great drawing-room, and was lumbered with all sorts of playthings, large and small. The biggest was a rocking-horse, that looked like a real pony ; and there was a whole family of wooden, waxen, plaster, and china dolls, besides rag-babies ; and blocks enough to build Bunker Hill Monument, and nine-pins, and balls, and humming-tops, and battledores, and grace-sticks, and skipping-ropes, and more of such valuable property than I could tell of in a printed page. But the children liked the snow-storm better than them all. It suggested so many brisk enjoyments for to-morrow, and all the remainder of the winter. The sleigh-ride ; the slides down hill into the valley ; the snow-images that were to be shaped out ; the snow-fortresses that were to be built ; and the snowballing to be carried on !

So the little folks blessed the snow-storm, and were glad to see it come thicker and thicker, and watched hopefully the long drift that was piling itself up in the avenue, and was already higher than any of their heads.

"Why, we shall be blocked up till spring!" cried they, with the hugest delight. "What a pity that the house is too high to be quite covered up! The little red house, down yonder, will be buried up to its eaves."

"You silly children, what do you want of more snow?" asked Eustace, who, tired of some novel that he was skimming through, had strolled into the play-room. "It has done mischief enough already, by spoiling the only skating that I could hope for through the winter. We shall see nothing more of the lake till April; and this was to have been my first day upon it! Don't you pity me, Primrose?"

"Oh, to be sure!" answered Primrose, laughing. "But, for your comfort, we will listen to another of your old stories, such as you told us under the porch, and down in the hollow, by Shadow Brook. Perhaps I shall like them better now, when there is nothing to do, than while there were nuts to be gathered, and beautiful weather to enjoy."

Hereupon, Periwinkle, Clover, Sweet Fern, and as many others of the little fraternity and cousinhood as were still at Tanglewood, gathered about Eustace, and earnestly besought him for a story. The student yawned, stretched himself, and then, to the vast admiration of the small people, skipped three times back and forth over the top of a chair, in order, as he explained to them, to set his wits in motion.

"Well, well, children," said he, after these preliminaries, "since you insist, and Primrose has set her heart upon it, I will see what can be done for you. And, that you may know what happy days there were before snow-storms came into fashion, I will tell you a story of the oldest of all old times, when the world was as new as Sweet Fern's bran-new humming-top. There was then but one season in the year, and that was the delightful summer; and but one age for mortals, and that was childhood."

"I never heard of that before," said Primrose.

"Of course, you never did," answered Eustace. "It shall be a story of what nobody but myself ever dreamed of, — a Paradise of children, — and how, by the naughtiness of just such a little imp as Primrose here, it all came to nothing."

So Eustace Bright sat down in the chair which he had just been skipping over, took Cowslip upon his knee, ordered silence throughout the auditory, and began a story about a sad naughty child, whose name was Pandora, and about her playfellow Epimetheus. You may read it, word for word, in the pages that come next.

THE PARADISE OF CHILDREN.

LONG, long ago, when this old world was in its tender infancy, there was a child, named Epimetheus, who never had either father or mother; and, that he might not be lonely, another child, fatherless and motherless like himself, was sent from a far country, to live with him, and be his playfellow and helpmate. Her name was Pandora.

The first thing that Pandora saw, when she entered the cottage where Epimetheus dwelt, was a great box. And almost the first question which she put to him, after crossing the threshold, was this, —

"Epimetheus, what have you in that box?"

"My dear little Pandora," answered Epimetheus, "that is a secret, and you must be kind enough not to ask any questions about it. The box was left here to be kept safely, and I do not myself know what it contains."

"But who gave it to you?" asked Pandora. "And where did it come from?"

"That is a secret, too," replied Epimetheus.

"How provoking!" exclaimed Pandora, pouting her lip. "I wish the great ugly box were out of the way!"

"Oh come, don't think of it any more," cried Epimetheus. "Let us run out of doors, and have some nice play with the other children."

It is thousands of years since Epimetheus and Pandora were alive; and the world, nowadays, is a very different sort of thing from what it was in their time. Then, everybody was a child. There needed no fathers and mothers to take care of the children ; because there was no danger, nor trouble of any kind, and no clothes to be mended, and there was always plenty to eat and drink. Whenever a child wanted his dinner, he found it growing on a tree ; and, if he looked at the tree in the morning, he could see the expanding blossom of that night's supper ; or, at eventide, he saw the tender bud of to-morrow's breakfast. It was a very pleasant life indeed. No labor to be done, no tasks to be studied ; nothing but sports and dances, and sweet voices of children talking, or carolling like birds, or gushing out in merry laughter, throughout the livelong day.

What was most wonderful of all, the children never quarrelled among themselves ; neither had they any crying fits ; nor, since time first began, had a single one of these little mortals ever gone apart into a corner, and sulked. Oh, what a good time was that to be alive in ? The truth is, those ugly little winged monsters, called Troubles, which are now almost as numerous as mosquitoes, had never yet been seen on the earth. It is probable that the very greatest disquietude which a child had ever experienced was Pandora's vexation at not being able to discover the secret of the mysterious box.

This was at first only the faint shadow of a Trouble ; but, every day, it grew more and more substantial, until, before a great while, the cottage of Epimetheus and Pandora was less sunshiny than those of the other children.

" Whence can the box have come ? " Pandora continually kept saying to herself and to Epimetheus. " And what in the world can be inside of it ? "

" Always talking about this box ! " said Epimetheus, at last ; for he had grown extremely tired of the subject. " I wish, dear Pandora, you would try to talk of something else. Come, let us go and gather some ripe figs, and eat them under the trees, for our supper. And I know a vine that has the sweetest and juiciest grapes you ever tasted."

" Always talking about grapes and figs ! " cried Pandora, pettishly.

" Well, then," said Epimetheus, who was a very good-tempered child, like a multitude of children in those days, " let us run out and have a merry time with our playmates."

" I am tired of merry times, and don't care if I never have any more ! " answered our pettish little Pandora. " And, besides, I never do have any. This ugly box ! I am so taken up with thinking about it all the time. I insist upon your telling me what is inside of it."

" As I have already said, fifty times over, I do not know ! " replied Epimetheus, getting a little vexed. " How, then, can I tell you what is inside ? "

" You might open it," said Pandora, looking sideways at Epimetheus, " and then we could see for ourselves."

" Pandora, what are you thinking of ? " exclaimed Epimetheus.

And his face expressed so much horror at the idea of looking into a box, which had been confided to him on the condition of his never opening it, that Pandora thought it best not to suggest it any more. Still, however, she could not help thinking and talking about the box.

" At least," said she, " you can tell me how it came here."

"It was left at the door," replied Epimetheus, "just before you came, by a person who looked very smiling and intelligent, and who could hardly forbear laughing as he put it down. He was dressed in an odd kind of a cloak, and had on a cap that seemed to be made partly of feathers, so that it looked almost as if it had wings."

"What sort of a staff had he?" asked Pandora.

"Oh, the most curious staff you ever saw!" cried Epimetheus. "It was like two serpents twisting around a stick, and was carved so naturally that I, at first, thought the serpents were alive."

"I know him," said Pandora, thoughtfully. "Nobody else has such a staff. It was Quicksilver; and he brought me hither, as well as the box. No doubt he intended it for me; and, most probably, it contains pretty dresses for me to wear, or toys for you and me to play with, or something very nice for us both to eat!"

"Perhaps so," answered Epimetheus, turning away. "But until Quicksilver comes back and tells us so, we have neither of us any right to lift the lid of the box."

"What a dull boy he is!" muttered Pandora, as Epimetheus left the cottage. "I do wish he had a little more enterprise!"

For the first time since her arrival, Epimetheus had gone out without asking Pandora to accompany him. He went to gather figs and grapes by himself, or to seek whatever amusement he could find, in other society than his little playfellow's. He was tired to death of hearing about the box, and heartily wished that Quicksilver, or whatever was the messenger's name, had left it at some other child's door, where Pandora would never have set eyes on it. So perseveringly as she did babble about this one thing! The box, the box, and nothing but the box! It seemed as if the box were bewitched, and as if the cottage were not big enough to hold it, without Pandora's continually stumbling over it, and making Epimetheus stumble over it likewise, and bruising all four of their shins.

Well, it was really hard that poor Epimetheus should have a box in his ears from morning till night; especially as the little people of the earth were so unaccustomed to vexations, in those happy days, that they knew not how to deal with them. Thus, a small vexation made as much disturbance then, as a far bigger one would in our own times.

After Epimetheus was gone, Pandora stood gazing at the box. She had called it ugly, above a hundred times; but, in spite of all that she had said against it, it was positively a very handsome article of furniture, and would have been quite an ornament to any room in which it should be placed. It was made of a beautiful kind of wood, with dark and rich veins spreading over its surface, which was so highly polished that little Pandora could see her face in it. As the child had no other looking-glass, it is odd that she did not value the box, merely on this account.

The edges and corners of the box were carved with most wonderful skill. Around the margin there were figures of graceful men and women, and the prettiest children ever seen, reclining or sporting amid a profusion of flowers and foliage; and these various objects were so exquisitely represented, and were wrought together in such harmony, that flowers, foliage, and human beings seemed to combine into a wreath of mingled beauty. But here and there, peeping forth from behind the carved foliage, Pandora once or twice fancied that she saw a face not so lovely, or something or other that was disagreeable, and which stole the beauty out of all the rest. Nevertheless, on looking more closely, and touching the spot with her finger, she could discover nothing of the kind. Some face, that was really beautiful, had been made to look ugly by her catching a sideway glimpse at it.

The most beautiful face of all was done in what is called high relief, in the centre of the lid. There was nothing else, save the dark, smooth richness of the polished wood, and this one face in the centre, with a garland of flowers about its brow. Pandora had looked at this face a great many times, and imagined that the mouth could smile if it liked, or be grave when it chose, the same as any living mouth. The features, indeed, all wore a very lively and rather mischievous expression, which looked almost as if it needs must burst out of the carved lips, and utter itself in words.

Had the mouth spoken, it would probably have been something like this:

"Do not be afraid, Pandora! What harm can there be in opening the box? Never mind that poor, simple Epimetheus! You are wiser than he, and have ten times as much spirit. Open the box, and see if you do not find something very pretty!"

The box, I had almost forgotten to say, was fastened; not by a lock, nor by any other such contrivance, but by a very intricate knot of gold cord. There appeared to be no end to this knot, and no beginning. Never was a knot so cunningly twisted, nor with so many ins and outs, which roguishly defied the skilfullest fingers to disentangle them. And yet, by the very difficulty that there was in it, Pandora was

the more tempted to examine the knot, and just see
how it was made. Two or three times, already, she
had stooped over the box, and taken the knot between
her thumb and forefinger, but without positively trying to undo it.

"I really believe," said she to herself, "that I begin
to see how it was done. Nay, perhaps I could tie it
up again, after undoing it. There would be no harm
in that, surely. Even Epimetheus would not blame
me for that. I need not open the box, and should
not, of course, without the foolish boy's consent, even
if the knot were untied."

It might have been better for Pandora if she had
had a little work to do, or anything to employ her
mind upon, so as not to be so constantly thinking of
this one subject. But children led so easy a life, before any Troubles came into the world, that they had
really a great deal too much leisure. They could not
be forever playing at hide-and-seek among the flower-
shrubs, or at blind-man's-buff with garlands over their
eyes, or at whatever other games had been found out,
while Mother Earth was in her babyhood. When life
is all sport, toil is the real play. There was absolutely
nothing to do. A little sweeping and dusting about
the cottage, I suppose, and the gathering of fresh
flowers (which were only too abundant everywhere),
and arranging them in vases, — and poor little Pandora's day's work was over. And then, for the rest of
the day, there was the box!

After all, I am not quite sure that the box was not
a blessing to her in its way. It supplied her with such
a variety of ideas to think of, and to talk about, whenever she had anybody to listen! When she was in
good-humor, she could admire the bright polish of its

sides, and the rich border of beautiful faces and foliage that ran all around it. Or, if she chanced to be ill-tempered, she could give it a push, or kick it with her naughty little foot. And many a kick did the box — (but it was a mischievous box, as we shall see, and deserved all it got) — many a kick did it receive. But, certain it is, if it had not been for the box, our active-minded little Pandora would not have known half so well how to spend her time as she now did.

For it was really an endless employment to guess what was inside. What could it be, indeed? Just imagine, my little hearers, how busy your wits would be, if there were a great box in the house, which, as you might have reason to suppose, contained something new and pretty for your Christmas or New-Year's gifts. Do you think that you should be less curious than Pandora? If you were left alone with the box, might you not feel a little tempted to lift the lid? But you would not do it. Oh, fie ! No, no ! Only, if you thought there were toys in it, it would be so very hard to let slip an opportunity of taking just one peep ! I know not whether Pandora expected any toys ; for none had yet begun to be made, probably, in those days, when the world itself was one great plaything for the children that dwelt upon it. But Pandora was convinced that there was something very beautiful and valuable in the box ; and therefore she felt just as anxious to take a peep as any of these little girls, here around me, would have felt. And, possibly, a little more so ; but of that I am not quite so certain.

On this particular day, however, which we have so long been talking about, her curiosity grew so much greater than it usually was, that, at last, she ap-

proached the box. She was more than half determined to open it, if she could. Ah, naughty Pandora!

First, however, she tried to lift it. It was heavy;
quite too heavy for the slender strength of a child,
like Pandora. She raised one end of the box a few
inches from the floor, and let it fall again, with a
pretty loud thump. A moment afterwards, she almost fancied that she heard something stir inside of
the box. She applied her ear as closely as possible,
and listened. Positively, there did seem to be a kind
of stifled murmur, within! Or was it merely the
singing in Pandora's ears? Or could it be the beating of her heart? The child could not quite satisfy
herself whether she had heard anything or no. But,
at all events, her curiosity was stronger than ever.

As she drew back her head, her eyes fell upon the
knot of gold cord.

"It must have been a very ingenious person who
tied this knot," said Pandora to herself. "But I think
I could untie it nevertheless. I am resolved, at least,
to find the two ends of the cord."

So she took the golden knot in her fingers, and
pried into its intricacies as sharply as she could. Almost without intending it, or quite knowing what she
was about, she was soon busily engaged in attempting
to undo it. Meanwhile, the bright sunshine came
through the open window; as did likewise the merry
voices of the children, playing at a distance, and perhaps the voice of Epimetheus among them. Pandora
stopped to listen. What a beautiful day it was!
Would it not be wiser, if she were to let the troublesome knot alone, and think no more about the box,
but run and join her little playfellows, and be happy?

All this time, however, her fingers were half un-
consciously busy with the knot; and happening to
glance at the flower-wreathed face on the lid of the
enchanted box, she seemed to perceive it slyly grinning at her.

"That face looks very mischievous," thought Pandora. "I wonder whether it smiles because I am doing wrong! I have the greatest mind in the world to
run away!"

But just then, by the merest accident, she gave the
knot a kind of a twist, which produced a wonderful
result. The gold cord untwined itself, as if by magic,
and left the box without a fastening.

"This is the strangest thing I ever knew!" said
Pandora. "What will Epimetheus say? And how
can I possibly tie it up again?"

She made one or two attempts to restore the knot,
but soon found it quite beyond her skill. It had dis-
entangled itself so suddenly that she could not in the
least remember how the strings had been doubled into
one another; and when she tried to recollect the shape
and appearance of the knot, it seemed to have gone
entirely out of her mind. Nothing was to be done,
therefore, but to let the box remain as it was until
Epimetheus should come in.

"But," said Pandora, "when he finds the knot untied, he will know that I have done it. How shall I
make him believe that I have not looked into the
box?"

And then the thought came into her naughty little
heart, that, since she would be suspected of having
looked into the box, she might just as well do so at
once. Oh, very naughty and very foolish Pandora!
You should have thought only of doing what was

right, and of leaving undone what was wrong, and not of what your playfellow Epimetheus would have said or believed. And so perhaps she might, if the enchanted face on the lid of the box had not looked so bewitchingly persuasive at her, and if she had not seemed to hear, more distinctly, than before, the murmur of small voices within. She could not tell whether it was fancy or no; but there was quite a little tumult of whispers in her ear, — or else it was her curiosity that whispered, —

"Let us out, dear Pandora, — pray let us out! We will be such nice pretty playfellows for you! Only let us out!"

"What can it be?" thought Pandora. "Is there something alive in the box? Well! — yes! — I am resolved to take just one peep! Only one peep; and then the lid shall be shut down as safely as ever! There cannot possibly be any harm in just one little peep!"

But it is now time for us to see what Epimetheus was doing.

This was the first time, since his little playmate had come to dwell with him, that he had attempted to enjoy any pleasure in which she did not partake. But nothing went right; nor was he nearly so happy as on other days. He could not find a sweet grape or a ripe fig (if Epimetheus had a fault, it was a little too much fondness for figs); or, if ripe at all, they were overripe, and so sweet as to be cloying. There was no mirth in his heart, such as usually made his voice gush out, of its own accord, and swell the merriment of his companions. In short, he grew so uneasy and discontented, that the other children could not imagine what was the matter with Epimetheus. Neither did he himself know what ailed him, any better than they did. For you must recollect that, at the time we are speaking of, it was everybody's nature, and constant habit, to be happy. The world had not yet learned to be otherwise. Not a single soul or body, since these children were first sent to enjoy themselves on the beautiful earth, had ever been sick or out of sorts.

At length, discovering that, somehow or other, he put a stop to all the play, Epimetheus judged it best to go back to Pandora, who was in a humor better suited to his own. But, with a hope of giving her pleasure, he gathered some flowers, and made them into a wreath, which he meant to put upon her head. The flowers were very lovely, — roses, and lilies, and orange-blossoms, and a great many more, which left a trail of fragrance behind, as Epimetheus carried them along; and the wreath was put together with as much skill as could reasonably be expected of a boy. The fingers of little girls, it has always appeared to me, are the fittest to twine flower-wreaths; but boys could do it, in those days, rather better than they can now.

And here I must mention that a great black cloud had been gathering in the sky, for some time past, although it had not yet overspread the sun. But, just as Epimetheus reached the cottage door, this cloud began to intercept the sunshine, and thus to make a sudden and sad obscurity.

He entered softly; for he meant, if possible, to steal behind Pandora, and fling the wreath of flowers over her head, before she should be aware of his approach. But, as it happened, there was no need of his treading so very lightly. He might have trod as heavily as he pleased, — as heavily as a grown man, — as heavily,

I was going to say, as an elephant, — without much probability of Pandora's hearing his footsteps. She was too intent upon her purpose. At the moment of his entering the cottage, the naughty child had put her hand to the lid, and was on the point of opening the mysterious box. Epimetheus beheld her.. If he had cried out, Pandora would probably have withdrawn her hand, and the fatal mystery of the box might never have been known.

But Epimetheus himself, although he said very little about it, had his own share of curiosity to know what was inside. Perceiving that Pandora was resolved to find out the secret, he determined that his playfellow should not be the only wise person in the cottage. And if there were anything pretty or valuable in the box, he meant to take half of it to himself. Thus, after all his sage speeches to Pandora about restraining her curiosity, Epimetheus turned out to be quite as foolish, and nearly as much in fault, as she. So, whenever we blame Pandora for what happened, we must not forget to shake our heads at Epimetheus likewise.

As Pandora raised the lid, the cottage grew very dark and dismal ; for the black cloud had now swept quite over the sun, and seemed to have buried it alive. There had, for a little while past, been a low growling and muttering, which all at once broke into a heavy peal of thunder. But Pandora, heeding nothing of all this, lifted the lid nearly upright, and looked inside. It seemed as if a sudden swarm of winged creatures brushed past her, taking flight out of the box, while, at the same instant, she heard the voice of Epimetheus, with a lamentable tone, as if he were in pain.

"Oh, I am stung ! " cried he. "I am stung !

Naughty Pandora! why have you opened this wicked box?"

Pandora let fall the lid, and, starting up, looked about her, to see what had befallen Epimetheus. The thunder-cloud had so darkened the room that she could not very clearly discern what was in it. But she heard a disagreeable buzzing, as if a great many huge flies, or gigantic mosquitoes, or those insects which we call dor-bugs, and pinching-dogs, were darting about. And, as her eyes grew more accustomed to the imperfect light, she saw a crowd of ugly little shapes, with bats' wings, looking abominably spiteful, and armed with terribly long stings in their tails. It was one of these that had stung Epimetheus. Nor was it a great while before Pandora herself began to scream, in no less pain and affright than her playfellow, and making a vast deal more hubbub about it. An odious little monster had settled on her forehead, and would have stung her I know not how deeply, if Epimetheus had not run and brushed it away.

Now, if you wish to know what these ugly things might be, which had made their escape out of the box, I must tell you that they were the whole family of earthly Troubles. There were evil Passions; there were a great many species of Cares; there were more than a hundred and fifty Sorrows; there were Diseases, in a vast number of miserable and painful shapes; there were more kinds of Naughtiness than it would be of any use to talk about. In short, everything that has since afflicted the souls and bodies of mankind had been shut up in the mysterious box, and given to Epimetheus and Pandora to be kept safely, in order that the happy children of the world might never be molested by them. Had they been faithful to their trust, all would have gone well. No grown person would ever have been sad, nor any child have had cause to shed a single tear, from that hour until this moment.

But — and you may see by this how a wrong act of any one mortal is a calamity to the whole world — by Pandora's lifting the lid of that miserable box, and by the fault of Epimetheus, too, in not preventing her, these Troubles have obtained a foothold among us, and do not seem very likely to be driven away in a hurry. For it was impossible, as you will easily guess, that the two children should keep the ugly swarm in their own little cottage. On the contrary, the first thing that they did was to fling open the doors and windows, in hopes of getting rid of them ; and, sure enough, away flew the winged Troubles all abroad, and so pestered and tormented the small people, everywhere about, that none of them so much as smiled for many days afterwards. And, what was very singular, all the flowers and dewy blossoms on earth, not one of which had hitherto faded, now began to droop and shed their leaves, after a day or two. The children, moreover, who before seemed immortal in their child hood, now grew older, day by day, and came soon to be youths and maidens, and men and women by and by, and aged people, before they dreamed of such a thing.

Meanwhile, the naughty Pandora, and hardly less naughty Epimetheus, remained in their cottage. Both of them had been grievously stung, and were in a good deal of pain, which seemed the more intolerable to them, because it was the very first pain that had ever been felt since the world began. Of course, they were entirely unaccustomed to it, and could have no idea what it meant. Besides all this, they were in exceedingly bad humor, both with themselves and with one another. In order to indulge it to the utmost, Epimetheus sat down sullenly in a corner with his back towards Pandora; while Pandora flung herself upon the floor and rested her head on the fatal and abominable box. She was crying bitterly, and sobbing as if her heart would break.

Suddenly there was a gentle little tap on the inside of the lid.

"What can that be?" cried Pandora, lifting her head.

But either Epimetheus had not heard the tap, or was too much out of humor to notice it. At any rate, he made no answer.

"You are very unkind," said Pandora, sobbing anew, "not to speak to me!"

Again the tap! It sounded like the tiny knuckles of a fairy's hand, knocking lightly and playfully on the inside of the box.

"Who are you?" asked Pandora, with a little of her former curiosity. "Who are you, inside of this naughty box?"

A sweet little voice spoke from within, —

"Only lift the lid, and you shall see."

"No, no," answered Pandora, again beginning to sob, "I have had enough of lifting the lid! You are inside of the box, naughty creature, and there you shall stay! There are plenty of your ugly brothers and sisters already flying about the world. You need never think that I shall be so foolish as to let you out!"

She looked towards Epimetheus, as she spoke, perhaps expecting that he would commend her for her wisdom. But the sullen boy only muttered that she was wise a little too late.

"Ah," said the sweet little voice again, "you had much better let me out. I am not like those naughty creatures that have stings in their tails. They are no brothers and sisters of mine, as you would see at once, if you were only to get a glimpse of me. Come, come, my pretty Pandora! I am sure you will let me out!"

And, indeed, there was a kind of cheerful witchery in the tone, that made it almost impossible to refuse anything which this little voice asked. Pandora's heart had insensibly grown lighter, at every word that came from within the box. Epimetheus, too, though still in the corner, had turned half round, and seemed to be in rather better spirits than before.

"My dear Epimetheus," cried Pandora, "have you heard this little voice?"

"Yes, to be sure I have," answered he, but in no very good-humor as yet. "And what of it?"

"Shall I lift the lid again?" asked Pandora.

"Just as you please," said Epimetheus. "You have done so much mischief already, that perhaps you may as well do a little more. One other Trouble, in such a swarm as you have set adrift about the world, can make no very great difference."

"You might speak a little more kindly!" murmured Pandora, wiping her eyes.

"Ah, naughty boy!" cried the little voice within the box, in an arch and laughing tone. "He knows he is longing to see me. Come, my dear Pandora, lift up the lid. I am in a great hurry to comfort you. Only let me have some fresh air, and you shall soon see that matters are not quite so dismal as you think them!"

"Epimetheus," exclaimed Pandora, "come what may, I am resolved to open the box!"

"And, as the lid seems very heavy," cried Epimetheus, running across the room, "I will help you!"

So, with one consent, the two children again lifted the lid. Out flew a sunny and smiling little personage, and hovered about the room, throwing a light wherever she went. Have you never made the sunshine dance into dark corners, by reflecting it from a bit of looking-glass? Well, so looked the winged cheerfulness of this fairy-like stranger, amid the gloom of the cottage. She flew to Epimetheus, and laid the least touch of her finger on the inflamed spot where the Trouble had stung him, and immediately the anguish of it was gone. Then she kissed Pandora on the forehead, and her hurt was cured likewise.

After performing these good offices, the bright stranger fluttered sportively over the children's heads, and looked so sweetly at them, that they both began to think it not so very much amiss to have opened the box, since, otherwise, their cheery guest must have been kept a prisoner among those naughty imps with stings in their tails.

"Pray, who are you, beautiful creature?" inquired Pandora.

"I am to be called Hope!" answered the sunshiny figure. "And because I am such a cheery little body, I was packed into the box, to make amends to the human race for that swarm of ugly Troubles, which was destined to be let loose among them. Never fear! we shall do pretty well in spite of them all."

"Your wings are colored like the rainbow!" exclaimed Pandora. "How very beautiful!"

"Yes, they are like the rainbow," said Hope, "because, glad as my nature is, I am partly made of tears as well as smiles."

"And will you stay with us," asked Epimetheus, "forever and ever?"

"As long as you need me," said Hope, with her pleasant smile, — "and that will be as long as you live in the world, — I promise never to desert you. There may come times and seasons, now and then, when you will think that I have utterly vanished. But again, and again, and again, when perhaps you least dream of it, you shall see the glimmer of my wings on the ceiling of your cottage. Yes, my dear children, and I know something very good and beautiful that is to be given you hereafter!"

"Oh tell us," they exclaimed, — "tell us what it is!"

"Do not ask me," replied Hope, putting her finger on her rosy mouth. "But do not despair, even if it should never happen while you live on this earth. Trust in my promise, for it is true."

"We do trust you!" cried Epimetheus and Pandora, both in one breath.

And so they did; and not only they, but so has everybody trusted Hope, that has since been alive. And to tell you the truth, I cannot help being glad — (though, to be sure, it was an uncommonly naughty thing for her to do) — but I cannot help being glad that our foolish Pandora peeped into the box. No doubt — no doubt — the Troubles are still flying about the world, and have increased in multitude, rather than lessened, and are a very ugly set of imps, and carry most venomous stings in their tails. I have felt them already, and expect to feel them more, as I grow older. But then that lovely and lightsome little figure of Hope! What in the world could we do without her? Hope spiritualizes the earth; Hope makes it always new; and, even in the earth's best and brightest aspect, Hope shows it to be only the shadow of an in-finite bliss hereafter!

TANGLEWOOD PLAY-ROOM.

" PRIMROSE," asked Eustace, pinching her ear, " how do you like my little Pandora? Don't you think her the exact picture of yourself? But you would not have hesitated half so long about opening the box."

" Then I should have been well punished for my naughtiness," retorted Primrose, smartly ; " for the first thing to pop out, after the lid was lifted, would have been Mr. Eustace Bright, in the shape of a Trouble."

" Cousin Eustace," said Sweet Fern, " did the box hold all the trouble that has ever come into the world ? "

" Every mite of it ! " answered Eustace. " This very snow-storm, which has spoiled my skating, was packed up there."

" And how big was the box ? " asked Sweet Fern.

" Why, perhaps three feet long," said Eustace, "two feet wide, and two feet and a half high."

" Ah," said the child, " you are making fun of me, Cousin Eustace ! I know there is not trouble enough in the world to fill such a great box as that. As for the snow-storm, it is no trouble at all, but a pleasure ; so it could not have been in the box."

" Hear the child ! " cried Primrose, with an air of superiority. " How little he knows about the troubles of this world! Poor fellow! He will be wiser when he has seen as much of life as I have."

So saying, she began to skip the rope.

Meantime, the day was drawing towards its close. Out of doors the scene certainly looked dreary. There was a gray drift, far and wide, through the gathering twilight; the earth was as pathless as the air; and the bank of snow over the steps of the porch proved that nobody had entered or gone out for a good many hours past. Had there been only one child at the window of Tanglewood, gazing at this wintry prospect, it would perhaps have made him sad. But half a dozen children together, though they cannot quite turn the world into a paradise, may defy old Winter and all his storms to put them out of spirits. Eustace Bright, moreover, on the spur of the moment, invented several new kinds of play, which kept them all in a roar of merriment till bedtime, and served for the next stormy day besides.

THE THREE GOLDEN APPLES.

------◆------

TANGLEWOOD FIRESIDE.

INTRODUCTORY TO "THE THREE GOLDEN APPLES."

THE snow-storm lasted another day; but what became of it afterwards, I cannot possibly imagine. At any rate, it entirely cleared away during the night; and when the sun arose the next morning, it shone brightly down on as bleak a tract of hill-country, here in Berkshire, as could be seen anywhere in the world. The frost-work had so covered the window-panes that it was hardly possible to get a glimpse at the scenery outside. But, while waiting for breakfast, the small populace of Tanglewood had scratched peep-holes with their finger-nails, and saw with vast delight that — unless it were one or two bare patches on a precipitous hill-side, or the gray effect of the snow, intermingled with the black pine forest — all nature was as white as a sheet. How exceedingly pleasant! And, to make it all the better, it was cold enough to nip one's nose short off! If people have but life enough in them to bear it, there is nothing that so raises the spirits, and makes the blood ripple and dance so nimbly, like a brook down the slope of a hill, as a bright, hard frost.

No sooner was breakfast over, than the whole party,

well muffled in furs and woollens, floundered forth
into the midst of the snow. Well, what a day of
frosty sport was this! They slid down hill into the
valley, a hundred times, nobody knows how far; and,
to make it all the merrier, upsetting their sledges, and
tumbling head over heels, quite as often as they came
safely to the bottom. And, once, Eustace Bright took
Periwinkle, Sweet Fern, and Squash-Blossom, on the
sledge with him, by way of insuring a safe passage;
and down they went, full speed. But, behold, half-
way down, the sledge hit against a hidden stump, and
flung all four of its passengers into a heap; and, on
gathering themselves up, there was no little Squash-
Blossom to be found! Why, what could have become
of the child? And while they were wondering and
staring about, up started Squash-Blossom out of a
snow-bank, with the reddest face you ever saw, and
looking as if a large scarlet flower had suddenly
sprouted up in midwinter. Then there was a great
laugh.

When they had grown tired of sliding down hill,
Eustace set the children to digging a cave in the
biggest snow-drift that they could find. Unluckily,
just as it was completed, and the party had squeezed
themselves into the hollow, down came the roof upon
their heads, and buried every soul of them alive! The
next moment, up popped all their little heads out of
the ruins, and the tall student's head in the midst of
them, looking hoary and venerable with the snow-dust
that had got amongst his brown curls. And then, to
punish Cousin Eustace for advising them to dig such
a tumble-down cavern, the children attacked him in a
body, and so bepelted him with snowballs that he was
fain to take to his heels.

So he ran away, and went into the woods, and thence to the margin of Shadow Brook, where he could hear the streamlet grumbling along, under great over-hanging banks of snow and ice, which would scarcely let it see the light of day. There were adamantine icicles glittering around all its little cascades. Thence he strolled to the shore of the lake, and beheld a white, untrodden plain before him, stretching from his own feet to the foot of Monument Mountain. And, it being now almost sunset, Eustace thought that he had never beheld anything so fresh and beautiful as the scene. He was glad that the children were not with him; for their lively spirits and tumble-about activity would quite have chased away his higher and graver mood, so that he would merely have been merry (as he had already been, the whole day long), and would not have known the loveliness of the winter sunset among the hills.

When the sun was fairly down, our friend Eustace went home to eat his supper. After the meal was over, he betook himself to the study, with a purpose, I rather imagine, to write an ode, or two or three sonnets, or verses of some kind or other, in praise of the purple and golden clouds which he had seen around the setting sun. But, before he had hammered out the very first rhyme, the door opened, and Primrose and Periwinkle made their appearance.

"Go away, children! I can't be troubled with you now!" cried the student, looking over his shoulder, with the pen between his fingers. "What in the world do you want here? I thought you were all in bed!"

"Hear him, Periwinkle, trying to talk like a grown man!" said Primrose. "And he seems to forget that

I am now thirteen years old, and may sit up almost as late as I please. But, Cousin Eustace, you must put off your airs, and come with us to the drawing-room. The children have talked so much about your stories, that my father wishes to hear one of them, in order to judge whether they are likely to do any mischief."

"Poh, poh, Primrose!" exclaimed the student, rather vexed. "I don't believe I can tell one of my stories in the presence of grown people. Besides, your father is a classical scholar; not that I am much afraid of his scholarship, neither, for I doubt not it is as rusty as an old case-knife by this time. But then he will be sure to quarrel with the admirable nonsense that I put into these stories, out of my own head, and which makes the great charm of the matter for children, like yourself. No man of fifty, who has read the classical myths in his youth, can possibly understand my merit as a reinventor and improver of them."

"All this may be very true," said Primrose, "but come you must! My father will not open his book, nor will mamma open the piano, till you have given us some of your nonsense, as you very correctly call it. So be a good boy, and come along."

Whatever he might pretend, the student was rather glad than otherwise, on second thoughts, to catch at the opportunity of proving to Mr. Pringle what an excellent faculty he had in modernizing the myths of ancient times. Until twenty years of age, a young man may, indeed, be rather bashful about showing his poetry and his prose; but, for all that, he is pretty apt to think that these very productions would place him at the tiptop of literature, if once they could be known. Accordingly, without much more resistance,

Eustace suffered Primrose and Periwinkle to drag him into the drawing-room.

It was a large, handsome apartment, with a semicircular window at one end, in the recess of which stood a marble copy of Greenough's Angel and Child. On one side of the fireplace there were many shelves of books, gravely but richly bound. The white light of the astral-lamp, and the red glow of the bright coal-fire, made the room brilliant and cheerful; and before the fire, in a deep arm-chair, sat Mr. Pringle, looking just fit to be seated in such a chair, and in such a room. He was a tall and quite a handsome gentleman, with a bald brow; and was always so nicely dressed, that even Eustace Bright never liked to enter his presence without at least pausing at the threshold to settle his shirt-collar. But now, as Primrose had hold of one of his hands, and Periwinkle of the other, he was forced to make his appearance with a rough-and-tumble sort of look, as if he had been rolling all day in a snow-bank. And so he had.

Mr. Pringle turned towards the student benignly enough, but in a way that made him feel how uncombed and unbrushed he was, and how uncombed and unbrushed, likewise, were his mind and thoughts.

"Eustace," said Mr. Pringle, with a smile, "I find that you are producing a great sensation among the little public of Tanglewood, by the exercise of your gifts of narrative. Primrose here, as the little folks choose to call her, and the rest of the children, have been so loud in praise of your stories, that Mrs. Pringle and myself are really curious to hear a specimen. It would be so much the more gratifying to myself, as the stories appear to be an attempt to render the fables of classical antiquity into the idiom of modern fancy and feeling. At least, so I judge from a few of the incidents which have come to me at second hand."

" You are not exactly the auditor that I should have chosen, sir," oberved the student, " for fantasies of this nature."

" Possibly not," replied Mr. Pringle. " I suspect, however, that a young author's most useful critic is precisely the one whom he would be least apt to choose. Pray oblige me, therefore."

"Sympathy, methinks, should have some little share in the critic's qualifications," murmured Eustace Bright. " However, sir, if you will find patience, I will find stories. But be kind enough to remember that I am addressing myself to the imagination and sympathies of the children, not to your own."

Accordingly, the student snatched hold of the first theme which presented itself.. It was suggested by a plate of apples that he happened to spy on the mantel-piece.

THE THREE GOLDEN APPLES.

DID you ever hear of the golden apples, that grew in the garden of the Hesperides? Ah, those were such apples as would bring a great price, by the bushel, if any of them could be found growing in the orchards of nowadays! But there is not, I suppose, a graft of that wonderful fruit on a single tree in the wide world. Not so much as a seed of those apples exists any longer.

And, even in the old, old, half-forgotten times, before the garden of the Hesperides was overrun with weeds, a great many people doubted whether there could be real trees that bore apples of solid gold upon their branches. All had heard of them, but nobody remembered to have seen any. Children, nevertheless, used to listen, open-mouthed, to stories of the golden apple-tree, and resolved to discover it, when they should be big enough. Adventurous young men, who desired to do a braver thing than any of their fellows, set out in quest of this fruit. Many of them returned no more; none of them brought back the apples. No wonder that they found it impossible to gather them! It is said that there was a dragon beneath the tree, with a hundred terrible heads, fifty of which were always on the watch, while the other fifty slept.

In my opinion it was hardly worth running so much risk for the sake of a solid golden apple. Had the apples been sweet, mellow, and juicy, indeed that would be another matter. There might then have been some sense in trying to get at them, in spite of the hundred-headed dragon.

But, as I have already told you, it was quite a common thing with young persons, when tired of too much peace and rest, to go in search of the garden of the Hesperides. And once the adventure was undertaken by a hero who had enjoyed very little peace or rest since he came into the world. At the time of which I am going to speak, he was wandering through the pleasant land of Italy, with a mighty club in his hand, and a bow and quiver slung across his shoulders. He was wrapt in the skin of the biggest and fiercest lion that ever had been seen, and which he himself had killed ; and though, on the whole, he was kind, and generous, and noble, there was a good deal of the lion's fierceness in his heart. As he went on his way, he continually inquired whether that were the right road to the famous garden. But none of the country people knew anything about the matter, and many looked as if they would have laughed at the question, if the stranger had not carried so very big a club.

So he journeyed on and on, still making the same inquiry, until, at last, he came to the brink of a river where some beautiful young women sat twining wreaths of flowers.

" Can you tell me, pretty maidens," asked the stranger, " whether this is the right way to the garden of the Hesperides ? "

The young women had been having a fine time together, weaving the flowers into wreaths, and crowning one another's heads. And there seemed to be a kind of magic in the touch of their fingers, that made the flowers more fresh and dewy, and of brighter hues, and sweeter fragrance, while they played with them, than even when they had been growing on their native stems. But, on hearing the stranger's question, they dropped all their flowers on the grass, and gazed at him with astonishment.

" The garden of the Hesperides ! " cried one. " We thought mortals had been weary of seeking it, after so many disappointments. And pray, adventurous traveller, what do you want there ? "

" A certain king, who is my cousin," replied he, " has ordered me to get him three of the golden apples."

" Most of the young men who go in quest of these apples," observed another of the damsels, " desire to obtain them for themselves, or to present them to some fair maiden whom they love. Do you, then, love this king, your cousin, so very much ? "

" Perhaps not," replied the stranger, sighing. " He has often been severe and cruel to me. But it is my destiny to obey him."

" And do you know," asked the damsel who had first spoken, " that a terrible dragon, with a hundred heads, keeps watch under the golden apple-tree ? "

" I know it well," answered the stranger, calmly. " But, from my cradle upwards, it has been my business, and almost my pastime, to deal with serpents and dragons."

The young women looked at his massive club, and at the shaggy lion's skin which he wore, and likewise at his heroic limbs and figure ; and they whispered to each other that the stranger appeared to be one who might reasonably expect to perform deeds far beyond the might of other men. But, then, the dragon with a hundred heads ! What mortal, even if he possessed a hundred lives, could hope to escape the fangs of such a monster ? So kind-hearted were the maidens, that they could not bear to see this brave and handsome traveller attempt what was so very dangerous, and devote himself, most probably, to become a meal for the dragon's hundred ravenous mouths.

" Go back," cried they all, — " go back to your own home ! Your mother, beholding you safe and sound, will shed tears of joy ; and what can she do more, should you win ever so great a victory ? No matter for the golden apples ! No matter for the king, your cruel cousin ! We do not wish the dragon with the hundred heads to eat you up ! "

The stranger seemed to grow impatient at these remonstrances. He carelessly lifted his mighty club, and let it fall upon a rock that lay half buried in the earth, near by. With the force of that idle blow, the great rock was shattered all to pieces. It cost the stranger no more effort to achieve this feat of a giant's strength than for one of the young maidens to touch her sister's rosy cheek with a flower.

" Do you not believe," said he, looking at the damsels with a smile, " that such a blow would have crushed one of the dragon's hundred heads ? "

Then he sat down on the grass, and told them the story of his life, or as much of it as he could remember, from the day when he was first cradled in a warrior's brazen shield. While he lay there, two immense serpents came gliding over the floor, and opened their hideous jaws to devour him ; and he, a baby of a few months old, had griped one of the fierce snakes in each of his little fists, and strangled them to death. When he was but a stripling, he had killed a huge lion, almost as big as the one whose vast and shaggy hide he now wore upon his shoulders. The next thing that he had done was to fight a battle with an ugly sort of monster, called a hydra, which had no less than nine heads, and exceedingly sharp teeth in every one.

" But the dragon of the Hesperides, you know," observed one of the damsels, " has a hundred heads ! "

" Nevertheless," replied the stranger, " I would rather fight two such dragons than a single hydra. For, as fast as I cut off a head, two others grew in its place ; and, besides, there was one of the heads that could not possibly be killed, but kept biting as fiercely as ever, long after it was cut off. So I was forced to bury it under a stone, where it is doubtless alive to this very day. But the hydra's body, and its eight other heads, will never do any further mischief."

The damsels, judging that the story was likely to last a good while, had been preparing a repast of bread and grapes, that the stranger might refresh himself in the intervals of his talk. They took pleasure in helping him to this simple food ; and, now and then, one of them would put a sweet grape between her rosy lips, lest it should make him bashful to eat alone.

The traveller proceeded to tell how he had chased a very swift stag, for a twelvemonth together, without ever stopping to take breath, and had at last caught it by the antlers, and carried it home alive. And he had fought with a very odd race of people, half horses and half men, and had put them all to death, from a sense of duty, in order that their ugly figures might never be seen any more. Besides all this, he took to himself great credit for having cleaned out a stable.

" Do you call that a wonderful exploit ? " asked one of the young maidens, with a smile. " Any clown in the country has done as much ! "

" Had it been an ordinary stable," replied the stranger, "I should not have mentioned it. But this was so gigantic a task that it would have taken me all my life to perform it, if I had not luckily thought of turning the channel of a river through the stable-door. That did the business in a very short time!"

Seeing how earnestly his fair auditors listened, he next told them how he had shot some monstrous birds, and had caught a wild bull alive and let him go again, and had tamed a number of very wild horses, and had conquered Hippolyta, the warlike queen of the Amazons. He mentioned, likewise, that he had taken off Hippolyta's enchanted girdle, and had given it to the daughter of his cousin, the king.

" Was it the girdle of Venus," inquired the prettiest of the damsels, " which makes women beautiful?"

" No," answered the stranger. " It had formerly been the sword-belt of Mars; and it can only make the wearer valiant and courageous."

" An old sword-belt!" cried the damsel, tossing her head. " Then I should not care about having it!"

" You are right," said the stranger.

Going on with his wonderful narrative, he informed the maidens that as strange an adventure as ever happened was when he fought with Geryon, the six-legged man. This was a very odd and frightful sort of figure, as you may well believe. Any person, looking at his tracks in the sand or snow, would suppose that three sociable companions had been walking along together. On hearing his footsteps at a little distance, it was no more than reasonable to judge that several people must be coming. But it was only the strange man Geryon clattering onward, with his six legs!

Six legs, and one gigantic body! Certainly, he must have been a very queer monster to look at; and, my stars, what a waste of shoe-leather!

When the stranger had finished the story of his adventures, he looked around at the attentive faces of the maidens.

"Perhaps you may have heard of me before," said he, modestly. "My name is Hercules!"

"We had already guessed it," replied the maidens; "for your wonderful deeds are known all over the world. We do not think it strange, any longer, that you should set out in quest of the golden apples of the Hesperides. Come, sisters, let us crown the hero with flowers!"

Then they flung beautiful wreaths over his stately head and mighty shoulders, so that the lion's skin was almost entirely covered with roses. They took possession of his ponderous club, and so entwined it about with the brightest, softest, and most fragrant blossoms, that not a finger's breadth of its oaken substance could be seen. It looked all like a huge bunch of flowers. Lastly, they joined hands, and danced around him, chanting words which became poetry of their own accord, and grew into a choral song, in honor of the illustrious Hercules.

And Hercules was rejoiced, as any other hero would have been, to know that these fair young girls had heard of the valiant deeds which it had cost him so much toil and danger to achieve. But, still, he was not satisfied. He could not think that what he had already done was worthy of so much honor, while there remained any bold or difficult adventure to be undertaken.

"Dear maidens," said he, when they paused to take breath, "now that you know my name, will you not tell me how I am to reach the garden of the Hesperides?"

" Ah! must you go so soon?" they exclaimed.
" You — that have performed so many wonders, and
spent such a toilsome life — cannot you content yourself to repose a little while on the margin of this
peaceful river?"

Hercules shook his head.

"I must depart now," said he.

"We will then give you the best directions we can,"
replied the damsels. "You must go to the sea-shore,
and find out the Old One, and compel him to inform
you where the golden apples are to be found."

"The Old One!" repeated Hercules, laughing at
this odd name. "And, pray, who may the Old One
be?"

"Why, the Old Man of the Sea, to be sure!" answered one of the damsels. "He has fifty daughters,
whom some people call very beautiful; but we do not
think it proper to be acquainted with them, because
they have sea-green hair, and taper away like fishes.
You must talk with this Old Man of the Sea. He is
a sea-faring person, and knows all about the garden
of the Hesperides; for it is situated in an island which
he is often in the habit of visiting."

Hercules then asked whereabouts the Old One was
most likely to be met with. When the damsels had
informed him, he thanked them for all their kindness,
— for the bread and grapes with which they had fed
him, the lovely flowers with which they had crowned
him, and the songs and dances wherewith they had
done him honor, — and he thanked them, most of all,
for telling him the right way, — and immediately set
forth upon his journey.

But, before he was out of hearing, one of the
maidens called after him.

" Keep fast hold of the Old One, when you catch him ! " cried she, smiling, and lifting her finger to make the caution more impressive. " Do not be astonished at anything that may happen. Only hold him fast, and he will tell you what you wish to know."

Hercules again thanked her, and pursued his way, while the maidens resumed their pleasant labor of making flower-wreaths. They talked about the hero, long after he was gone.

" We will crown him with the loveliest of our garlands," said they, " when he returns hither with the three golden apples, after slaying the dragon with a hundred heads."

Meanwhile, Hercules travelled constantly onward, over hill and dale, and through the solitary woods. Sometimes he swung his club aloft, and splintered a mighty oak with a downright blow. His mind was so full of the giants and monsters with whom it was the business of his life to fight, that perhaps he mistook the great tree for a giant or a monster. And so eager was Hercules to achieve what he had undertaken, that he almost regretted to have spent so much time with the damsels, wasting idle breath upon the story of his adventures. But thus it always is with persons who are destined to perform great things. What they have already done seems less than nothing. What they have taken in hand to do seems worth toil, danger, and life itself.

Persons who happened to be passing through the forest must have been affrighted to see him smite the trees with his great club. With but a single blow, the trunk was riven as by the stroke of lightning, and the broad boughs came rustling and crashing down.

Hastening forward, without ever pausing or looking

behind, he by and by heard the sea roaring at a distance. At this sound, he increased his speed, and
soon came to a beach, where the great surf-waves tumbled themselves upon the hard sand, in a long line of
snowy foam. At one end of the beach, however, there
was a pleasant spot, where some green shrubbery
clambered up a cliff, making its rocky face look soft
and beautiful. A carpet of verdant grass, largely intermixed with sweet-smelling clover, covered the narrow space between the bottom of the cliff and the sea.
And what should Hercules espy there, but an old man,
fast asleep!

But was it really and truly an old man? Certainly,
at first sight, it looked very like one; but, on closer
inspection, it rather seemed to be some kind of a creature that lived in the sea. For, on his legs and arms
there were scales, such as fishes have; he was web-
footed and web-fingered, after the fashion of a duck;
and his long beard, being of a greenish tinge, had more
the appearance of a tuft of sea-weed than of an ordinary beard. Have you never seen a stick of timber,
that has been long tossed about by the waves, and has
got all overgrown with barnacles, and, at last drifting
ashore, seems to have been thrown up from the very
deepest bottom of the sea? Well, the old man would
have put you in mind of just such a wave-tost spar!
But Hercules, the instant he set eyes on this strange
figure, was convinced that it could be no other than
the Old One, who was to direct him on his way.

Yes, it was the selfsame Old Man of the Sea whom
the hospitable maidens had talked to him about.
Thanking his stars for the lucky accident of finding
the old fellow asleep, Hercules stole on tiptoe towards
him, and caught him by the arm and leg.

"Tell me," cried he, before the Old One was well awake, "which is the way to the garden of the Hesperides?"

As you may easily imagine, the Old Man of the Sea awoke in a fright. But his astonishment could hardly have been greater than was that of Hercules, the next moment. For, all of a sudden, the Old One seemed to disappear out of his grasp, and he found himself holding a stag by the fore and hind leg! But still he kept fast hold. Then the stag disappeared, and in its stead there was a sea-bird, fluttering and screaming, while Hercules clutched it by the wing and claw! But the bird could not get away. Immediately afterwards, there was an ugly three-headed dog, which growled and barked at Hercules, and snapped fiercely at the hands by which he held him! But Hercules would not let him go. In another minute, instead of the three-headed dog, what should appear but Geryon, the six-legged man-monster, kicking at Hercules with five of his legs, in order to get the remaining one at liberty! But Hercules held on. By and by, no Geryon was there, but a huge snake, like one of those which Hercules had strangled in his babyhood, only a hundred times as big; and it twisted and twined about the hero's neck and body, and threw its tail high into the air, and opened its deadly jaws as if to devour him outright; so that it was really a very terrible spectacle! But Hercules was no whit disheartened, and squeezed the great snake so tightly that he soon began to hiss with pain.

You must understand that the Old Man of the Sea, though he generally looked so much like the wave-beaten figure-head of a vessel, had the power of assuming any shape he pleased. When he found himself so roughly seized by Hercules, he had been in hopes of putting him into such surprise and terror, by these magical transformations, that the hero would be glad to let him go. If Hercules had relaxed his grasp, the Old One would certainly have plunged down to the very bottom of the sea, whence he would not soon have given himself the trouble of coming up, in order to answer any impertinent questions. Ninety-nine people out of a hundred, I suppose, would have been frightened out of their wits by the very first of his ugly shapes, and would have taken to their heels at once. For, one of the hardest things in this world is, to see the difference between real dangers and imaginary ones.

But, as Hercules held on so stubbornly, and only squeezed the Old One so much the tighter at every change of shape, and really put him to no small torture, he finally thought it best to reappear in his own figure. So there he was again, a fishy, scaly, web-footed sort of personage, with something like a tuft of sea-weed at his chin.

" Pray, what do you want with me ? " cried the Old One, as soon as he could take breath ; for it is quite a tiresome affair to go through so many false shapes. " Why do you squeeze me so hard ? Let me go, this moment, or I shall begin to consider you an extremely uncivil person ! "

" My name is Hercules ! " roared the mighty stranger. " And you will never get out of my clutch, until you tell me the nearest way to the garden of the Hesperides ! "

When the old fellow heard who it was that had caught him, he saw, with half an eye, that it would be necessary to tell him everything that he wanted to

know. The Old One was an inhabitant of the sea,
you must recollect, and roamed about everywhere, like
other sea-faring people. Of course, he had often
heard of the fame of Hercules, and of the wonderful
things that he was constantly performing, in various
parts of the earth, and how determined he always was
to accomplish whatever he undertook. He therefore
made no more attempts to escape, but told the hero
how to find the garden of the Hesperides, and likewise warned him of many difficulties which must be
overcome, before he could arrive thither.

"You must go on, thus and thus," said the Old
Man of the Sea, after taking the points of the compass, "till you come in sight of a very tall giant, who
holds the sky on his shoulders. And the giant, if he
happens to be in the humor, will tell you exactly
where the garden of the Hesperides lies."

"And if the giant happens not to be in the humor," remarked Hercules, balancing his club on the
tip of his finger, "perhaps I shall find means to persuade him!"

Thanking the Old Man of the Sea, and begging his
pardon for having squeezed him so roughly, the hero
resumed his journey. He met with a great many
strange adventures, which would be well worth your
hearing, if I had leisure to narrate them as minutely
as they deserve.

It was in this journey, if I mistake not, that he encountered a prodigious giant, who was so wonderfully
contrived by nature, that, every time he touched the
earth, he became ten times as strong as ever he had
been before. His name was Antæus. You may see,
plainly enough, that it was a very difficult business
to fight with such a fellow; for, as often as he got a

knock-down blow, up he started again, stronger, fiercer, and abler to use his weapons, than if his enemy had let him alone. Thus, the harder Hercules pounded the giant with his club, the further he seemed from winning the victory. I have sometimes argued with such people, but never fought with one. The only way in which Hercules found it possible to finish the battle, was by lifting Antæus off his feet into the air, and squeezing, and squeezing, and squeezing him, until, finally, the strength was quite squeezed out of his enormous body.

When this affair was finished, Hercules continued his travels, and went to the land of Egypt, where he was taken prisoner, and would have been put to death, if he had not slain the king of the country, and made his escape. Passing through the deserts of Africa, and going as fast as he could, he arrived at last on the shore of the great ocean. And here, unless he could walk on the crests of the billows, it seemed as if his journey must needs be at an end.

Nothing was before him, save the foaming, dashing, measureless ocean. But, suddenly, as he looked towards the horizon, he saw something, a great way off, which he had not seen the moment before. It gleamed very brightly, almost as you may have beheld the round, golden disk of the sun, when it rises or sets over the edge of the world. It evidently drew nearer; for, at every instant, this wonderful object became larger and more lustrous. At length, it had come so nigh that Hercules discovered it to be an immense cup or bowl, made either of gold or burnished brass. How it had got afloat upon the sea is more than I can tell you. There it was, at all events, rolling on the tumultuous billows, which tossed it up and down, and heaved their foamy tops against its sides, but without ever throwing their spray over the brim.

"I have seen many giants, in my time," thought Hercules, "but never one that would need to drink his wine out of a cup like this!"

And, true enough, what a cup it must have been! It was as large — as large — but, in short, I am afraid to say how immeasurably large it was. To speak within bounds, it was ten times larger than a great mill-wheel; and, all of metal as it was, it floated over the heaving surges more lightly than an acorn-cup adown the brook. The waves tumbled it onward, until it grazed against the shore, within a short distance of the spot where Hercules was standing.

As soon as this happened, he knew what was to be done; for he had not gone through so many remarkable adventures without learning pretty well how to conduct himself, whenever anything came to pass a little out of the common rule. It was just as clear as daylight that this marvellous cup had been set adrift by some unseen power, and guided hitherward, in order to carry Hercules across the sea, on his way to the garden of the Hesperides. Accordingly, without a moment's delay, he clambered over the brim, and slid down on the inside, where, spreading out his lion's skin, he proceeded to take a little repose. He had scarcely rested, until now, since he bade farewell to the damsels on the margin of the river. The waves dashed, with a pleasant and ringing sound, against the circumference of the hollow cup; it rocked lightly to and fro, and the motion was so soothing that it speedily rocked Hercules into an agreeable slumber.

His nap had probably lasted a good while, when the cup chanced to graze against a rock, and, in consequence, immediately resounded and reverberated through its golden or brazen substance, a hundred times as loudly as ever you heard a church-bell. The noise awoke Hercules, who instantly started up and gazed around him, wondering whereabouts he was. He was not long in discovering that the cup had floated across a great part of the sea, and was approaching the shore of what seemed to be an island. And, on that island, what do you think he saw?

No; you will never guess it, not if you were to try fifty thousand times! It positively appears to me that this was the most marvellous spectacle that had ever been seen by Hercules, in the whole course of his wonderful travels and adventures. It was a greater marvel than the hydra with nine heads, which kept growing twice as fast as they were cut off; greater than the six-legged man-monster; greater than Antæus; greater than anything that was ever beheld by anybody, before or since the days of Hercules, or than anything that remains to be beheld, by travellers in all time to come. It was a giant!

But such an intolerably big giant! A giant as tall as a mountain; so vast a giant, that the clouds rested about his midst, like a girdle, and hung like a hoary beard from his chin, and flitted before his huge eyes, so that he could neither see Hercules nor the golden cup in which he was voyaging. And, most wonderful of all, the giant held up his great hands and appeared to support the sky, which, so far as Hercules could discern through the clouds, was resting upon his head! This does really seem almost too much to believe.

Meanwhile, the bright cup continued to float onward, and finally touched the strand. Just then a breeze wafted away the clouds from before the giant's visage, and Hercules beheld it, with all its enormous features ; eyes each of them as big as yonder lake, a nose a mile long, and a mouth of the same width. It was a countenance terrible from its enormity of size, but disconsolate and weary, even as you may see the faces of many people, nowadays, who are compelled to sustain burdens above their strength. What the sky was to the giant, such are the cares of earth to those who let themselves be weighed down by them. And whenever men undertake what is beyond the just measure of their abilities, they encounter precisely such a doom as had befallen this poor giant.

Poor fellow! He had evidently stood there a long while. An ancient forest had been growing and decaying around his feet ; and oak-trees, of six or seven centuries old, had sprung from the acorn, and forced themselves between his toes.

The giant now looked down from the far height of his great eyes, and, perceiving Hercules, roared out, in a voice that resembled thunder, proceeding out of the cloud that had just flitted away from his face.

" Who are you, down at my feet there ? And whence do you come, in that little cup ? "

" I am Hercules ! " thundered back the hero, in a voice pretty nearly or quite as loud as the giant's own. " And I am seeking for the garden of the Hesperides ! "

" Ho ! ho ! ho ! " roared the giant, in a fit of immense laughter. " That is a wise adventure, truly ! "

" And why not ? " cried Hercules, getting a little angry at the giant's mirth. " Do you think I am afraid of the dragon with a hundred heads ! "

Just at this time, while they were talking together, some black clouds gathered about the giant's middle,

and burst into a tremendous storm of thunder and
lightning, causing such a pother that Hercules found
it impossible to distinguish a word. Only the giant's
immeasurable legs were to be seen, standing up into
the obscurity of the tempest; and, now and then, a
momentary glimpse of his whole figure, mantled in a
volume of mist. He seemed to be speaking, most of
the time ; but his big, deep, rough voice chimed in
with the reverberations of the thunder-claps, and rolled
away over the hills, like them. Thus, by talking out
of season, the foolish giant expended an incalculable
quantity of breath, to no purpose ; for the thunder
spoke quite as intelligibly as he.

At last, the storm swept over, as suddenly as it had
come. And there again was the clear sky, and the
weary giant holding it up, and the pleasant sunshine
beaming over his vast height, and illuminating it
against the background of the sullen thunder-clouds.
So far above the shower had been his head, that not a
hair of it was moistened by the rain-drops!

When the giant could see Hercules still standing on
the sea-shore, he roared out to him anew.

"I am Atlas, the mightiest giant in the world!
And I hold the sky upon my head ! "

"So I see," answered Hercules. " But, can you
show me the way to the garden of the Hesperides?"

"What do you want there ? " asked the giant.

"I want three of the golden apples," shouted Hercules, "for my cousin, the king."

"There is nobody but myself," quoth the giant,
"that can go to the garden of the Hesperides, and
gather the golden apples. If it were not for this little business of holding up the sky, I would make half
a dozen steps across the sea, and get them for you."

"You are very kind," replied Hercules. "And cannot you rest the sky upon a mountain?"

"None of them are quite high enough," said Atlas, shaking his head. "But, if you were to take your stand on the summit of that nearest one, your head would be pretty nearly on a level with mine. You seem to be a fellow of some strength. What if you should take my burden on your shoulders, while I do your errand for you?"

Hercules, as you must be careful to remember, was a remarkably strong man; and though it certainly requires a great deal of muscular power to uphold the sky, yet, if any mortal could be supposed capable of such an exploit, he was the one. Nevertheless, it seemed so difficult an undertaking, that, for the first time in his life, he hesitated.

"Is the sky very heavy?" he inquired.

"Why, not particularly so, at first," answered the giant, shrugging his shoulders. "But it gets to be a little burdensome, after a thousand years!"

"And how long a time," asked the hero, "will it take you to get the golden apples?"

"Oh, that will be done in a few moments," cried Atlas. "I shall take ten or fifteen miles at a stride, and be at the garden and back again before your shoulders begin to ache."

"Well, then," answered Hercules, "I will climb the mountain behind you there, and relieve you of your burden."

The truth is, Hercules had a kind heart of his own, and considered that he should be doing the giant a favor, by allowing him this opportunity for a ramble. And, besides, he thought that it would be still more for his own glory, if he could boast of upholding the

sky, than merely to do so ordinary a thing as to conquer a dragon with a hundred heads. Accordingly,
without more words, the sky was shifted from the
shoulders of Atlas, and placed upon those of Hercules.

When this was safely accomplished, the first thing
that the giant did was to stretch himself; and you
may imagine what a prodigious spectacle he was then.
Next, he slowly lifted one of his feet out of the forest
that had grown up around it; then, the other. Then,
all at once, he began to caper, and leap, and dance,
for joy at his freedom; flinging himself nobody knows
how high into the air, and floundering down again
with a shock that made the earth tremble. Then he
laughed — Ho! ho! ho! — with a thunderous roar that
was echoed from the mountains, far and near, as if
they and the giant had been so many rejoicing brothers.
When his joy had a little subsided, he stepped into
the sea; ten miles at the first stride, which brought
him midleg deep; and ten miles at the second, when
the water came just above his knees; and ten miles
more at the third, by which he was immersed nearly
to his waist. This was the greatest depth of the sea.

Hercules watched the giant, as he still went onward;
for it was really a wonderful sight, this immense human form, more than thirty miles off, half hidden in
the ocean, but with his upper half as tall, and misty,
and blue, as a distant mountain. At last the gigantic
shape faded entirely out of view. And now Hercules
began to consider what he should do, in case Atlas
should be drowned in the sea, or if he were to be stung
to death by the dragon with the hundred heads, which
guarded the golden apples of the Hesperides. If any
such misfortune were to happen, how could he ever

get rid of the sky ? And, by the by, its weight began already to be a little irksome to his head and shoulders.

" I really pity the poor giant," thought Hercules. " If it wearies me so much in ten minutes, how must it have wearied him in a thousand years ! "

O my sweet little people, you have no idea what a weight there was in that same blue sky, which looks so soft and aerial above our heads ! And there, too, was the bluster of the wind, and the chill and watery clouds, and the blazing sun, all taking their turns to make Hercules uncomfortable! He began to be afraid that the giant would never come back. He gazed wistfully at the world beneath him, and acknowledged to himself that it was a far happier kind of life to be a shepherd at the foot of a mountain, than to stand on its dizzy summit, and bear up the firmament with his might and main. For, of course, as you will easily understand, Hercules had an immense responsibility on his mind, as well as a weight on his head and shoulders. Why, if he did not stand perfectly still, and keep the sky immovable, the sun would perhaps be put ajar ! Or, after nightfall, a great many of the stars might be loosened from their places, and shower down, like fiery rain, upon the people's heads ! And how ashamed would the hero be, if, owing to his unsteadiness beneath its weight, the sky should crack, and show a great fissure quite across it !

I know not how long it was before, to his unspeakable joy, he beheld the huge shape of the giant, like a cloud, on the far-off edge of the sea. At his nearer approach, Atlas held up his hand, in which Hercules could perceive three magnificent golden apples, as big as pumpkins, all hanging from one branch. .

"I am glad to see you again," shouted Hercules, when the giant was within hearing. "So you have got the golden apples?"

"Certainly, certainly," answered Atlas; "and very fair apples they are. I took the finest that grew on the tree, I assure you. Ah! it is a beautiful spot, that garden of the Hesperides. Yes; and the dragon with a hundred heads is a sight worth any man's seeing. After all, you had better have gone for the apples yourself."

"No matter," replied Hercules. "You have had a pleasant ramble, and have done the business as well as I could. I heartily thank you for your trouble. And now, as I have a long way to go, and am rather in haste, — and as the king, my cousin, is anxious to receive the golden apples, — will you be kind enough to take the sky off my shoulders again?"

"Why, as to that," said the giant, chucking the golden apples into the air twenty miles high, or thereabouts and catching them as they came down, — "as to that, my good friend, I consider you a little unreasonable. Cannot I carry the golden apples to the king, your cousin, much quicker than you could? As his majesty is in such a hurry to get them, I promise you to take my longest strides. And, besides, I have no fancy for burdening myself with the sky, just now."

Here Hercules grew impatient, and gave a great shrug of his shoulders. It being now twilight, you might have seen two or three stars tumble out of their places. Everybody on earth looked upward in affright, thinking that the sky might be going to fall next.

"Oh, that will never do!" cried Giant Atlas, with

a great roar of laughter. " I have not let fall so many stars within the last five centuries. By the time you have stood there as long as I did, you will begin to learn patience ! "

" What ! " shouted Hercules, very wrathfully, " do you intend to make me bear this burden forever ? "

" We will see about that, one of these days," answered the giant. " At all events, you ought not to complain, if you have to bear it the next hundred years, or perhaps the next thousand. I bore it a good while longer, in spite of the back-ache. Well, then, after a thousand years, if I happen to feel in the mood, we may possibly shift about again. You are certainly a very strong man, and can never have a better opportunity to prove it. Posterity will talk of you, I warrant it ! "

" Pish ! a fig for its talk ! " cried Hercules, with another hitch of his shoulders. " Just take the sky upon your head one instant, will you ? I want to make a cushion of my lion's skin, for the weight to rest upon. It really chafes me, and will cause unnecessary inconvenience in so many centuries as I am to stand here."

" That 's no more than fair, and I 'll do it ! " quoth the giant ; for he had no unkind feeling towards Hercules, and was merely acting with a too selfish consideration of his own ease. " For just five minutes, then, I 'll take back the sky. Only for five minutes, recollect ! I have no idea of spending another thousand years as I spent the last. Variety is the spice of life, say I."

Ah, the thick-witted old rogue of a giant ! He threw down the golden apples, and received back the sky, from the head and shoulders of Hercules, upon his own, where it rightly belonged. And Hercules picked up the three golden apples, that were as big or bigger than pumpkins, and straightway set out on his journey homeward, without paying the slightest heed to the thundering tones of the giant, who bellowed after him to come back. Another forest sprang up around his feet, and grew ancient there; and again might be seen oak-trees, of six or seven centuries old, that had waxed thus aged betwixt his enormous toes.

And there stands the giant to this day; or, at any rate, there stands a mountain as tall as he, and which bears his name; and when the thunder rumbles about its summit, we may imagine it to be the voice of Giant Atlas, bellowing after Hercules!

TANGLEWOOD FIRESIDE.

"Cousin Eustace," demanded Sweet Fern, who had been sitting at the story-teller's feet, with his mouth wide open, "exactly how tall was this giant?"

"O Sweet Fern, Sweet Fern!" cried the student, "do you think I was there, to measure him with a yard-stick? Well, if you must know to a hair's-breadth, I suppose he might be from three to fifteen miles straight upward, and that he might have seated himself on Taconic, and had Monument Mountain for a footstool."

"Dear me!" ejaculated the good little boy, with a contented sort of a grunt, "that was a giant, sure enough! And how long was his little finger?"

"As long as from Tanglewood to the lake," said Eustace.

"Sure enough, that was a giant!" repeated Sweet Fern, in an ecstasy at the precision of these measurements. "And how broad, I wonder, were the shoulders of Hercules?"

"That is what I have never been able to find out," answered the student. "But I think they must have been a great deal broader than mine, or than your father's, or than almost any shoulders which one sees nowadays."

"I wish," whispered Sweet Fern, with his mouth close to the student's ear, "that you would tell me how big were some of the oak-trees that grew between the giant's toes."

"They were bigger," said Eustáce, "than the great chestnut-tree which stands beyond Captain Smith's house."

"Eustace," remarked Mr. Pringle, after some deliberation, "I find it impossible to express such an opinion of this story as will be likely to gratify, in the smallest degree, your pride of authorship. Pray let me advise you never more to meddle with a classical myth. Your imagination is altogether Gothic, and will inevitably Gothicize everything that you touch. The effect is like bedaubing a marble statue with paint. This giant, now! How can you have ventured to thrust his huge, disproportioned mass among the seemly outlines of Grecian fable, the tendency of which is to reduce even the extravagant within limits, by its pervading elegance?"

"I described the giant as he appeared to me," replied the student, rather piqued. "And, sir, if you would only bring your mind into such a relation with these fables as is necessary in order to remodel them, you would see at once that an old Greek had no more exclusive right to them than a modern Yankee has. They are the common property of the world, and of all time. The ancient poets remodelled them at pleasure, and held them plastic in their hands; and why should they not be plastic in my hands as well?"

Mr. Pringle could not forbear a smile.

"And besides," continued Eustace, "the moment you put any warmth of heart, any passion or affection, any human or divine morality, into a classic mould, you make it quite another thing from what it was before. My own opinion is, that the Greeks, by taking

possession of these legends (which were the immemorial birthright of mankind), and putting them into
shapes of indestructible beauty, indeed, but cold and
heartless, have done all subsequent ages an incalculable injury."

"Which you, doubtless, were born to remedy," said
Mr. Pringle, laughing outright. "Well, well, go on;
but take my advice, and never put any of your traves-
ties on paper. And, as your next effort, what if you
should try your hand on some one of the legends of
Apollo?"

"Ah, sir, you propose it as an impossibility," observed the student, after a moment's meditation;
"and, to be sure, at first thought, the idea of a Gothic
Apollo strikes one rather ludicrously. But I will turn
over your suggestion in my mind, and do not quite
despair of success."

During the above discussion, the children (who understood not a word of it) had grown very sleepy, and
were now sent off to bed. Their drowsy babble was
heard, ascending the staircase, while a northwest-wind
roared loudly among the tree-tops of Tanglewood, and
played an anthem around the house. Eustace Bright
went back to the study, and again endeavored to hammer out some verses, but fell asleep between two of
the rhymes.

THE MIRACULOUS PITCHER.

THE HILL–SIDE.

INTRODUCTORY TO "THE MIRACULOUS PITCHER."

AND when, and where, do you think we find the children next? No longer in the winter-time, but in the merry month of May. No longer in Tanglewood play-room, or at Tanglewood fireside, but more than half-way up a monstrous hill, or a mountain, as perhaps it would be better pleased to have us call it. They had set out from home with the mighty purpose of climbing this high hill, even to the very tiptop of its bald head. To be sure, it was not quite so high as Chimborazo, or Mont Blanc, and was even a good deal lower than old Graylock. But, at any rate, it was higher than a thousand ant-hillocks, or a million of mole-hills; and, when measured by the short strides of little children, might be reckoned a very respectable mountain.

And was Cousin Eustace with the party? Of that you may be certain; else how could the book go on a step further? He was now in the middle of the spring vacation, and looked pretty much as we saw him four or five months ago, except that, if you gazed quite closely at his upper lip, you could discern the funniest little bit of a mustache upon it. Setting aside this

mark of mature manhood, you might have considered
Cousin Eustace just as much a boy as when you first
became acquainted with him. He was as merry, as
playful, as good-humored, as light of foot and of spirits, and equally a favorite with the little folks, as he
had always been. This expedition up the mountain
was entirely of his contrivance. All the way up the
steep ascent, he had encouraged the elder children
with his cheerful voice ; and when Dandelion, Cowslip, and Squash-Blossom grew weary, he had lugged
them along, alternately, on his back. In this manner,
they had passed through the orchards and pastures on
the lower part of the hill, and had reached the wood,
which extends thence towards its bare summit.

The month of May, thus far, had been more amiable than it often is, and this was as sweet and genial
a day as the heart of man or child could wish. In
their progress up the hill, the small people had found
enough of violets, blue and white, and some that were
as golden as if they had the touch of Midas on them.
That sociablest of flowers, the little Houstonia, was
very abundant. It is a flower that never lives alone,
but which loves its own kind, and is always fond of
dwelling with a great many friends and relatives
around it. Sometimes you see a family of them, covering a space no bigger than the palm of your hand ;
and sometimes a large community, whitening a whole
tract of pasture, and all keeping one another in cheerful heart and life.

Within the verge of the wood there were colum-
bines, looking more pale than red, because they were
so modest, and had thought proper to seclude themselves too anxiously from the sun. There were wild
geraniums, too, and a thousand white blossoms of the

strawberry. The trailing arbutus was not yet quite out of bloom; but it hid its precious flowers under the last year's withered forest-leaves, as carefully as a mother-bird hides its little young ones. It knew, I suppose, how beautiful and sweet-scented they were. So cunning was their concealment, that the children sometimes smelt the delicate richness of their perfume before they knew whence it proceeded.

Amid so much new life, it was strange and truly pitiful to behold, here and there, in the fields and pastures, the hoary periwigs of dandelions that had already gone to seed. They had done with summer before the summer came. Within those small globes of winged seeds it was autumn now!

Well, but we must not waste our valuable pages with any more talk about the spring-time and wild flowers. There is something, we hope, more interesting to be talked about. If you look at the group of children, you may see them all gathered around Eustace Bright, who, sitting on the stump of a tree, seems to be just beginning a story. The fact is, the younger part of the troop have found out that it takes rather too many of their short strides to measure the long ascent of the hill. Cousin Eustace, therefore, has decided to leave Sweet Fern, Cowslip, Squash-Blossom, and Dandelion, at this point, midway up, until the return of the rest of the party from the summit. And because they complain a little, and do not quite like to stay behind, he gives them some apples out of his pocket, and proposes to tell them a very pretty story. Hereupon they brighten up, and change their grieved looks into the broadest kind of smiles.

As for the story, I was there to hear it, hidden behind a bush, and shall tell it over to you in the pages that come next.

THE MIRACULOUS PITCHER.

ONE evening, in times long ago, old Philemon and his old wife Baucis sat at their cottage-door, enjoying the calm and beautiful sunset. They had already eaten their frugal supper, and intended now to spend a quiet hour or two before bedtime. So they talked together about their garden, and their cow, and their bees, and their grapevine, which clambered over the cottage-wall, and on which the grapes were beginning to turn purple. But the rude shouts of children, and the fierce barking of dogs, in the village near at hand, grew louder and louder, until, at last, it was hardly possible for Baucis and Philemon to hear each other speak.

"Ah, wife," cried Philemon, "I fear some poor traveller is seeking hospitality among our neighbors yonder, and, instead of giving him food and lodging, they have set their dogs at him, as their custom is!"

"Well-a-day!" answered old Baucis, "I do wish our neighbors felt a little more kindness for their fellow-creatures. And only think of bringing up their children in this naughty way, and patting them on the head when they fling stones at strangers!"

"Those children will never come to any good," said Philemon, shaking his white head. "To tell you the truth, wife, I should not wonder if some terrible thing were to happen to all the people in the village, unless they mend their manners. But, as for you and me, so long as Providence affords us a crust of bread, let us be ready to give half to any poor, homeless stranger, that may come along and need it."

"That's right, husband!" said Baucis. "So we will!"

These old folks, you must know, were quite poor, and had to work pretty hard for a living. Old Philemon toiled diligently in his garden, while Baucis was always busy with her distaff, or making a little butter and cheese with their cow's milk, or doing one thing and another about the cottage. Their food was seldom anything but bread, milk, and vegetables, with sometimes a portion of honey from their beehive, and now and then a bunch of grapes, that had ripened against the cottage wall. But they were two of the kindest old people in the world, and would cheerfully have gone without their dinners, any day, rather than refuse a slice of their brown loaf, a cup of new milk, and a spoonful of honey, to the weary traveller who might pause before their door. They felt as if such guests had a sort of holiness, and that they ought, therefore, to treat them better and more bountifully than their own selves.

Their cottage stood on a rising ground, at some short distance from a village, which lay in a hollow valley, that was about half a mile in breadth. This valley, in past ages, when the world was new, had probably been the bed of a lake. There, fishes had glided to and fro in the depths, and water-weeds had grown along the margin, and trees and hills had seen their reflected images in the broad and peaceful mirror. But, as the waters subsided, men had cultivated the soil, and built houses on it, so that it was now a fertile spot, and bore no traces of the ancient lake, except a very small brook, which meandered through the midst of the village, and supplied the inhabitants with water. The valley had been dry land so long, that oaks had sprung up, and grown great and high, and perished with old age, and been succeeded by others, as tall and stately as the first. Never was there a prettier or more fruitful valley. The very sight of the plenty around them should have made the inhabitants kind and gentle, and ready to show their gratitude to Providence by doing good to their fellow-creatures.

But, we are sorry to say, the people of this lovely village were not worthy to dwell in a spot on which Heaven had smiled so beneficently. They were a very selfish and hard-hearted people, and had no pity for the poor, nor sympathy with the homeless. They would only have laughed, had anybody told them that human beings owe a debt of love to one another, because there is no other method of paying the debt of love and care which all of us owe to Providence. You will hardly believe what I am going to tell you. These naughty people taught their children to be no better than themselves, and used to clap their hands, by way of encouragement, when they saw the little boys and girls run after some poor stranger, shouting at his heels, and pelting him with stones. They kept large and fierce dogs, and whenever a traveller ventured to show himself in the village street, this pack of disagreeable curs scampered to meet him, barking, snarling, and showing their teeth. Then they would seize him by his leg, or by his clothes, just as it happened; and if he were ragged when he came, he was generally a pitiable object before he had time to run away. This was a very terrible thing to poor travellers, as you may suppose, especially when they chanced to be sick, or feeble, or lame, or old. Such persons (if they once

knew how badly these unkind people, and their unkind children and curs, were in the habit of behaving) would go miles and miles out of their way, rather
than try to pass through the village again.

What made the matter seem worse, if possible, was
that when rich persons came in their chariots, or riding on beautiful horses, with their servants in rich liveries attending on them, nobody could be more civil
and obsequious than the inhabitants of the village.
They would take off their hats, and make the humblest bows you ever saw. If the children were rude,
they were pretty certain to get their ears boxed ; and
as for the dogs, if a single cur in the pack presumed
to yelp, his master instantly beat him with a club, and
tied him up without any supper. This would have
been all very well, only it proved that the villagers
cared much about the money that a stranger had in
his pocket, and nothing whatever for the human soul,
which lives equally in the beggar and the prince.

So now you can understand why old Philemon
spoke so sorrowfully, when he heard the shouts of the
children and the barking of the dogs, at the farther
extremity of the village street. There was a confused
din, which lasted a good while, and seemed to pass
quite through the breadth of the valley.

"I never heard the dogs so loud!" observed the
good old man.

"Nor the children so rude!" answered his good old
wife.

They sat shaking their heads, one to another, while
the noise came nearer and nearer; until, at the foot of
the little eminence on which their cottage stood, they
saw two travellers approaching on foot. Close behind
them came the fierce dogs, snarling at their very heels.

A little farther off, ran a crowd of children, who sent up shrill cries, and flung stones at the two strangers, with all their might. Once or twice, the younger of the two men (he was a slender and very active figure) turned about and drove back the dogs with a staff which he carried in his hand. His companion, who was a very tall person, walked calmly along, as if disdaining to notice either the naughty children, or the pack of curs, whose manners the children seemed to imitate.

Both of the travellers were very humbly clad, and looked as if they might not have money enough in their pockets to pay for a night's lodging. And this, I am afraid, was the reason why the villagers had allowed their children and dogs to treat them so rudely.

"Come, wife," said Philemon to Baucis, "let us go and meet these poor people. No doubt, they feel almost too heavy-hearted to climb the hill."

"Go you and meet them," answered Baucis, "while I make haste within doors, and see whether we can get them anything for supper. A comfortable bowl of bread and milk would do wonders towards raising their spirits."

Accordingly, she hastened into the cottage. Philemon, on his part, went forward, and extended his hand with so hospitable an aspect that there was no need of saying what nevertheless he did say, in the heartiest tone imaginable, —

"Welcome, strangers! welcome!"

"Thank you!" replied the younger of the two, in a lively kind of way, notwithstanding his weariness and trouble. "This is quite another greeting than we have met with yonder in the village. Pray, why do you live in such a bad neighborhood?"

" Ah ! " observed old Philemon, with a quiet and benign smile, " Providence put me here, I hope, among other reasons, in order that I may make you what amends I can for the inhospitality of my neighbors."

" Well said, old father ! " cried the traveller, laughing ; " and, if the truth must be told, my companion and myself need some amends. Those children (the little rascals !) have bespattered us finely with their mud-balls ; and one of the curs has torn my cloak, which was ragged enough already. But I took him across the muzzle with my staff ; and I think you may have heard him yelp, even thus far off."

Philemon was glad to see him in such good spirits ; nor, indeed, would you have fancied, by the traveller's look and manner, that he was weary with a long day's journey, besides being disheartened by rough treatment at the end of it. He was dressed in rather an odd way, with a sort of cap on his head, the brim of which stuck out over both ears. Though it was a summer evening, he wore a cloak, which he kept wrapt closely about him, perhaps because his under garments were shabby. Philemon perceived, too, that he had on a singular pair of shoes ; but, as it was now growing dusk, and as the old man's eyesight was none the sharpest, he could not precisely tell in what the strangeness consisted. One thing, certainly, seemed queer. The traveller was so wonderfully light and active, that it appeared as if his feet sometimes rose from the ground of their own accord, or could only be kept down by an effort.

" I used to be light-footed, in my youth," said Philemon to the traveller. " But I always found my feet grow heavier towards nightfall."

" There is nothing like a good staff to help one

along," answered the stranger; "and I happen to have an excellent one, as you see."

This staff, in fact, was the oddest-looking staff that Philemon had ever beheld. It was made of olive-wood, and had something like a little pair of wings near the top. Two snakes, carved in the wood, were represented as twining themselves about the staff, and were so very skilfully executed that old Philemon (whose eyes, you know, were getting rather dim) almost thought them alive, and that he could see them wriggling and twisting.

" A curious piece of work, sure enough ! " said he. " A staff with wings ! It would be an excellent kind of stick for a little boy to ride astride of ! "

By this time, Philemon and his two guests had reached the cottage door.

" Friends," said the old man, " sit down and rest yourselves here on this bench. My good wife Baucis has gone to see what you can have for supper. We are poor folks; but you shall be welcome to whatever we have in the cupboard."

The younger stranger threw himself carelessly on the bench, letting his staff fall, as he did so. And here happened something rather marvellous, though trifling enough, too. The staff seemed to get up from the ground of its own accord, and, spreading its little pair of wings, it half hopped, half flew, and leaned itself against the wall of the cottage. There it stood quite still, except that the snakes continued to wriggle. But, in my private opinion, old Philemon's eyesight had been playing him tricks again.

Before he could ask any questions, the elder stranger drew his attention from the wonderful staff, by speaking to him.

"Was there not," asked the stranger, in a remarkably deep tone of voice, "a lake, in very ancient times, covering the spot where now stands yonder village?"

"Not in my day, friend," answered Philemon ; "and yet I am an old man, as you see. There were always the fields and meadows, just as they are now, and the old trees, and the little stream murmuring through the midst of the valley. My father, nor his father before him, ever saw it otherwise, so far as I know; and doubtless it will still be the same, when old Philemon shall be gone and forgotten!"

"That is more than can be safely foretold," observed the stranger; and there was something very stern in his deep voice. He shook his head, too, so that his dark and heavy curls were shaken with the movement. "Since the inhabitants of yonder village have forgotten the affections and sympathies of their nature, it were better that the lake should be rippling over their dwellings again!"

The traveller looked so stern, that Philemon was really almost frightened; the more so, that, at his frown, the twilight seemed suddenly to grow darker, and that, when he shook his head, there was a roll as of thunder in the air.

But, in a moment afterwards, the stranger's face became so kindly and mild, that the old man quite forgot his terror. Nevertheless, he could not help feeling that this elder traveller must be no ordinary personage, although he happened now to be attired so humbly and to be journeying on foot. Not that Philemon fancied him a prince in disguise, or any character of that sort; but rather some exceedingly wise man, who went about the world in this poor garb, despising wealth and all worldly objects, and seeking everywhere to add a mite to his wisdom. This idea appeared the more probable, because, when Philemon raised his eyes to the stranger's face, he seemed to see more thought there, in one look, than he could have studied out in a lifetime.

While Baucis was getting the supper, the travellers both began to talk very sociably with Philemon. The younger, indeed, was extremely loquacious, and made such shrewd and witty remarks, that the good old man continually burst out a-laughing, and pronounced him the merriest fellow whom he had seen for many a day.

"Pray, my young friend," said he, as they grew familiar together, "what may I call your name?"

"Why, I am very nimble, as you see," answered the traveller. "So, if you call me Quicksilver, the name will fit tolerably well."

"Quicksilver? Quicksilver?" repeated Philemon, looking in the traveller's face, to see if he were making fun of him. "It is a very odd name! And your companion there? Has he as strange a one?"

"You must ask the thunder to tell it you!" replied Quicksilver, putting on a mysterious look. "No other voice is loud enough."

This remark, whether it were serious or in jest, might have caused Philemon to conceive a very great awe of the elder stranger, if, on venturing to gaze at him, he had not beheld so much beneficence in his visage. But, undoubtedly, here was the grandest figure that ever sat so humbly beside a cottage door. When the stranger conversed, it was with gravity, and in such a way that Philemon felt irresistibly moved to tell him everything which he had most at heart. This is always the feeling that people have, when they meet with any one wise enough to comprehend all their good and evil, and to despise not a tittle of it.

But Philemon, simple and kind-hearted old man that he was, had not many secrets to disclose. He talked, however, quite garrulously, about the events of his past life, in the whole course of which he had never been a score of miles from this very spot. His wife Baucis and himself had dwelt in the cottage from their youth upward, earning their bread by honest labor, always poor, but still contented. He told what excellent butter and cheese Baucis made, and how nice were the vegetables which he raised in his garden. He said, too, that, because they loved one another so very much, it was the wish of both that death might not separate them, but that they should die, as they had lived, together.

As the stranger listened, a smile beamed over his countenance, and made its expression as sweet as it was grand.

"You are a good old man," said he to Philemon, "and you have a good old wife to be your helpmeet. It is fit that your wish be granted."

And it seemed to Philemon, just then, as if the sunset clouds threw up a bright flash from the west, and kindled a sudden light in the sky.

Baucis had now got supper ready, and, coming to the door, began to make apologies for the poor fare which she was forced to set before her guests.

"Had we known you were coming," said she, "my good man and myself would have gone without a morsel, rather than you should lack a better supper. But I took the most part of to-day's milk to make cheese; and our last loaf is already half eaten. Ah me! I never feel the sorrow of being poor, save when a poor traveller knocks at our door."

"All will be very well; do not trouble yourself, my

good dame," replied the elder stranger, kindly.   " An
honest, hearty welcome to a guest works miracles with
the fare, and is capable of turning the coarsest food to
nectar and ambrosia."

" A welcome you shall have," cried Baucis, "and
likewise a little honey that we happen to have left,
and a bunch of purple grapes besides."

" Why, Mother Baucis, it is a feast ! " exclaimed
Quicksilver, laughing, " an absolute feast! and you
shall see how bravely I will play my part at it!   I
think I never felt hungrier in my life."

" Mercy on us ! " whispered Baucis to her husband.
" If the young man has such a terrible appetite, I am
afraid there will not be half enough supper ! "

They all went into the cottage.

And now, my little auditors, shall I tell you something that will make you open your eyes very wide ?
It is really one of the oddest circumstances in the
whole story.   Quicksilver's staff, you recollect, had
set itself up against the wall of the cottage.   Well ;
when its master entered the door, leaving this wonderful staff behind, what should it do but immediately
spread its little wings, and go hopping and fluttering
up the door steps !   Tap, tap, went the staff, on the
kitchen floor ; nor did it rest until it had stood itself
on end, with the greatest gravity and decorum, beside
Quicksilver's chair.   Old Philemon, however, as well
as his wife, was so taken up in attending to their
guests, that no notice was given to what the staff had
been about.

As Baucis had said, there was but a scanty supper
for two hungry travellers.   In the middle of the table
was the remnant of a brown loaf, with a piece of
cheese on one side of it, and a dish of honeycomb on

the other. There was a pretty good bunch of grapes for each of the guests. A moderately sized earthen pitcher, nearly full of milk, stood at a corner of the board; and when Baucis had filled two bowls, and set them before the strangers, only a little milk remained in the bottom of the pitcher. Alas! it is a very sad business, when a bountiful heart finds itself pinched and squeezed among narrow circumstances. Poor Baucis kept wishing that she might starve for a week to come, if it were possible, by so doing, to provide these hungry folks a more plentiful supper.

And, since the supper was so exceedingly small, she could not help wishing that their appetites had not been quite so large. Why, at their very first sitting down, the travellers both drank off all the milk in their two bowls, at a draught.

"A little more milk, kind Mother Baucis, if you please," said Quicksilver. "The day has been hot, and I am very much athirst."

"Now, my dear people," answered Baucis, in great confusion, "I am so sorry and ashamed! But the truth is, there is hardly a drop more milk in the pitcher. O husband! husband! why did n't we go without our supper?"

"Why, it appears to me," cried Quicksilver, starting up from table and taking the pitcher by the handle, "it really appears to me that matters are not quite so bad as you represent them. Here is certainly more milk in the pitcher."

So saying, and to the vast astonishment of Baucis, he proceeded to fill, not only his own bowl, but his companion's likewise, from the pitcher, that was supposed to be almost empty. The good woman could scarcely believe her eyes. She had certainly poured

out nearly all the milk, and had peeped in afterwards,
and seen the bottom of the pitcher, as she set it down
upon the table.

"But I am old," thought Baucis to herself, "and
apt to be forgetful. I suppose I must have made a
mistake. At all events, the pitcher cannot help being
empty now, after filling the bowls twice over."

"What excellent milk!" observed Quicksilver,
after quaffing the contents of the second bowl. "Excuse me, my kind hostess, but I must really ask you
for a little more."

Now Baucis had seen, as plainly as she could see
anything, that Quicksilver had turned the pitcher up-
side down, and consequently had poured out every
drop of milk, in filling the last bowl. Of course,
there could not possibly be any left. However, in
order to let him know precisely how the case was, she
lifted the pitcher, and made a gesture as if pouring
milk into Quicksilver's bowl, but without the remotest
idea that any milk would stream forth. What was
her surprise, therefore, when such an abundant cascade
fell bubbling into the bowl, that it was immediately
filled to the brim, and overflowed upon the table! The
two snakes that were twisted about Quicksilver's staff
(but neither Baucis nor Philemon happened to observe
this circumstance) stretched out their heads, and began to lap up the spilt milk.

And then what a delicious fragrance the milk had!
It seemed as if Philemon's only cow must have pas-
tured, that day, on the richest herbage that could be
found anywhere in the world. I only wish that each
of you, my beloved little souls, could have a bowl of
such nice milk, at supper-time!

"And now a slice of your brown loaf, Mother

Baucis," said Quicksilver, " and a little of that honey ! "

Baucis cut him a slice, accordingly; and though the loaf, when she and her husband ate of it, had been rather too dry and crusty to be palatable, it was now as light and moist as if but a few hours out of the oven. Tasting a crumb, which had fallen on the table, she found it more delicious than bread ever was before, and could hardly believe that it was a loaf of her own kneading and baking. Yet, what other loaf could it possibly be ?

But, oh the honey ! I may just as well let it alone, without trying to describe how exquisitely it smelt and looked. Its color was that of the purest and most transparent gold; and it had the odor of a thousand flowers; but of such flowers as never grew in an earthly garden, and to seek which the bees must have flown high above the clouds. The wonder is, that, after alighting on a flower-bed of so delicious fragrance and immortal bloom, they should have been content to fly down again to their hive in Philemon's garden. Never was such honey tasted, seen, or smelt. The perfume floated around the kitchen, and made it so delightful, that, had you closed your eyes, you would instantly have forgotten the low ceiling and smoky walls, and have fancied yourself in an arbor, with celestial honeysuckles creeping over it.

Although good Mother Baucis was a simple old dame, she could not but think that there was something rather out of the common way, in all that had been going on. So, after helping the guests to bread and honey, and laying a bunch of grapes by each of their plates, she sat down by Philemon, and told him what she had seen, in a whisper.

" Did you ever hear the like ? " asked she.

" No, I never did," answered Philemon, with a smile. " And I rather think, my dear old wife, you have been walking about in a sort of a dream. If I had poured out the milk, I should have seen through the business at once. There happened to be a little more in the pitcher than you thought, — that is all."

" Ah, husband," said Baucis, " say what you will, these are very uncommon people."

" Well, well," replied Philemon, still smiling, " perhaps they are. They certainly do look as if they had seen better days ; and I am heartily glad to see them making so comfortable a supper."

Each of the guests had now taken his bunch of grapes upon his plate. Baucis (who rubbed her eyes, in order to see the more clearly) was of opinion that the clusters had grown larger and richer, and that each separate grape seemed to be on the point of bursting with ripe juice. It was entirely a mystery to her how such grapes could ever have been produced from the old stunted vine that climbed against the cottage wall.

" Very admirable grapes these ! " observed Quicksilver, as he swallowed one after another, without apparently diminishing his cluster. " Pray,· my good host, whence did you gather them ? "

" From my own vine," answered Philemon. " You may see one of its branches twisting across the window, yonder. But wife and I never thought the grapes very fine ones."

" I never tasted better," said the guest. " Another cup of this delicious milk, if you please, and I shall then have supped better than a prince."

This time, old Philemon bestirred himself, and took

up the pitcher ; for he was curious to discover whether there was any reality in the marvels which Baucis had whispered to him. He knew that his good old wife was incapable of falsehood, and that she was seldom mistaken in what she supposed to be true ; but this was so very singular a case, that he wanted to see into it with his own eyes. On taking up the pitcher, there-fore, he slyly peeped into it, and was fully satisfied that it contained not so much as a single drop. All at once, however, he beheld a little white fountain, which gushed up from the bottom of the pitcher, and speed-ily filled it to the brim with foaming and deliciously fragrant milk. It was lucky that Philemon, in his surprise, did not drop the miraculous pitcher from his hand.

" Who are ye, wonder-working strangers ! " cried he, even more bewildered than his wife had been.

"Your guests, my good Philemon, and your friends," replied the elder traveller, in his mild, deep voice, that had something at once sweet and awe-inspiring in it. " Give me likewise a cup of the milk ; and may your pitcher never be empty for kind Baucis and yourself, any more than for the needy wayfarer ! "

The supper being now over, the strangers requested to be shown to their place of repose. The old people would gladly have talked with them a little longer, and have expressed the wonder which they felt, and their delight at finding the poor and meagre supper prove so much better and more abundant than they hoped. But the elder traveller had inspired them with such reverence, that they dared not ask him any questions. And when Philemon drew Quicksilver aside, and in-quired how under the sun a fountain of milk could have got into an old earthen pitcher, this latter person-age pointed to his staff.

" There is the whole mystery of the affair," quoth
Quicksilver ; " and if you can make it out, I 'll thank
you to let me know. I can't tell what to make of my
staff. It is always playing such odd tricks as this ;
sometimes getting me a supper, and, quite as often,
stealing it away. If I had any faith in such nonsense,
I should say the stick was bewitched ! "

He said no more, but looked so slyly in their faces,
that they rather fancied he was laughing at them. The
magic staff went hopping at his heels, as Quicksilver
quitted the room. When left alone, the good old
couple spent some little time in conversation about the
events of the evening, and then lay down on the floor,
and fell fast asleep. They had given up their sleep-
ing-room to the guests, and had no other bed for
themselves, save these planks, which I wish had been
as soft as their own hearts.

The old man and his wife were stirring betimes in
the morning, and the strangers likewise arose with the
sun, and made their preparations to depart. Philemon
hospitably entreated them to remain a little longer,
until Baucis could milk the cow, and bake a cake upon
the hearth, and, perhaps, find them a few fresh eggs,
for breakfast. The guests, however, seemed to think
it better to accomplish a good part of their journey
before the heat of the day should come on. They,
therefore, persisted in setting out immediately, but
asked Philemon and Baucis to walk forth with them
a short distance, and show them the road which they
were to take.

So they all four issued from the cottage, chatting together like old friends. It was very remarkable, indeed, how familiar the old couple insensibly grew with
the elder traveller, and how their good and simple spir-

its melted into his, even as two drops of water would melt into the illimitable ocean. And as for Quicksilver, with his keen, quick, laughing wits, he appeared to discover every little thought that but peeped into their minds, before they suspected it themselves. They sometimes wished, it is true, that he had not been quite so quick-witted, and also that he would fling away his staff, which looked so mysteriously mischievous, with the snakes always writhing about it. But then, again, Quicksilver showed himself so very good-humored, that they would have been rejoiced to keep him in their cottage, staff, snakes, and all, every day, and the whole day long.

"Ah me! Well-a-day!" exclaimed Philemon, when they had walked a little way from their door. "If our neighbors only knew what a blessed thing it is to show hospitality to strangers, they would tie up all their dogs, and never allow their children to fling another stone."

"It is a sin and shame for them to behave so,—that it is!" cried good old Baucis, vehemently. "And I mean to go this very day, and tell some of them what naughty people they are!"

"I fear," remarked Quicksilver, slyly smiling, "that you will find none of them at home."

The elder traveller's brow, just then, assumed such a grave, stern, and awful grandeur, yet serene withal, that neither Baucis nor Philemon dared to speak a word. They gazed reverently into his face, as if they had been gazing at the sky.

"When men do not feel towards the humblest stranger as if he were a brother," said the traveller, in tones so deep that they sounded like those of an organ, "they are unworthy to exist on earth, which was created as the abode of a great human brotherhood!"

" And, by the by, my dear old people," cried Quick-silver, with the liveliest look of fun and mischief in his eyes, " where is this same village that you talk about? On which side of us does it lie ? Methinks I do not see it hereabouts."

Philemon and his wife turned towards the valley, where, at sunset, only the day before, they had seen the meadows, the houses, the gardens, the clumps of trees, the wide, green-margined street, with children playing in it, and all the tokens of business, enjoyment, and prosperity. But what was their astonishment! There was no longer any appearance of a village! Even the fertile vale, in the hollow of which it lay, had ceased to have existence. In its stead, they beheld the broad, blue surface of a lake, which filled the great basin of the valley from brim to brim, and reflected the surrounding hills in its bosom with as tranquil an image as if it had been there ever since the creation of the world. For an instant, the lake remained perfectly smooth. Then, a little breeze sprang up, and caused the water to dance, glitter, and sparkle in the early sunbeams, and to dash, with a pleasant rippling murmur, against the hither shore.

The lake seemed so strangely familiar, that the old couple were greatly perplexed, and felt as if they could only have been dreaming about a village having lain there. But, the next moment, they remembered the vanished dwellings, and the faces and characters of the inhabitants, far too distinctly for a dream. The village had been there yesterday, and now was gone!

" Alas ! " cried these kind-hearted old people, " what has become of our poor neighbors ? "

" They exist no lónger as men and women," said the elder traveller, in his grand and deep voice, while a roll of thunder seemed to echo it at a distance. "There was neither use nor beauty in such a life as theirs; for they never softened or sweetened the hard lot of mortality by the exercise of kindly affections between man and man. They retained no image of the better life in their bosoms; therefore, the lake, that was of old, has spread itself forth again, to reflect the sky!"

"And as for those foolish people," said Quicksilver, with his mischievous smile, "they are all transformed to fishes. There needed but little change, for they were already a scaly set of rascals, and the coldest-blooded beings in existence. So, kind Mother Baucis, whenever you or your husband have an appetite for a dish of broiled trout, he can throw in a line, and pull out half a dozen of your old neighbors!"

"Ah," cried Baucis, shuddering, "I would not, for the world, put one of them on the gridiron!"

"No," added Philemon, making a wry face, "we could never relish them!"

"As for you, good Philemon," continued the elder traveller, — "and you, kind Baucis, — you, with your scanty means, have mingled so much heartfelt hospitality with your entertainment of the homeless stranger, that the milk became an inexhaustible fount of nectar, and the brown loaf and the honey were ambrosia. Thus, the divinities have feasted, at your board, off the same viands that supply their banquets on Olympus. You have done well, my dear old friends. Wherefore, request whatever favor you have most at heart, and it is granted."

Philemon and Baucis looked at one another, and then, — I know not which of the two it was who spoke, but that one uttered the desire of both their hearts.

" Let us live together, while we live, and leave the
world at the same instant, when we die ! For we have
always loved one another ! "

" Be it so!" replied the stranger, with majestic
kindness. " Now, look towards your cottage ! "

They did so. But what was their surprise on beholding a tall edifice of white marble, with a wide-
open portal, occupying the spot where their humble
residence had so lately stood !

" There is your home," said the stranger, beneficently
smiling on them both. " Exercise your hospitality in
yonder palace as freely as in the poor hovel to which
you welcomed us last evening."

The old folks fell on their knees to thank him ; but,
behold ! neither he nor Quicksilver was there.

So Philemon and Baucis took up their residence in
the marble palace, and spent their time, with vast satisfaction to themselves, in making everybody jolly and
comfortable who happened to pass that way. The
milk-pitcher, I must not forget to say, retained its marvellous quality of being never empty, when it was desirable to have it full. Whenever an honest, good-
humored, and free-hearted guest took a draught from
this pitcher, he invariably found it the sweetest and
most invigorating fluid that ever ran down his throat.
But, if a cross and disagreeable curmudgeon happened
to sip, he was pretty certain to twist his visage into a
hard knot, and pronounce it a pitcher of sour milk !

Thus the old couple lived in their palace a great, great
while, and grew older and older, and very old indeed.
At length, however, there came a summer morning
when Philemon and Baucis failed to make their appearance, as on other mornings, with one hospitable
smile overspreading both their pleasant faces, to invite

the guests of over-night to breakfast. The guests
searched everywhere, from top to bottom of the spacious palace, and all to no purpose. But, after a great
deal of perplexity, they espied, in front of the portal,
two venerable trees, which nobody could remember to
have seen there the day before. Yet there they stood,
with their roots fastened deep into the soil, and a huge
breadth of foliage overshadowing the whole front of
the edifice. One was an oak, and the other a linden-
tree. Their boughs — it was strange and beautiful to
see — were intertwined together, and embraced one
another, so that each tree seemed to live in the other
tree's bosom much more than in its own.

While the guests were marvelling how these trees,
that must have required at least a century to grow,
could have come to be so tall and venerable in a single night, a breeze sprang up, and set their intermingled boughs astir. And then there was a deep, broad
murmur in the air, as if the two mysterious trees were
speaking.

" I am old Philemon ! " murmured the oak.

" I am old Baucis ! " murmured the linden-tree.

But, as the breeze grew stronger, the trees both
spoke at once, — " Philemon ! Baucis ! Baucis ! Philemon ! " — as if one were both and both were one, and
talking together in the depths of their mutual heart.
It was plain enough to perceive that the good old
couple had renewed their age, and were now to spend
a quiet and delightful hundred years or so, Philemon
as an oak, and Baucis as a linden-tree. And oh, what
a hospitable shade did they fling around them. Whenever a wayfarer paused beneath it, he heard a pleasant
whisper of the leaves above his head, and wondered

how the sound should so much resemble words like
these : —

"Welcome, welcome, dear traveller, welcome!"

And some kind soul, that knew what would have
pleased old Baucis and old Philemon best, built a cir-
cular seat around both their trunks, where, for a great
while afterwards, the weary, and the hungry, and the
thirsty used to repose themselves, and quaff milk abundantly out of the miraculous pitcher.

And I wish, for all our sakes, that we had the
pitcher here now!

THE HILL-SIDE.

"How much did the pitcher hold?" asked Sweet Fern.

"It did not hold quite a quart," answered the student; "but you might keep pouring milk out of it, till you should fill a hogshead, if you pleased. The truth is, it would run on forever, and not be dry even at midsummer, — which is more than can be said of yonder rill, that goes babbling down the hill-side."

"And what has become of the pitcher now?" inquired the little boy.

"It was broken, I am sorry to say, about twenty-five thousand years ago," replied Cousin Eustace. "The people mended it as well as they could, but, though it would hold milk pretty well, it was never afterwards known to fill itself of its own accord. So, you see, it was no better than any other cracked earthen pitcher."

"What a pity!" cried all the children at once.

The respectable dog Ben had accompanied the party, as did likewise a half-grown Newfoundland puppy, who went by the name of Bruin, because he was just as black as a bear. Ben, being elderly, and of very circumspect habits, was respectfully requested, by Cousin Eustace, to stay behind with the four little children, in order to keep them out of mischief. As for black Bruin, who was himself nothing but a child,

the student thought it best to take him along, lest, in
his rude play with the other children, he should trip
them up, and send them rolling and tumbling down
the hill.   Advising Cowslip, Sweet Fern, Dandelion,
and Squash-Blossom to sit pretty still, in the spot
where he left them, the student, with Primrose and
the elder children, began to ascend, and were soon out
of sight among the trees.

THE CHIMÆRA.

BALD–SUMMIT.

UPWARD, along the steep and wooded hill-side, went Eustace Bright and his companions. The trees were not yet in full leaf, but had budded forth sufficiently to throw an airy shadow, while the sunshine filled them with green light. There were moss-grown rocks, half hidden among the old, brown, fallen leaves; there were rotten tree-trunks, lying at full length where they had long ago fallen; there were decayed boughs, that had been shaken down by the wintry gales, and were scattered everywhere about. But still, though these things looked so aged, the aspect of the wood was that of the newest life; for, whichever way you turned your eyes, something fresh and green was springing forth, so as to be ready for the summer.

At last, the young people reached the upper verge of the wood, and found themselves almost at the summit of the hill. It was not a peak, nor a great round ball, but a pretty wide plain, or table-land, with a house and barn upon it, at some distance. That house was the home of a solitary family; and oftentimes the clouds, whence fell the rain, and whence the snow-storm drifted down into the valley, hung lower than this bleak and lonely dwelling-place.

On the highest point of the hill was a heap of stones, in the centre of which was stuck a long pole, with a little flag fluttering at the end of it. Eustace led the children thither, and bade them look around, and see how large a tract of our beautiful world they could take in at a glance. And their eyes grew wider as they looked.

Monument Mountain, to the southward, was still in the centre of the scene, but seemed to have sunk and subsided, so that it was now but an undistinguished member of a large family of hills. Beyond it, the Taconic range looked higher and bulkier than before. Our pretty lake was seen, with all its little bays and inlets; and not that alone, but two or three new lakes were opening their blue eyes to the sun. Several white villages, each with its steeple, were scattered about in the distance. There were so many farm-houses, with their acres of woodland, pasture, mowing-fields, and tillage, that the children could hardly make room in their minds to receive all these different objects. There, too, was Tanglewood, which they had hitherto thought such an important apex of the world. It now occupied so small a space, that they gazed far beyond it, and on either side, and searched a good while with all their eyes, before discovering whereabout it stood.

White, fleecy clouds were hanging in the air, and threw the dark spots of their shadow here and there over the landscape. But, by and by, the sunshine was where the shadow had been, and the shadow was somewhere else.

Far to the westward was a range of blue mountains, which Eustace Bright told the children were the Catskills. Among those misty hills, he said, was a spot where some old Dutchmen were playing an everlasting game of ninepins, and where an idle fellow, whose name was Rip Van Winkle, had fallen asleep, and slept twenty years at a stretch. The children eagerly besought Eustace to tell them all about this wonderful affair. But the student replied that the story had been told once already, and better than it ever could be told again; and that nobody would have a right to alter a word of it, until it should have grown as old as "The Gorgon's Head," and "The Three Golden Apples," and the rest of those miraculous legends.

"At least," said Periwinkle, "while we rest ourselves here, and are looking about us, you can tell us another of your own stories."

"Yes, Cousin Eustace," cried Primrose, "I advise you to tell us a story here. Take some lofty subject or other, and see if your imagination will not come up to it. Perhaps the mountain air may make you poetical, for once. And no matter how strange and wonderful the story may be, now that we are up among the clouds, we can believe anything."

"Can you believe," asked Eustace, "that there was once a winged horse?"

"Yes," said saucy Primrose; "but I am afraid you will never be able to catch him."

"For that matter, Primrose," rejoined the student, "I might possibly catch Pegasus, and get upon his back, too, as well as a dozen other fellows that I know of. At any rate, here is a story about him; and, of all places in the world, it ought certainly to be told upon a mountain-top."

So, sitting on the pile of stones, while the children clustered themselves at its base, Eustace fixed his eyes on a white cloud that was sailing by, and began as follows.

THE CHIMÆRA.

ONCE, in the old, old times (for all the strange things which I tell you about happened long before anybody can remember), a fountain gushed out of a hill-side, in the marvellous land of Greece. And, for aught I know, after so many thousand years, it is still gushing out of the very selfsame spot. At any rate, there was the pleasant fountain, welling freshly forth and sparkling adown the hill-side, in the golden sunset, when a handsome young man named Bellerophon drew near its margin. In his hand he held a bridle, studded with brilliant gems, and adorned with a golden bit. Seeing an old man, and another of middle age, and a little boy, near the fountain, and likewise a maiden, who was dipping up some of the water in a pitcher, he paused, and begged that he might refresh himself with a draught.

"This is very delicious water," he said to the maiden as he rinsed and filled her pitcher, after drinking out of it. "Will you be kind enough to tell me whether the fountain has any name?"

"Yes; it is called the Fountain of Pirene," answered the maiden; and then she added, "My grandmother has told me that this clear fountain was once a beautiful woman; and when her son was killed by the arrows of the huntress Diana, she melted all away into tears. And so the water, which you find so cool and sweet, is the sorrow of that poor mother's heart!"

"I should not have dreamed," observed the young

stranger, " that so clear a well-spring, with its gush and gurgle, and its cheery dance out of the shade into the sunlight, had so much as one tear-drop in its bosom! And this, then, is Pirene? I thank you, pretty maiden, for telling me its name. I have come from a far-away country to find this very spot."

A middle-aged country fellow (he had driven his cow to drink out of the spring) stared hard at young Bellerophon, and at the handsome bridle which he carried in his hand.

" The water-courses must be getting low, friend, in your part of the world," remarked he, " if you come so far only to find the Fountain of Pirene. But, pray, have you lost a horse? I see you carry the bridle in your hand; and a very pretty one it is with that double row of bright stones upon it. If the horse was as fine as the bridle, you are much to be pitied for losing him."

" I have lost no horse," said Bellerophon, with a smile. " But I happen to be seeking a very famous one, which, as wise people have informed me, must be found hereabouts, if anywhere. Do you know whether the winged horse Pegasus still haunts the Fountain of Pirene, as he used to do in your forefathers' days?"

But then the country fellow laughed.

Some of you, my little friends, have probably heard that this Pegasus was a snow-white steed, with beautiful silvery wings, who spent most of his time on the summit of Mount Helicon. He was as wild, and as swift, and as buoyant, in his flight through the air, as any eagle that ever soared into the clouds. There was nothing else like him in the world. He had no mate; he never had been backed or bridled by a master; and, for many a long year, he led a solitary and a happy life.

Oh, how fine a thing it is to be a winged horse! Sleeping at night, as he did, on a lofty mountain-top, and passing the greater part of the day in the air, Pegasus seemed hardly to be a creature of the earth. Whenever he was seen, up very high above people's heads, with the sunshine on his silvery wings, you would have thought that he belonged to the sky, and that, skimming a little too low, he had got astray among our mists and vapors, and was seeking his way back again. It was very pretty to behold him plunge into the fleecy bosom of a bright cloud, and be lost in it, for a moment or two, and then break forth from the other side. Or, in a sullen rain-storm, when there was a gray pavement of clouds over the whole sky, it would sometimes happen that the winged horse descended right through it, and the glad light of the upper region would gleam after him. In another instant, it is true, both Pegasus and the pleasant light would be gone away together. But any one that was fortunate enough to see this wondrous spectacle felt cheerful the whole day afterwards, and as much longer as the storm lasted.

In the summer-time, and in the beautifullest of weather, Pegasus often alighted on the solid earth, and, closing his silvery wings, would gallop over hill and dale for pastime, as fleetly as the wind. Oftener than in any other place, he had been seen near the Fountain of Pirene, drinking the delicious water, or rolling himself upon the soft grass of the margin. Sometimes, too (but Pegasus was very dainty in his food), he would crop a few of the clover-blossoms that happened to be sweetest.

To the Fountain of Pirene, therefore, people's great-grandfathers had been in the habit of going (as long

as they were youthful, and retained their faith in
winged horses), in hopes of getting a glimpse at the
beautiful Pegasus. But, of late years, he had been
very seldom seen. Indeed, there were many of the
country folks, dwelling within half an hour's walk of
the fountain, who had never beheld Pegasus, and did
not believe that there was any such creature in existence. The country fellow to whom Bellerophon was
speaking chanced to be one of those incredulous per
sons.

And that was the reason why he laughed.

" Pegasus, indeed! " cried he, turning up his nose
as high as such a flat nose could be turned up, —
" Pegasus, indeed! A winged horse, truly! Why,
friend, are you in your senses? Of what use would
wings be to a horse? Could he drag the plough so
well, think you? To be sure, there might be a little
saving in the expense of shoes; but then, how would
a man like to see his horse flying out of the stable
window? — yes, or whisking him up above the clouds,
when he only wanted to ride to mill? No, no! I
don't believe in Pegasus. There never was such a ridiculous kind of a horse-fowl made! "

" I have some reason to think otherwise," said Bellerophon, quietly.

And then he turned to an old, gray man, who was
leaning on a staff, and listening very attentively, with
his head stretched forward, and one hand at his ear,
because, for the last twenty years, he had been getting
rather deaf.

" And what say you, venerable sir? " inquired he.
"In your younger days, I should imagine, you must
frequently have seen the winged steed! "

" Ah, young stranger, my memory is very poor! "

said the aged man. " When I was a lad, if I remember rightly, I used to believe there was such a horse, and so did everybody else. But, nowadays, I hardly know what to think, and very seldom think about the winged horse at all. If I ever saw the creature, it was a long, long while ago; and, to tell you the truth, I doubt whether I ever did see him. One day, to be sure, when I was quite a youth, I remember seeing some hoof-tramps round about the brink of the fountain. Pegasus might have made those hoof-marks; and so might some other horse."

" And have you never seen him, my fair maiden ? " asked Bellerophon of the girl, who stood with the pitcher on her head, while this talk went on. " You certainly could see Pegasus, if anybody can, for your eyes are very bright."

" Once I thought I saw him," replied the maiden, with a smile and a blush. " It was either Pegasus, or a large white bird, a very great way up in the air. And one other time, as I was coming to the fountain with my pitcher, I heard a neigh. Oh, such a brisk and melodious neigh as that was! My very heart leaped with delight at the sound. But it startled me, nevertheless ; so that I ran home without filling my pitcher."

" That was truly a pity ! " said Bellerophon.

And he turned to the child, whom I mentioned at the beginning of the story, and who was gazing at him, as children are apt to gaze at strangers, with his rosy mouth wide open.

" Well, my little fellow," cried Bellerophon, playfully pulling one of his curls, " I suppose you have often seen the winged horse."

" That I have," answered the child, very readily. " I saw him yesterday, and many times before."

"You are a fine little man!" said Bellerophon, drawing the child closer to him. "Come, tell me all about it."

"Why," replied the child, "I often come here to sail little boats in the fountain, and to gather pretty pebbles out of its basin. And sometimes, when I look down into the water, I see the image of the winged horse, in the picture of the sky that is there. I wish he would come down, and take me on his back, and let me ride him up to the moon! But, if I so much as stir to look at him, he flies far away out of sight."

And Bellerophon put his faith in the child, who had seen the image of Pegasus in the water, and in the maiden, who had heard him neigh so melodiously, rather than in the middle-aged clown, who believed only in cart-horses, or in the old man who had forgotten the beautiful things of his youth.

Therefore, he haunted about the Fountain of Pirene for a great many days afterwards. He kept continually on the watch, looking upward at the sky, or else down into the water, hoping forever that he should see either the reflected image of the winged horse, or the marvellous reality. He held the bridle, with its bright gems and golden bit, always ready in his hand. The rustic people, who dwelt in the neighborhood, and drove their cattle to the fountain to drink, would often laugh at poor Bellerophon, and sometimes take him pretty severely to task. They told him that an able-bodied young man, like himself, ought to have better business than to be wasting his time in such an idle pursuit. They offered to sell him a horse, if he wanted one; and when Bellerophon declined the purchase, they tried to drive a bargain with him for his fine bridle.

Even the country boys thought him so very foolish, that they used to have a great deal of sport about him, and were rude enough not to care a fig, although Bellerophon saw and heard it. One little urchin, for example, would play Pegasus, and cut the oddest imaginable capers, by way of flying; while one of his schoolfellows would scamper after him, holding forth a twist of bulrushes, which was intended to represent Bellerophon's ornamental bridle. But the gentle child, who had seen the picture of Pegasus in the water, comforted the young stranger more than all the naughty boys could torment him. The dear little fellow, in his play-hours, often sat down beside him, and, without speaking a word, would look down into the fountain and up towards the sky, with so innocent a faith, that Bellerophon could not help feeling encouraged.

Now you will, perhaps, wish to be told why it was that Bellerophon had undertaken to catch the winged horse. And we shall find no better opportunity to speak about this matter than while he is waiting for Pegasus to appear.

If I were to relate the whole of Bellerophon's previous adventures, they might easily grow into a very long story. It will be quite enough to say, that, in a certain country of Asia, a terrible monster, called a Chimæra, had made its appearance, and was doing more mischief than could be talked about between now and sunset. According to the best accounts which I have been able to obtain, this Chimæra was nearly, if not quite, the ugliest and most poisonous creature, and the strangest and unaccountablest, and the hardest to fight with, and the most difficult to run away from, that ever came out of the earth's inside.

It had a tail like a boa-constrictor; its body was like I do not care what; and it had three separate heads, one of which was a lion's, the second a goat's, and the third an abominably great snake's. And a hot blast of fire came flaming out of each of its three mouths! Being an earthly monster, I doubt whether it had any wings; but, wings or no, it ran like a goat and a lion, and wriggled along like a serpent, and thus contrived to make about as much speed as all the three together.

Oh, the mischief, and mischief, and mischief that this naughty creature did! With its flaming breath, it could set a forest on fire, or burn up a field of grain, or, for that matter, a village, with all its fences and houses. It laid waste the whole country round about, and used to eat up people and animals alive, and cook them afterwards in the burning oven of its stomach. Mercy on us, little children, I hope neither you nor I will ever happen to meet a Chimæra!

While the hateful beast (if a beast we can anywise call it) was doing all these horrible things, it so chanced that Bellerophon came to that part of the world, on a visit to the king. The king's name was Iobates, and Lycia was the country which he ruled over. Bellerophon was one of the bravest youths in the world, and desired nothing so much as to do some valiant and beneficent deed, such as would make all mankind admire and love him. In those days, the only way for a young man to distinguish himself was by fighting battles, either with the enemies of his country, or with wicked giants, or with troublesome dragons, or with wild beasts, when he could find nothing more dangerous to encounter. King Iobates, perceiving the courage of his youthful visitor, proposed to him to go and fight the Chimæra, which everybody else was afraid of, and which, unless it should be soon killed, was likely to convert Lycia into a desert. Bellerophon hesitated not a moment, but assured the king that he would either slay this dreaded Chimæra, or perish in the attempt.

But, in the first place, as the monster was so prodigiously swift, he bethought himself that he should never win the victory by fighting on foot. The wisest thing he could do, therefore, was to get the very best and fleetest horse that could anywhere be found. And what other horse, in all the world, was half so fleet as the marvellous horse Pegasus, who had wings as well as legs, and was even more active in the air than on the earth? To be sure, a great many people denied that there was any such horse with wings, and said that the stories about him were all poetry and nonsense. But, wonderful as it appeared, Bellerophon believed that Pegasus was a real steed, and hoped that he himself might be fortunate enough to find him; and, once fairly mounted on his back, he would be able to fight the Chimæra at better advantage.

And this was the purpose with which he had travelled from Lycia to Greece, and had brought the beautifully ornamented bridle in his hand. It was an enchanted bridle. If he could only succeed in putting the golden bit into the mouth of Pegasus, the winged horse would be submissive, and would own Bellerophon for his master, and fly whithersoever he might choose to turn the rein.

But, indeed, it was a weary and anxious time, while Bellerophon waited and waited for Pegasus, in hopes that he would come and drink at the Fountain of Pirene. He was afraid lest King Iobates should imagine that he had fled from the Chimæra. It pained him, too, to think how much mischief the monster was doing, while he himself, instead of fighting with it, was compelled to sit idly poring over the bright waters of Pirene, as they gushed out of the sparkling sand. And as Pegasus came thither so seldom in these latter years, and scarcely alighted there more than once in a lifetime, Bellerophon feared that he might grow an old man, and have no strength left in his arms nor courage in his heart, before the winged horse would appear. Oh, how heavily passes the time, while an adventurous youth is yearning to do his part in life, and to gather in the harvest of his renown! How hard a lesson it is to wait! Our life is brief, and how much of it is spent in teaching us only this!

Well was it for Bellerophon that the gentle child had grown so fond of him, and was never weary of keeping him company. Every morning the child gave him a new hope to put in his bosom, instead of yesterday's withered one.

"Dear Bellerophon," he would cry, looking up hopefully into his face, " I think we shall see Pegasus today!"

And, at length, if it had not been for the little boy's unwavering faith, Bellerophon would have given up all hope, and would have gone back to Lycia, and have done his best to slay the Chimæra without the help of the winged horse. And in that case poor Bellerophon would at least have been terribly scorched by the creature's breath, and would most probably have been killed and devoured. Nobody should ever try to fight an earth-born Chimæra, unless he can first get upon the back of an aerial steed.

One morning the child spoke to Bellerophon even more hopefully than usual.

" Dear, dear Bellerophon," cried he, " I know not why it is, but I feel as if we should certainly see Pegasus to-day ! "

And all that day he would not stir a step from Bellerophon's side; so they ate a crust of bread together, and drank some of the water of the fountain. In the afternoon, there they sat, and Bellerophon had thrown his arm around the child, who likewise had put one of his little hands into Bellerophon's. The latter was lost in his own thoughts, and was fixing his eyes vacantly on the trunks of the trees that overshadowed the fountain, and on the grapevines that clambered up among their branches. But the gentle child was gazing down into the water; he was grieved, for Bellerophon's sake, that the hope of another day should be deceived, like so many before it ; and two or three quiet tear-drops fell from his eyes, and mingled with what were said to be the many tears of Pirene, when she wept for her slain children.

But, when he least thought of it, Bellerophon felt the pressure of the child's little hand, and heard a soft, almost breathless, whisper.

" See there, dear Bellerophon ! There is an image in the water ! "

The young man looked down into the dimpling mirror of the fountain, and saw what he took to be the reflection of a bird which seemed to be flying at a great height in the air, with a gleam of sunshine on its snowy or silvery wings.

" What a splendid bird it must be!" said he. " And how very large it looks, though it must really be flying higher than the clouds ! "

" It makes me tremble !" whispered the child. " I am afraid to look up into the air ! It is very beautiful, and yet I dare only look at its image in the water. Dear Bellerophon, do you not see that it is no bird? It is the winged horse Pegasus!"

Bellerophon's heart began to throb! He gazed keenly upward, but could not see the winged creature, whether bird or horse; because, just then, it had plunged into the fleecy depths of a summer cloud. It was but a moment, however, before the object reappeared, sinking lightly down out of the cloud, although still at a vast distance from the earth. Bellerophon caught the child in his arms, and shrank back with him, so that they were both hidden among the thick shubbery which grew all around the fountain. Not that he was afraid of any harm, but he dreaded lest, if Pegasus caught a glimpse of them, he would fly far away, and alight in some inaccessible mountain-top. For it was really the winged horse. After they had expected him so long, he was coming to quench his thirst with the water of Pirene.

Nearer and nearer came the aerial wonder, flying in great circles, as you may have seen a dove when about to alight. Downward came Pegasus, in those wide, sweeping circles, which grew narrower, and narrower still, as he gradually approached the earth. The nigher the view of him, the more beautiful he was, and the more marvellous the sweep of his silvery wings. At last, with so light a pressure as hardly to bend the grass about the fountain, or imprint a hoof-tramp in the sand of its margin, he alighted, and, stooping his wild head, began to drink. He drew in the water, with long and pleasant sighs, and tranquil pauses of enjoyment; and then another draught, and another, and another. For, nowhere in the world, or up among the clouds, did Pegasus love any water as he loved this of Pirene.   And when his thirst was slaked, he cropped a few of the honey-blossoms of the clover, delicately tasting them, but not caring to make a hearty meal, because the herbage, just beneath the clouds, on the lofty sides of Mount Helicon, suited his palate better than this ordinary grass.

After thus drinking to his heart's content, and in his dainty fashion, condescending to take a little food, the winged horse began to caper to and fro, and dance as it were, out of mere idleness and sport.   There never was a more playful creature made than this very Pegasus.   So there he frisked, in a way that it delights me to think about, fluttering his great wings as lightly as ever did a linnet, and running little races, half on earth and half in air, and which I know not whether to call a flight or a gallop.   When a creature is perfectly able to fly, he sometimes chooses to run, just for the pastime of the thing; and so did Pegasus, although it cost him some little trouble to keep his hoofs so near the ground.   Bellerophon, meanwhile, holding the child's hand, peeped forth from the shrubbery, and thought that never was any sight so beautiful as this, nor ever a horse's eyes so wild and spirited as those of Pegasus.   It seemed a sin to think of bridling him and riding on his back.

Once or twice, Pegasus stopped, and snuffed the air, pricking up his ears, tossing his head, and turning it on all sides, as if he partly suspected some mischief or other.   Seeing nothing, however, and hearing no sound, he soon began his antics again.

At length, — not that he was weary, but only idle and luxurious, — Pegasus folded his wings, and lay down on the soft green turf.   But, being too full of aerial life to remain quiet for many moments together, he soon rolled over on his back, with his four slender legs in the air. It was beautiful to see him, this one solitary creature, whose mate had never been created, but who needed no companion, and, living a great many hundred years, was as happy as the centuries were long. The more he did such things as mortal horses are accustomed to do, the less earthly and the more wonderful he seemed. Bellerophon and the child almost held their breath, partly from a delightful awe, but still more because they dreaded lest the slightest stir or murmur should send him up, with the speed of an arrow-flight, into the farthest blue of the sky.

Finally, when he had had enough of rolling over and over, Pegasus turned himself about, and, indolently, like any other horse, put out his fore legs, in order to rise from the ground; and Bellerophon, who had guessed that he would do so, darted suddenly from the thicket, and leaped astride of his back.

Yes, there he sat, on the back of the winged horse!

But what a bound did Pegasus make, when, for the first time, he felt the weight of a mortal man upon his loins! A bound, indeed! Before he had time to draw a breath, Bellerophon found himself five hundred feet aloft, and still shooting upward, while the winged horse snorted and trembled with terror and anger. Upward he went, up, up, up, until he plunged into the cold misty bosom of a cloud, at which, only a little while before, Bellerophon had been gazing, and fancying it a very pleasant spot. Then again, out of the heart of the cloud, Pegasus shot down like a thunderbolt, as if he meant to dash both himself and his rider headlong against a rock. Then he went through about a thousand of the wildest caprioles that had ever been performed either by a bird or a horse.

I cannot tell you half that he did. He skimmed straight forward, and sideways, and backward. He reared himself erect, with his fore legs on a wreath of mist, and his hind legs on nothing at all. He flung out his heels behind, and put down his head between his legs, with his wings pointing right upward. At about two miles' height above the earth, he turned a somerset, so that Bellerophon's heels were where his head should have been, and he seemed to look down into the sky, instead of up. He twisted his head about, and, looking Bellerophon in the face, with fire flashing from his eyes, made a terrible attempt to bite him. He fluttered his pinions so wildly that one of the silver feathers was shaken out, and floating earthward, was picked up by the child, who kept it as long as he lived, in memory of Pegasus and Bellerophon.

But the latter (who, as you may judge, was as good a horseman as ever galloped) had been watching his opportunity, and at last clapped the golden bit of the enchanted bridle between the winged steed's jaws. No sooner was this done, than Pegasus became as manageable as if he had taken food, all his life, out of Bellerophon's hand. To speak what I really feel, it was almost a sadness to see so wild a creature grow suddenly so tame. And Pegasus seemed to feel it so, likewise. He looked round to Bellerophon, with the tears in his beautiful eyes, instead of the fire that so recently flashed from them. But when Bellerophon patted his head, and spoke a few authoritative, yet kind and soothing words, another look came into the eyes of Pegasus; for he was glad at heart, after so many lonely centuries, to have found a companion and a master.

Thus it always is with winged horses, and with all such wild and solitary creatures. If you can catch and overcome them, it is the surest way to win their love.

While Pegasus had been doing his utmost to shake Bellerophon off his back, he had flown a very long distance; and they had come within sight of a lofty mountain by the time the bit was in his mouth. Bellerophon had seen this mountain before, and knew it to be Helicon, on the summit of which was the winged horse's abode. Thither (after looking gently into his rider's face, as if to ask leave) Pegasus now flew, and, alighting, waited patiently until Bellerophon should please to dismount. The young man, accordingly, leaped from his steed's back, but still held him fast by the bridle. Meeting his eyes, however, he was so affected by the gentleness of his aspect, and by the thought of the free life which Pegasus had heretofore lived, that he could not bear to keep him a a prisoner, if he really desired his liberty.

Obeying this generous impulse he slipped the enchanted bridle off the head of Pegasus, and took the bit from his mouth.

" Leave me, Pegasus ! " said he. "Either leave me, or love me."

In an instant, the winged horse shot almost out of sight, soaring straight upward from the summit of Mount Helicon. Being long after sunset, it was now twilight on the mountain-top, and dusky evening over all the country round about. But Pegasus flew so high that he overtook the departed day, and was bathed in the upper radiance of the sun. Ascending higher and higher, he looked like a bright speck, and, at last, could no longer be seen in the hollow waste of the sky. And Bellerophon was afraid that he should never behold him more. But, while he was lamenting his own folly, the bright speck reappeared, and drew nearer and nearer, until it descended lower than the sunshine; and, behold, Pegasus had come back! After this trial there was no more fear of the winged horse's making his escape. He and Bellerophon were friends, and put loving faith in one another.

That night they lay down and slept together, with Bellerophon's arm about the neck of Pegasus, not as a caution, but for kindness. And they awoke at peep of day, and bade one another good morning, each in his own language.

In this manner, Bellerophon and the wondrous steed spent several days, and grew better acquainted and fonder of each other all the time. They went on long aerial journeys, and sometimes ascended so high that the earth looked hardly bigger than — the moon. They visited distant countries, and amazed the inhabitants, who thought that the beautiful young man, on the back of the winged horse, must have come down out of the sky. A thousand miles a day was no more than an easy space for the fleet Pegasus to pass over. Bellerophon was delighted with this kind of life, and would have liked nothing better than to live always in the same way, aloft in the clear atmosphere; for it was always sunny weather up there, however cheerless and rainy it might be in the lower region. But he could not forget the horrible Chimæra, which he had promised King Iobates to slay. So, at last, when he had become well accustomed to feats of horsemanship in the air, and could manage Pegasus with the least motion of his hand, and had taught him to obey his voice, he determined to attempt the performance of this perilous adventure.

At daybreak, therefore, as soon as he unclosed his eyes, he gently pinched the winged horse's ear, in order to arouse him. Pegasus immediately started from the ground, and pranced about a quarter of a mile aloft, and made a grand sweep around the mountain-top, by way of showing that he was wide awake, and ready for any kind of an excursion. During the whole of this little flight, he uttered a loud, brisk, and melodious neigh, and finally came down at Bellerophon's side, as lightly as ever you saw a sparrow hop upon a twig.

"Well done, dear Pegasus! well done, my sky-skimmer!" cried Bellerophon, fondly stroking the horse's neck. "And now, my fleet and beautiful friend, we must break our fast. To-day we are to fight the terrible Chimæra."

As soon as they had eaten their morning meal, and drank some sparkling water from a spring called Hippocrene, Pegasus held out his head, of his own accord, so that his master might put on the bridle. Then, with a great many playful leaps and airy caperings, he showed his impatience to be gone; while Bellerophon was girding on his sword, and hanging his shield about his neck, and preparing himself for battle. When everything was ready, the rider mounted, and (as was his custom, when going a long distance) ascended five miles perpendicularly, so as the better to see whither he was directing his course. He then turned the head of Pegasus towards the east, and set out for Lycia. In their flight they overtook an eagle, and came so nigh him, before he could get out of their way, that Bellerophon might easily have caught him by the leg. Hastening onward at this rate, it was still early in the forenoon when they beheld the lofty mountains of Lycia, with their deep and shaggy valleys. If

Bellerophon had been told truly, it was in one of those dismal valleys that the hideous Chimæra had taken up its abode.

Being now so near their journey's end, the winged horse gradually descended with his rider ; and they took advantage of some clouds that were floating over the mountain-tops, in order to conceal themselves. Hovering on the upper surface of a cloud, and peeping over its edge, Bellerophon had a pretty distinct view of the mountainous part of Lycia, and could look into all its shadowy vales at once. At first there appeared to be nothing remarkable. It was a wild, savage, and rocky tract of high and precipitous hills. In the more level part of the country, there were the ruins of houses that had been burnt, and, here and there, the carcasses of dead cattle, strewn about the pastures where they had been feeding.

" The Chimæra must have done this mischief," thought Bellerophon. " But where can the monster be ? "

As I have already said, there was nothing remarkable to be detected, at first sight, in any of the valleys and dells that lay among the precipitous heights of the mountains. Nothing at all ; unless, indeed, it were three spires of black smoke, which issued from what seemed to be the mouth of a cavern, and clambered sullenly into the atmosphere. Before reaching the mountain-top, these three black smoke-wreaths mingled themselves into one. The cavern was almost directly beneath the winged horse and his rider, at the distance of about a thousand feet. The smoke, as it crept heavily upward, had an ugly, sulphurous, stifling scent, which caused Pegasus to snort and Bellerophon to sneeze. So disagreeable was it to the marvellous steed (who was accustomed to breathe only the purest air), that he waved his wings, and shot half a mile out of the range of this offensive vapor.

But, on looking behind him, Bellerophon saw some- thing that induced him first to draw the bridle, and then to turn Pegasus about. He made a sign, which the winged horse understood, and sunk slowly through the air, until his hoofs were scarcely more than a man's height above the rocky bottom of the valley. In front, as far off as you could throw a stone, was the cavern's mouth, with the three smoke-wreaths ooz- ing out of it. And what else did Bellerophon behold there?

There seemed to be a heap of strange and terrible creatures curled up within the cavern. Their bodies lay so close together, that Bellerophon could not dis- tinguish them apart; but, judging by their heads, one of these creatures was a huge snake, the second a fierce lion, and the third an ugly goat. The lion and the goat were asleep; the snake was broad awake, and kept staring around him with a great pair of fiery eyes. But — and this was the most wonderful part of the matter — the three spires of smoke evidently issued from the nostrils of these three heads! So strange was the spectacle, that, though Bellerophon had been all along expecting it, the truth did not im- mediately occur to him, that here was the terrible three-headed Chimæra. He had found out the Chi- mæra's cavern. The snake, the lion, and the goat, as he supposed them to be, were not three separate crea- tures, but one monster!

The wicked, hateful thing! Slumbering as two thirds of it were, it still held, in its abominable claws, the remnant of an unfortunate lamb, — or possibly

(but I hate to think so) it was a dear little boy, —-
which its three mouths had been gnawing, before two
of them fell asleep!

All at once, Bellerophon started as from a dream,
and knew it to be the Chimæra. Pegasus seemed to
know it, at the same instant, and sent forth a neigh,
that sounded like the call of a trumpet to battle. At
this sound the three heads reared themselves erect, and
belched out great flashes of flame. Before Bellerophon
had time to consider what to do next, the monster
flung itself out of the cavern and sprung straight towards him, with its immense claws extended, and its
snaky tail twisting itself venomously behind. If Pegasus had not been as nimble as a bird, both he and his
rider would have been overthrown by the Chimæra's
headlong rush, and thus the battle have been ended
before it was well begun. But the winged horse was
not to be caught so. In the twinkling of an eye he
was up aloft, half-way to the clouds, snorting with
anger. He shuddered, too, not with affright, but with
utter disgust at the loathsomeness of this poisonous
thing with three heads.

The Chimæra, on the other hand, raised itself up so
as to stand absolutely on the tip-end of its tail, with
its talons pawing fiercely in the air, and its three heads
spluttering fire at Pegasus and his rider. My stars,
how it roared, and hissed, and bellowed! Bellerophon,
meanwhile, was fitting his shield on his arm, and drawing his sword.

"Now, my beloved Pegasus," he whispered in the
winged horse's ear, "thou must help me to slay this
insufferable monster; or else thou shalt fly back to
thy solitary mountain-peak without thy friend Bellerophon. For either the Chimæra dies, or its three

mouths shall gnaw this head of mine, which has slumbered upon thy neck!"

Pegasus whinnied, and, turning back his head, rubbed his nose tenderly against his rider's cheek. It was his way of telling him that, though he had wings and was an immortal horse, yet he would perish, if it were possible for immortality to perish, rather than leave Bellerophon behind.

"I thank you, Pegasus," answered Bellerophon. "Now, then, let us make a dash at the monster!"

Uttering these words, he shook the bridle; and Pegasus darted down aslant, as swift as the flight of an arrow, right towards the Chimæra's threefold head, which, all this time, was poking itself as high as it could into the air. As he came within arm's-length, Bellerophon made a cut at the monster, but was carried onward by his steed, before he could see whether the blow had been successful. Pegasus continued his course, but soon wheeled round, at about the same distance from the Chimæra as before. Bellerophon then perceived that he had cut the goat's head of the monster almost off, so that it dangled downward by the skin, and seemed quite dead.

But, to make amends, the snake's head and the lion's head had taken all the fierceness of the dead one into themselves, and spit flame, and hissed, and roared, with a vast deal more fury than before.

"Never mind, my brave Pegasus!" cried Bellerophon. "With another stroke like that, we will stop either its hissing or its roaring."

And again he shook the bridle. Dashing aslantwise, as before, the winged horse made another arrow-flight towards the Chimæra, and Bellerophon aimed another downright stroke at one of the two remaining

heads, as he shot by. But this time, neither he nor
Pegasus escaped so well as at first. With one of its
claws, the Chimæra had given the young man a deep
scratch in his shoulder, and had slightly damaged the
left wing of the flying steed with the other. On his
part, Bellerophon had mortally wounded the lion's
head of the monster, insomuch that it now hung downward, with its fire almost extinguished, and sending
out gasps of thick black smoke. The snake's head,
however (which was the only one now left), was twice
as fierce and venomous as ever before. It belched
forth shoots of fire five hundred yards long, and
emitted hisses so loud, so harsh, and so ear-piercing,
that King Iobates heard them, fifty miles off, and
trembled till the throne shook under him.

" Well-a-day ! " thought the poor king ; " the Chimæra is certainly coming to devour me ! "

Meanwhile Pegasus had again paused in the air,
and neighed angrily, while sparkles of a pure crystal
flame darted out of his eyes. How unlike the lurid
fire of the Chimæra ! The aerial steed's spirit was all
aroused, and so was that of Bellerophon.

" Dost thou bleed, my immortal horse ? " cried the
young man, caring less for his own hurt than for the
anguish of this glorious creature, that ought never to
have tasted pain. " The execrable Chimæra shall pay
for this mischief with his last head ! "

Then he shook the bridle, shouted loudly, and
guided Pegasus, not aslantwise as before, but straight
at the monster's hideous front. So rapid was the
onset, that it seemed but a dazzle and a flash before
Bellerophon was at close gripes with his enemy.

The Chimæra, by this time, after losing its second
head, had got into a red-hot passion of pain and ram-

pant rage. It so flounced about, half on earth and
partly in the air, that it was impossible to say which
element it rested upon. It opened its snake-jaws to
such an abominable width, that Pegasus might almost,
I was going to say, have flown right down its throat,
wings outspread, rider and all! At their approach it
shot out a tremendous blast of its fiery breath, and en-
veloped Bellerophon and his steed in a perfect atmosphere of flame, singeing the wings of Pegasus, scorching off one whole side of the young man's golden
ringlets, and making them both far hotter than was
comfortable, from head to foot.

But this was nothing to what followed.

When the airy rush of the winged horse had
brought him within the distance of a hundred yards,
the Chimæra gave a spring, and flung its huge, awkward, venomous, and utterly detestable carcass right
upon poor Pegasus, clung round him with might and
main, and tied up its snaky tail into a knot! Up
flew the aerial steed, higher, higher, higher, above the
mountain-peaks, above the clouds, and almost out of
sight of the solid earth. But still the earth-born
monster kept its hold, and was borne upward, along
with the creature of light and air. Bellerophon, meanwhile, turning about, found himself face to face with
the ugly grimness of the Chimæra's visage, and could
only avoid being scorched to death, or bitten right in
twain, by holding up his shield. Over the upper edge
of the shield, he looked sternly into the savage eyes of
the monster.

But the Chimæra was so mad and wild with pain,
that it did not guard itself so well as might else have
been the case. Perhaps, after all, the best way to fight
a Chimæra is by getting as close to it as you can. In

its efforts to stick its horrible iron claws into its enemy, the creature left its own breast quite exposed; and perceiving this, Bellerophon thrust his sword up to the hilt into its cruel heart.   Immediately the snaky tail untied its knot.   The monster let go its hold of Pegasus, and fell from that vast height, downward ; while the fire within its bosom, instead of being put out, burned fiercer than ever, and quickly began to consume the dead carcass.   Thus it fell out of the sky, all a-flame, and (it being nightfall before it reached the earth) was mistaken for a shooting star or a comet. But, at early sunrise, some cottagers were going to their day's labor, and saw, to their astonishment, that several acres of ground were strewn with black ashes. In the middle of a field, there was a heap of whitened bones, a great deal higher than a haystack.   Nothing else was ever seen of the dreadful Chimæra !

And when Bellerophon had won the victory, he bent forward and kissed Pegasus, while the tears stood in his eyes.

" Back now, my beloved steed ! " said he.   " Back to the Fountain of Pirene ! "

Pegasus skimmed through the air, quicker than ever he did before, and reached the fountain in a very short time.   And there he found the old man leaning on his staff, and the country fellow watering his cow, and the pretty maiden filling her pitcher.

" I remember now," quoth the old man, " I saw this winged horse once before, when I was quite a lad.   But he was ten times handsomer in those days."

" I own a cart-horse, worth three of him ! " said the country fellow.   " If this pony were mine, the first thing I should do would be to clip his wings ! "

But the poor maiden said nothing, for she had al

ways the luck to be afraid at the wrong time. So she ran away, and let her pitcher tumble down, and broke it.

"Where is the gentle child," asked Bellerophon, "who used to keep me company, and never lost his faith, and never was weary of gazing into the fountain?"

"Here am I, dear Bellerophon!" said the child, softly.

For the little boy had spent day after day, on the margin of Pirene, waiting for his friend to come back; but when he perceived Bellerophon descending through the clouds, mounted on the winged horse, he had shrunk back into the shrubbery. He was a delicate and tender child, and dreaded lest the old man and the country fellow should see the tears gushing from his eyes.

"Thou hast won the victory," said he, joyfully, running to the knee of Bellerophon, who still sat on the back of Pegasus. "I knew thou wouldst."

"Yes, dear child!" replied Bellerophon, alighting from the winged horse. "But if thy faith had not helped me, I should never have waited for Pegasus, and never have gone up above the clouds, and never have conquered the terrible Chimæra. Thou, my beloved little friend, hast done it all. And now let us give Pegasus his liberty."

So he slipped off the enchanted bridle from the head of the marvellous steed.

"Be free, forevermore, my Pegasus!" cried he, with a shade of sadness in his tone. "Be as free as thou art fleet!"

But Pegasus rested his head on Bellerophon's shoulder, and would not be persuaded to take flight.

"Well then," said Bellerophon, caressing the airy horse, "thou shalt be with me, as long as thou wilt; and we will go together, forthwith, and tell King Iobates that the Chimæra is destroyed."

Then Bellerophon embraced the gentle child, and promised to come to him again, and departed. But, in after years, that child took higher flights upon the aerial steed than ever did Bellerophon, and achieved more honorable deeds than his friend's victory over the Chimæra. For, gentle and tender as he was, he grew to be a mighty poet!

BALD–SUMMIT.

AFTER THE STORY.

EUSTACE BRIGHT told the legend of Bellerophon with as much fervor and animation as if he had really been taking a gallop on the winged horse. At the conclusion, he was gratified to discern, by the glowing countenances of his auditors, how greatly they had been interested. All their eyes were dancing in their heads, except those of Primrose. In her eyes there were positively tears; for she was conscious of something in the legend which the rest of them were not yet old enough to feel. Child's story as it was, the student had contrived to breathe through it the ardor, the generous hope, and the imaginative enterprise of youth.

"I forgive you, now, Primrose," said he, " for all your ridicule of myself and my stories. One tear pays for a great deal of laughter."

"Well, Mr. Bright," answered Primrose, wiping her eyes, and giving him another of her mischievous smiles, "it certainly does elevate your ideas, to get your head above the clouds. I advise you never to tell another story, unless it be, as at present, from the top of a mountain."

"Or from the back of Pegasus," replied Eustace, laughing. "Don't you think that I succeeded pretty well in catching that wonderful pony?"

"It was so like one of your madcap pranks!'

cried Primrose, clapping her hands. " I think I see you now on his back, two miles high, and with your head downward! It is well that you have not really an opportunity of trying your horsemanship on any wilder steed than our sober Davy, or Old Hundred."

"For my part, I wish I had Pegasus here, at this moment," said the student. " I would mount him forthwith, and gallop about the country, within a circumference of a few miles, making literary calls on my brother-authors. Dr. Dewey would be within my reach, at the foot of Taconic. In Stockbridge, yonder, is Mr. James, conspicuous to all the world on his mountain-pile of history and romance. Longfellow, I believe, is not yet at the Ox-bow, else the winged horse would neigh at the sight of him. But, here in Lenox, I should find our most truthful novelist, who has made the scenery and life of Berkshire all her own. On the hither side of Pittsfield sits Herman Melville, shaping out the gigantic conception of his ' White Whale,' while the gigantic shape of Graylock looms upon him from his study-window. Another bound of my flying steed would bring me to the door of Holmes, whom I mention last, because Pegasus would certainly unseat me, the next minute, and claim the poet as his rider."

"Have we not an author for our next neighbor?" asked Primrose. " That silent man, who lives in the old red house, near Tanglewood Avenue, and whom we sometimes meet, with two children at his side, in the woods or at the lake. I think I have heard of his having written a poem, or a romance, or an arithmetic, or a school-history, or some other kind of a book."

"Hush, Primrose, hush!" exclaimed Eustace, in a thrilling whisper, and putting his finger on his lip.

"Not a word about that man, even on a hill-top! If our babble were to reach his ears, and happen not to please him, he has but to fling a quire or two of paper into the stove, and you, Primrose, and I, and Periwinkle, Sweet Fern, Squash-Blossom, Blue Eye, Huckleberry, Clover, Cowslip, Plantain, Milkweed, Dandelion, and Buttercup, — yes, and wise Mr. Pringle, with his unfavorable criticisms on my legends, and poor Mrs. Pringle, too, — would all turn to smoke, and go whisking up the funnel! Our neighbor in the red house is a harmless sort of person enough, for aught I know, as concerns the rest of the world; but something whispers to me that he has a terrible power over ourselves, extending to nothing short of annihilation."

"And would Tanglewood turn to smoke, as well as we?" asked Periwinkle, quite appalled at the threatened destruction. "And what would become of Ben and Bruin?"

"Tanglewood would remain," replied the student, "looking just as it does now, but occupied by an entirely different family. And Ben and Bruin would be still alive, and would make themselves very comfortable with the bones from the dinner-table, without ever thinking of the good times which they and we have had together!"

"What nonsense you are talking!" exclaimed Primrose.

With idle chat of this kind, the party had already begun to descend the hill, and were now within the shadow of the woods. Primrose gathered some mountain-laurel, the leaf of which, though of last year's growth, was still as verdant and elastic as if the frost and thaw had not alternately tried their force upon its texture. Of these twigs of laurel she twined a wreath, and took off the student's cap, in order to place it on his brow.

"Nobody else is likely to crown you for your stories," observed saucy Primrose, "so take this from me."

"Do not be too sure," answered Eustace, looking really like a youthful poet, with the laurel among his glossy curls, "that I shall not win other wreaths by these wonderful and admirable stories. I mean to spend all my leisure, during the rest of the vacation, and throughout the summer term at college, in writing them out for the press. Mr. J. T. Fields (with whom I became acquainted when he was in Berkshire, last summer, and who is a poet, as well as a publisher) will see their uncommon merit at a glance. He will get them illustrated, I hope, by Billings, and will bring them before the world under the very best of auspices, through the eminent house of TICKNOR & Co. In about five months from this moment, I make no doubt of being reckoned among the lights of the age!"

"Poor boy!" said Primrose, half aside. "What a disappointment awaits him!"

Descending a little lower, Bruin began to bark, and was answered by the graver bow-wow of the respectable Ben. They soon saw the good old dog, keeping careful watch over Dandelion, Sweet Fern, Cowslip, and Squash-Blossom. These little people, quite recovered from their fatigue, had set about gathering checkerberries, and now came clambering to meet their playfellows. Thus reunited, the whole party went down through Luther Butler's orchard, and made the best of their way home to Tanglewood.

TANGLEWOOD TALES,

FOR GIRLS AND BOYS.

BEING A SECOND WONDER-BOOK.

INTRODUCTORY NOTE.

TANGLEWOOD TALES.

HAWTHORNE's first "Wonder Book" was so well received, that he was induced to undertake another within eighteen months from the time of finishing the first. To this new volume, made up in the same way of Greek myths retold with a modern, free, half realistic and half fanciful tone, he gave the name "Tanglewood Tales." The previous series having been ostensibly narrated by one Eustace Bright, among the hills of Berkshire, these additional stories in the like vein were represented as having been brought by Eustace Bright to Hawthorne, at his new home, The Wayside, in Concord.

This place Hawthorne had bought and moved into, early in the summer of 1852, after finishing "The Blithedale Romance" at West Newton, during the preceding winter.[1] Some slight references to it are made in the Introduction headed "The Wayside," where "my predecessor's little ruined, rustic summer-house, midway on the hill-side," is mentioned. The predecessor was Mr. A. Bronson Alcott, one of the so-called Transcendental school of thinkers, the intimate friend of Ralph Waldo Emerson, and the father of

[1] For a detailed account of The Wayside, the prefatory note to *Septimius Felton*, in this edition of the works, may be consulted.

Miss Louisa M. Alcott, since become one of the most popular of writers for children. This summer-house, therefore, becomes to the mind a sort of station between the new generation and the old, a link between Hawthorne in his capacity of tale-teller to the little folks of America, and the woman who, at that time a child, has in later years assembled from the young people a vast audience of her own. The romancer speaks of this rustic structure in a letter to George William Curtis, dated July 14, 1852 : —

" Mr. Alcott expended a good deal of taste and some money (to no great purpose) in forming the hillside behind the house into terraces, and building arbors and summer-houses of rough stems and branches and trees, on a system of his own. They must have been very pretty in their day, and are so still, although much decayed, and shattered more and more by every breeze that blows."

No vestige of this sylvan edifice now remains.

Prior to his return to Concord and installation at The Wayside, Hawthorne had contemplated giving up that humble abode at Lenox, which, in a letter to George William Curtis, he had called " the ugliest little old red farm-house you ever saw," and renting the country-seat of Mrs. Fanny Kemble, in the same vicinity. But as I have mentioned in the Introductory Note prefixed to the " Wonder-Book," he had already begun to languish somewhat in the inland air of the Berkshire Valley; added to which was the not altogether favorable influence of the striking scenery in that picturesque mountain-district. In October, 1851, he wrote from Lenox to a friend: " We shall leave here (with much joy) on the first day of December."

The sojourn at West Newton, however, served only

to occupy the interval between Lenox and his settlement at Concord. After he had arrived at the latter place, he wrote to Horatio Bridge (October 13, 1852): "In a day or two I intend to begin a new romance, which, if possible, I intend to make more genial than the last." The "last" was "The Blithedale Romance;" but of the newly projected work here mentioned we find no further trace, and it is impossible to conjecture what scheme for a fresh work of fiction was then occupying the author's mind. The "campaign" Life of Franklin Pierce had already been produced after his coming to The Wayside, and he was apparently free to turn his attention to this projected romance; but instead of pursuing the design, whatever it may have been, he took up the composition of the "Tanglewood Tales," which were completed in the early spring of 1853. On the 13th of March, that year, he wrote the preface for them. Ten days later his appointment to the consulate at Liverpool by President Pierce was confirmed by the Senate of the United States.

G. P. L.

THE WAYSIDE.

A SHORT time ago, I was favored with a flying visit
from my young friend Eustace Bright, whom I had
not before met with since quitting the breezy mountains of Berkshire. It being the winter vacation at
his college, Eustace was allowing himself a little re-
laxation, in the hope, he told me, of repairing the in-
roads which severe application to study had made
upon his health; and I was happy to conclude, from
the excellent physical condition in which I saw him,
that the remedy had already been attended with very
desirable success. He had now run up from Boston
by the noon train, partly impelled by the friendly regard with which he is pleased to honor me, and
partly, as I soon found, on a matter of literary business.

It delighted me to receive Mr. Bright, for the first
time, under a roof, though a very humble one, which
I could really call my own. Nor did I fail (as is the
custom of landed proprietors all about the world) to
parade the poor fellow up and down over my half a
dozen acres; secretly rejoicing, nevertheless, that the
disarray of the inclement season, and particularly the
six inches of snow then upon the ground, prevented
him from observing the ragged neglect of soil and
shrubbery into which the place has lapsed. It was
idle, however, to imagine that an airy guest from

Monument Mountain, Bald-Summit, and old Gray-lock, shaggy with primeval forests, could see anything to admire in my poor little hill-side, with its growth of frail and insect-eaten locust-trees. Eustace very frankly called the view from my hill-top tame; and so, no doubt, it was, after rough, broken, rugged, head-long Berkshire, and especially the northern parts of the county, with which his college residence had made him familiar. But to me there is a peculiar, quiet charm in these broad meadows and gentle eminences. They are better than mountains, because they do not stamp and stereotype themselves into the brain, and thus grow wearisome with the same strong impression, repeated day after day. A few summer weeks among mountains, a lifetime among green meadows and placid slopes, with outlines forever new, because continually fading out of the memory, — such would be my sober choice.

I doubt whether Eustace did not internally pro-nounce the whole thing a bore, until I led him to my predecessor's little ruined, rustic summer-house, mid-way on the hill-side. It is a mere skeleton of slender, decaying tree-trunks, with neither walls nor a roof; nothing but a tracery of branches and twigs, which the next wintry blast will be very likely to scatter in fragments along the terrace. It looks, and is, as evan-escent as a dream; and yet, in its rustic net-work of boughs, it has somehow enclosed a hint of spiritual beauty, and has become a true emblem of the subtile and ethereal mind that planned it. I made Eustace Bright sit down on a snow-bank, which had heaped it-self over the mossy seat, and gazing through the arched window opposite, he acknowledged that the scene at once grew picturesque.

"Simple as it looks," said he, "this little edifice seems to be the work of magic. It is full of suggestiveness, and, in its way, is as good as a cathedral. Ah, it would be just the spot for one to sit in, of a summer afternoon, and tell the children some more of those wild stories from the classic myths!"

"It would, indeed," answered I. "The summerhouse itself, so airy and so broken, is like one of those old tales, imperfectly remembered; and these living branches of the Baldwin apple-tree, thrusting themselves so rudely in, are like your unwarrantable interpolations. But, by the by, have you added any more legends to the series, since the publication of the Wonder Book?"

"Many more," said Eustace; "Primrose, Periwinkle, and the rest of them allow me no comfort of my life, unless I tell them a story every day or two. I have run away from home partly to escape the importunity of those little wretches! But I have written out six of the new stories, and have brought them for you to look over."

"Are they as good as the first?" I inquired.

"Better chosen, and better handled," replied Eustace Bright. "You will say so when you read them."

"Possibly not," I remarked. "I know, from my own experience, that an author's last work is always his best one, in his own estimate, until it quite loses the red heat of composition. After that, it falls into its true place, quietly enough. But let us adjourn to my study, and examine these new stories. It would hardly be doing yourself justice, were you to bring me acquainted with them, sitting here on this snowbank!"

So we descended the hill to my small, old cottage,

and shut ourselves up in the southeastern room, where the sunshine comes in, warmly and brightly, through the better half of a winter's day. Eustace put his bundle of manuscript into my hands ; and I skimmed through it pretty rapidly, trying to find out its merits and demerits by the touch of my fingers, as a veteran story-teller ought to know how to do.

It will be remembered, that Mr. Bright conde-scended to avail himself of my literary experience by constituting me editor of the Wonder Book. As he had no reason to complain of the reception of that erudite work by the public, he was now disposed to re-tain me in a similar position, with respect to the pres-ent volume, which he entitled "TANGLEWOOD TALES." Not, as Eustace hinted, that there was any real neces-sity for my services as introductor, inasmuch as his own name had become established, in some good de-gree of favor, with the literary world. But the con-nection with myself, he was kind enough to say, had been highly agreeable ; nor was he by any means de-sirous, as most people are, of kicking away the ladder that had perhaps helped him to reach his present ele-vation. My young friend was willing, in short, that the fresh verdure of his growing reputation should spread over my straggling and half - naked boughs ; even as I have sometimes thought of training a vine, with its broad leafiness, and purple fruitage, over the worm-eaten posts and rafters of the rustic sum-mer-house. I was not insensible to the advantages of his proposal, and gladly assured him of my accept-ance.

Merely from the titles of the stories, I saw at once that the subjects were not less rich than those of the former volume ; nor did I at all doubt that Mr.

Bright's audacity (so far as that endowment might avail) had enabled him to take full advantage of whatever capabilities they offered. Yet, in spite of my experience of his free way of handling them, I did not quite see, I confess, how he could have obviated all the difficulties in the way of rendering them presentable to children. These old legends, so brimming over with everything that is most abhorrent to our Christianized moral sense, — some of them so hideous, others so melancholy and miserable, amid which the Greek tragedians sought their themes, and moulded them into the sternest forms of grief that ever the world saw; was such material the stuff that children's playthings should be made of! How were they to be purified? How was the blessed sunshine to be thrown into them? ·

But Eustace told me that these myths were the most singular things in the world, and that he was invariably astonished, whenever he began to relate one, by the readiness with which it adapted itself to the childish purity of his auditors. The objectionable characteristics seem to be a parasitical growth, having no essential connection with the original fable. They fall away, and are thought of no more, the instant he puts his imagination in sympathy with the innocent little circle, whose wide-open eyes are fixed so eagerly upon him. Thus the stories (not by any strained effort of the narrator's, but in harmony with their inherent germ) transform themselves, and reassume the shapes which they might be supposed to possess in the pure childhood of the world. When the first poet or romancer told these marvellous legends (such is Eustace Bright's opinion), it was still the Golden Age. Evil had never yet existed; and sorrow, misfortune, crime, were mere shadows which the mind fancifully created for itself, as a shelter against too sunny realities; or, at most, but prophetic dreams, to which the dreamer himself did not yield a waking credence. Children are now the only representatives of the men and women of that happy era; and therefore it is that we must raise the intellect and fancy to the level of childhood, in order to re-create the original myths.

I let the youthful author talk as much and as extravagantly as he pleased, and was glad to see him commencing life with such confidence in himself and his performances. A few years will do all that is necessary towards showing him the truth in both respects. Meanwhile, it is but right to say, he does really appear to have overcome the moral objections against these fables, although at the expense of such liberties with their structure as must be left to plead their own excuse, without any help from me. Indeed, except that there was a necessity for it, — and that the inner life of the legends cannot be come at save by making them entirely one's own property, — there is no defence to be made.

Eustace informed me that he had told his stories to the children in various situations, — in the woods, on the shore of the lake, in the dell of Shadow Brook, in the play-room, at Tanglewood fireside, and in a magnificent palace of snow, with ice windows, which he helped his little friends to build. His auditors were even more delighted with the contents of the present volume than with the specimens which have already been given to the world. The classically learned Mr. Pringle, too, had listened to two or three of the tales, and censured them even more bitterly than he did THE THREE GOLDEN APPLES; so that, what with praise, and what with criticism, Eustace Bright thinks that there is good hope of at least as much success with the public as in the case of the Wonder Book.

I made all sorts of inquiries about the children, not doubting that there would be great eagerness to hear of their welfare among some good little folks who have written to me, to ask for another volume of myths. They are all, I am happy to say (unless we except Clover), in excellent health and spirits. Primrose is now almost a young lady, and, Eustace tells me, is just as saucy as ever. She pretends to consider herself quite beyond the age to be interested by such idle stories as these; but, for all that, whenever a story is to be told, Primrose never fails to be one of the listeners, and to make fun of it when finished. Periwinkle is very much grown, and is expected to shut up her baby-house and throw away her doll in a month or two more. Sweet Fern has learned to read and write, and has put on a jacket and pair of pantaloons, — all of which improvements I am sorry for. Squash-Blossom, Blue Eye, Plantain, and Buttercup have had the scarlet fever, but came easily through it. Huckleberry, Milkweed, and Dandelion were attacked with the hooping-cough, but bore it bravely, and kept out of doors whenever the sun shone. Cowslip, during the autumn, had either the measles, or some eruption that looked very much like it, but was hardly sick a day. Poor Clover has been a good deal troubled with her second teeth, which have made her meagre in aspect and rather fractious in temper ; nor, even when she smiles, is the matter much mended, since it discloses a gap just within her lips, almost as wide as the barn door. But all this will pass over, and it is predicted that she will turn out a very pretty girl.

As for Mr. Bright himself, he is now in his senior year at Williams College, and has a prospect of graduating with some degree of honorable distinction at the next Commencement. In his oration for the bachelor's degree, he gives me to understand, he will treat of the classical myths, viewed in the aspect of baby stories, and has a great mind to discuss the expediency of using up the whole of ancient history for the same purpose. I do not know what he means to do with himself after leaving college, but trust that, by dabbling so early with the dangerous and seductive business of authorship, he will not be tempted to become an author by profession. If so, I shall be very sorry for the little that I have had to do with the matter, in encouraging these first beginnings.

I wish there were any likelihood of my soon seeing Primrose, Periwinkle, Dandelion, Sweet Fern, Clover, Plantain, Huckleberry, Milkweed, Cowslip, Buttercup, Blue Eye, and Squash-Blossom again. But as I do not know when I shall revisit Tanglewood, and as Eustace Bright probably will not ask me to edit a third Wonder Book, the public of little folks must not expect to hear any more about those dear children from me. Heaven bless them, and everybody else, whether grown people or children!

THE WAYSIDE, CONCORD, MASS,
March 13, 1853.

THE MINOTAUR.

In the old city of Trœzene, at the foot of a lofty mountain, there lived, a very long time ago, a little boy named Theseus. His grandfather, King Pittheus, was the sovereign of that country, and was reckoned a very wise man; so that Theseus, being brought up in the royal palace, and being naturally a bright lad, could hardly fail of profiting by the old king's instructions. His mother's name was Æthra. As for his father, the boy had never seen him. But, from his earliest remembrance, Æthra used to go with little Theseus into a wood, and sit down upon a moss-grown rock, which was deeply sunken into the earth. Here she often talked with her son about his father, and said that he was called Ægeus, and that he was a great king, and ruled over Attica, and dwelt at Athens, which was as famous a city as any in the world. Theseus was very fond of hearing about King Ægeus, and often asked his good mother Æthra why he did not come and live with them at Trœzene.

"Ah, my dear son," answered Æthra, with a sigh, "a monarch has his people to take care of. The men and women over whom he rules are in the place of children to him; and he can seldom spare time to love his own children as other parents do. Your father will never be able to leave his kingdom for the sake of seeing his little boy."

"Well, but, dear mother," asked the boy, "why cannot I go to this famous city of Athens, and tell King Ægeus that I am his son?"

"That may happen by and by," said Æthra. "Be patient, and we shall see. You are not yet big and strong enough to set out on such an errand."

"And how soon shall I be strong enough?" Theseus persisted in inquiring.

"You are but a tiny boy as yet," replied his mother. "See if you can lift this rock on which we are sitting?"

The little fellow had a great opinion of his own strength. So, grasping the rough protuberances of the rock, he tugged and toiled amain, and got himself quite out of breath, without being able to stir the heavy stone. It seemed to be rooted into the ground. No wonder he could not move it; for it would have taken all the force of a very strong man to lift it out of its earthy bed.

His mother stood looking on, with a sad kind of a smile on her lips and in her eyes, to see the zealous and yet puny efforts of her little boy. She could not help being sorrowful at finding him already so impatient to begin his adventures in the world.

"You see how it is, my dear Theseus," said she. "You must possess far more strength than now before I can trust you to go to Athens, and tell King Ægeus that you are his son. But when you can lift this rock, and show me what is hidden beneath it, I promise you my permission to depart."

Often and often, after this, did Theseus ask his mother whether it was yet time for him to go to Athens; and still his mother pointed to the rock, and told him that, for years to come, he could not be strong enough to move it. And again and again the rosy-cheeked and curly-headed boy would tug and strain at the huge mass of stone, striving, child as he was, to do what a giant could hardly have done without taking both of his great hands to the task. Meanwhile the rock seemed to be sinking farther and farther into the ground. The moss grew over it thicker and thicker, until at last it looked almost like a soft green seat, with only a few gray knobs of granite peeping out. The overhanging trees, also, shed their brown leaves upon it, as often as the autumn came; and at its base grew ferns and wild flowers, some of which crept quite over its surface. To all appearance, the rock was as firmly fastened as any other portion of the earth's substance.

But, difficult as the matter looked, Theseus was now growing up to be such a vigorous youth, that, in his own opinion, the time would quickly come when he might hope to get the upper hand of this ponderous lump of stone.

"Mother, I do believe it has started!" cried he, after one of his attempts. "The earth around it is certainly a little cracked!"

"No, no, child!" his mother hastily answered. "It is not possible you can have moved it, such a boy as you still are!"

Nor would she be convinced, although Theseus showed her the place where he fancied that the stem of a flower had been partly uprooted by the movement of the rock. But Æthra sighed and looked disquieted; for, no doubt, she began to be conscious that her son was no longer a child, and that, in a little while hence, she must send him forth among the perils and troubles of the world.

It was not more than a year afterwards when they were again sitting on the moss-covered stone. Æthra had once more told him the oft-repeated story of his father, and how gladly he would receive Theseus at his stately palace, and how he would present him to his courtiers and the people, and tell them that here was the heir of his dominions. The eyes of Theseus glowed with enthusiasm, and he would hardly sit still to hear his mother speak.

" Dear mother Æthra," he exclaimed, " I never felt half so strong as now ! I am no longer a child, nor a boy, nor a mere youth ! I feel myself a man ! It is now time to make one earnest trial to remove the stone."

" Ah, my dearest Theseus," replied his mother, " not yet ! not yet !"

" Yes, mother," said he, resolutely, " the time has come."

Then Theseus bent himself in good earnest to the task, and strained every sinew, with manly strength and resolution. He put his whole brave heart into the effort. He wrestled with the big and sluggish stone, as if it had been a living enemy. He heaved, he lifted, he resolved now to succeed, or else to perish there, and let the rock be his monument forever ! Æthra stood gazing at him, and clasped her hands, partly with a mother's pride, and partly with a mother's sorrow. The great rock stirred ! Yes, it was raised slowly from the bedded moss and earth, uprooting the shrubs and flowers along with it, and was turned upon its side. Theseus had conquered !

While taking breath, he looked joyfully at his mother, and she smiled upon him through her tears.

" Yes, Theseus," she said, " the time has come, and you must stay no longer at my side ! See what King Ægeus, your royal father, left for you, beneath the stone, when he lifted it in his mighty arms, and laid it on the spot whence you have now removed it."

Theseus looked, and saw that the rock had been placed over another slab of stone, containing a cavity within it; so that it somewhat resembled a roughly made chest or coffer, of which the upper mass had served as the lid. Within the cavity lay a sword, with a golden hilt, and a pair of sandals.

"That was your father's sword," said Æthra, "and those were his sandals. When he went to be king of Athens, he bade me treat you as a child until you should prove yourself a man by lifting this heavy stone. That task being accomplished, you are to put on his sandals, in order to follow in your father's footsteps, and to gird on his sword, so that you may fight giants and dragons, as King Ægeus did in his youth."

"I will set out for Athens this very day!" cried Theseus.

But his mother persuaded him to stay a day or two longer, while she got ready some necessary articles for his journey. When his grandfather, the wise King Pittheus, heard that Theseus intended to present himself at his father's palace, he earnestly advised him to get on board of a vessel, and go by sea; because he might thus arrive within fifteen miles of Athens, without either fatigue or danger.

"The roads are very bad by land," quoth the venerable king; "and they are terribly infested with robbers and monsters. A mere lad, like Theseus, is not fit to be trusted on such a perilous journey, all by himself. No, no; let him go by sea!"

But when Theseus heard of robbers and monsters, he pricked up his ears, and was so much the more eager to take the road along which they were to be met with. On the third day, therefore, he bade a respectful farewell to his grandfather, thanking him for all his kindness, and, after affectionately embracing his mother, he set forth, with a good many of her tears glistening on his cheeks, and some, if the truth must be told, that had gushed out of his own eyes. But he let the sun and wind dry them, and walked stoutly on, playing with the golden hilt of his sword and taking very manly strides in his father's sandals.

I cannot stop to tell you hardly any of the adventures that befell Theseus on the road to Athens. It is enough to say, that he quite cleared that part of the country of the robbers, about whom King Pittheus had been so much alarmed. One of these bad people was named Procrustes; and he was indeed a terrible fellow, and had an ugly way of making fun of the poor travellers who happened to fall into his clutches. In his cavern he had a bed, on which, with great pretence of hospitality, he invited his guests to lie down; but if they happened to be shorter than the bed, this wicked villain stretched them out by main force; or, if they were too long, he lopped off their heads or feet, and laughed at what he had done, as an excellent joke. Thus, however weary a man might be, he never liked to lie in the bed of Procrustes. Another of these robbers, named Scinis, must likewise have been a very great scoundrel. He was in the habit of flinging his victims off a high cliff into the sea; and, in order to give him exactly his deserts, Theseus tossed him off the very same place. But if you will believe me, the sea would not pollute itself by receiving such a bad person into its bosom, neither would the earth, having once got rid of him, consent to take him back; so that, between the cliff and the sea, Scinis stuck fast in the air, which was forced to bear the burden of his naughtiness.

After these memorable deeds, Theseus heard of an enormous sow, which ran wild, and was the terror of all the farmers round about; and, as he did not consider himself above doing any good thing that came in his way, he killed this monstrous creature, and gave the carcass to the poor people for bacon. The great sow had been an awful beast, while ramping about the woods and fields, but was a pleasant object enough when cut up into joints, and smoking on I know not how many dinner tables.

Thus, by the time he reached his journey's end, Theseus had done many valiant feats with his father's golden-hilted sword, and had gained the renown of being one of the bravest young men of the day. His fame travelled faster than he did, and reached Athens before him. As he entered the city, he heard the inhabitants talking at the street-corners, and saying that Hercules was brave, and Jason too, and Castor and Pollux likewise, but that Theseus, the son of their own king, would turn out as great a hero as the best of them. Theseus took longer strides on hearing this, and fancied himself sure of a magnificent reception at his father's court, since he came thither with Fame to blow her trumpet before him, and cry to King Ægeus, "Behold your son!"

He little suspected, innocent youth that he was, that here, in this very Athens, where his father reigned, a greater danger awaited him than any which he had encountered on the road. Yet this was the truth. You must understand that the father of Theseus, though not very old in years, was almost worn out with the cares of government, and had thus grown aged before his time. His nephews, not expecting him to live a very great while, intended to get all the power of the

kingdom into their own hands. But when they heard
that Theseus had arrived in Athens, and learned what
a gallant young man he was, they saw that he would
not be at all the kind of person to let them steal away
his father's crown and sceptre, which ought to be his
own by right of inheritance. Thus these bad-hearted
nephews of King Ægeus, who were the own cousins of
Theseus, at once became his enemies. A still more
dangerous enemy was Medea, the wicked enchantress;
for she was now the king's wife, and wanted to give
the kingdom to her son Medus, instead of letting it be
given to the son of Æthra, whom she hated.

It so happened that the king's nephews met Theseus, and found out who he was, just as he reached
the entrance of the royal palace. With all their evil
designs against him, they pretended to be their cousin's best friends, and expressed great joy at making
his acquaintance. They proposed to him that he
should come into the king's presence as a stranger, in
order to try whether Ægeus would discover in the
young man's features any likeness either to himself or
his mother Æthra, and thus recognize him for a son.
Theseus consented; for he fancied that his father
would know him in a moment, by the love that was in
his heart. But, while he waited at the door, the nephews ran and told King Ægeus that a young man had
arrived in Athens, who, to their certain knowledge, intended to put him to death, and get possession of his
royal crown.

"And he is now waiting for admission to your Majesty's presence," added they.

"Aha!" cried the old king, on hearing this.
"Why, he must be a very wicked young fellow indeed! Pray, what would you advise me to do with
him?"

In reply to this question, the wicked Medea put in
her word. As I have already told you, she was a famous enchantress. According to some stories, she
was in the habit of boiling old people in a large caldron, under pretence of making them young again ;
but King Ægeus, I suppose, did not fancy such an uncomfortable way of growing young, or perhaps was
contented to be old, and therefore would never let
himself be popped into the caldron. If there were
time to spare from more important matters, I should
be glad to tell you of Medea's fiery chariot, drawn by
winged dragons, in which the enchantress used often
to take an airing among the clouds. This chariot, in
fact, was the vehicle that first brought her to Athens,
where she had done nothing but mischief ever since
her arrival. But these and many other wonders must
be left untold ; and it is enough to say, that Medea,
amongst a thousand other bad things, knew how to
prepare a poison, that was instantly fatal to whomsoever might so much as touch it with his lips.

So, when the king asked what he should do with
Theseus, this naughty woman had an answer ready at
her tongue's end.

" Leave that to me, please your Majesty," she replied. " Only admit this evil-minded young man to
your presence, treat him civilly, and invite him to
drink a goblet of wine. Your Majesty is well aware
that I sometimes amuse myself with distilling very
powerful medicines. Here is one of them in this
small phial. As to what it is made of, that is one of
my secrets of state. Do but let me put a single drop
into the goblet, and let the young man taste it; and I
will answer for it, he shall quite lay aside the bad designs with which he comes hither."

As she said this, Medea smiled; but, for all her smiling face, she meant nothing less than to poison the poor innocent Theseus, before his father's eyes. And King Ægeus, like most other kings, thought any punishment mild enough for a person who was accused of plotting against his life. He therefore made little or no objection to Medea's scheme, and as soon as the poisonous wine was ready, gave orders that the young stranger should be admitted into his presence. The goblet was set on a table beside the king's throne; and a fly, meaning just to sip a little from the brim, immediately tumbled into it, dead. Observing this, Medea looked round at the nephews, and smiled again.

When Theseus was ushered into the royal apartment, the only object that he seemed to behold was the white-bearded old king. There he sat on his magnificent throne, a dazzling crown on his head, and a sceptre in his hand. His aspect was stately and majestic, although his years and infirmities weighed heavily upon him, as if each year were a lump of lead, and each infirmity a ponderous stone, and all were bundled up together, and laid upon his weary shoulders. The tears both of joy and sorrow sprang into the young man's eyes; for he thought how sad it was to see his dear father so infirm, and how sweet it would be to support him with his own youthful strength, and to cheer him up with the alacrity of his loving spirit. When a son takes his father into his warm heart, it renews the old man's youth in a better way than by the heat of Medea's magic caldron. And this was what Theseus resolved to do. He could scarcely wait to see whether King Ægeus would recognize him, so eager was he to throw himself into his arms.

Advancing to the foot of the throne, he attempted to make a little speech, which he had been thinking about, as he came up the stairs. But he was almost choked by a great many tender feelings that gushed out of his heart and swelled into his throat, all struggling to find utterance together. And therefore, unless he could have laid his full, over-brimming heart into the king's hand, poor Theseus knew not what to do or say. The cunning Medea observed what was passing in the young man's mind. She was more wicked at that moment than ever she had been before; for (and it makes me tremble to tell you of it) she did her worst to turn all this unspeakable love with which Theseus was agitated, to his own ruin and destruction.

"Does your Majesty see his confusion?" she whispered in the king's ear. "He is so conscious of guilt, that he trembles and cannot speak. The wretch lives too long! Quick! offer him the wine!"

Now King Ægeus had been gazing earnestly at the young stranger, as he drew near the throne. There was something, he knew not what, either in his white brow, or in the fine expression of his mouth, or in his beautiful and tender eyes, that made him indistinctly feel as if he had seen this youth before; as if, indeed, he had trotted him on his knee when a baby, and had beheld him growing to be a stalwart man, while he himself grew old. But Medea guessed how the king felt, and would not suffer him to yield to these natural sensibilities; although they were the voice of his deepest heart, telling him, as plainly as it could speak, that here was his dear son, and Æthra's son, coming to claim him for a father. The enchantress again whispered in the king's ear, and compelled him, by her witchcraft, to see everything under a false aspect.

He made up his mind, therefore, to let Theseus drink off the poisoned wine.

"Young man," said he, "you are welcome! I am proud to show hospitality to so heroic a youth. Do me the favor to drink the contents of this goblet. It is brimming over, as you see, with delicious wine, such as I bestow only on those who are worthy of it! None is more worthy to quaff it than yourself!"

So saying, King Ægeus took the golden goblet from the table, and was about to offer it to Theseus. But, partly through his infirmities, and partly because it seemed so sad a thing to take away this young man's life, however wicked he might be, and partly, no doubt, because his heart was wiser than his head, and quaked within him at the thought of what he was going to do, — for all these reasons, the king's hand trembled so much that a great deal of the wine slopped over. In order to strengthen his purpose, and fearing lest the whole of the precious poison should be wasted, one of his nephews now whispered to him, —

"Has your Majesty any doubt of this stranger's guilt? There is the very sword with which he meant to slay you. How sharp, and bright, and terrible it is! Quick! — let him taste the wine; or perhaps he may do the deed even yet."

At these words, Ægeus drove every thought and feeling out of his breast, except the one idea of how justly the young man deserved to be put to death. He sat erect on his throne, and held out the goblet of wine with a steady hand, and bent on Theseus a frown of kingly severity; for, after all, he had too noble a spirit to murder even a treacherous enemy with a deceitful smile upon his face.

"Drink!" said he, in the stern tone with which

he was wont to condemn a criminal to be beheaded. " You have well deserved of me such wine as this ! "

Theseus held out his hand to take the wine. But, before he touched it, King Ægeus trembled again. His eyes had fallen on the gold-hilted sword that hung at the young man's side. He drew back the goblet.

" That sword ! " he cried ; " how came you by it ? "

" It was my father's sword," replied Theseus, with a tremulous voice. " These were his sandals. My dear mother (her name is Æthra) told me his story while I was yet a little child. But it is only a month since I grew strong enough to lift the heavy stone, and take the sword and sandals from beneath it, and come to Athens to seek my father."

" My son ! my son ! " cried King Ægeus, flinging away the fatal goblet, and tottering down from the throne to fall into the arms of Theseus. " Yes, these are Æthra's eyes. It is my son."

I have quite forgotten what became of the king's nephews. But when the wicked Medea saw this new turn of affairs, she hurried out of the room, and going to her private chamber, lost no time in setting her enchantments at work. In a few moments, she heard a great noise of hissing snakes outside of the chamber window ; and, behold ! there was her fiery chariot, and four huge winged serpents, wriggling and twisting in the air, flourishing their tails higher than the top of the palace, and all ready to set off on an aerial journey. Medea stayed only long enough to take her son with her, and to steal the crown jewels, together with the king's best robes, and whatever other valuable things she could lay hands on ; and getting into the chariot, she whipped up the snakes, and ascended high over the city.

The king, hearing the hiss of the serpents, scrambled as fast as he could to the window, and bawled out to the abominable enchantress never to come back. The whole people of Athens, too, who had run out of doors to see this wonderful spectacle, set up a shout of joy at the prospect of getting rid of her. Medea, almost bursting with rage, uttered precisely such a hiss as one of her own snakes, only ten times more venomous and spiteful ; and glaring fiercely out of the blaze of the chariot, she shook her hands over the multitude below, as if she were scattering a million of curses among them. In so doing, however, she unintentionally let fall about five hundred diamonds of the first water, together with a thousand great pearls, and two thousand emeralds, rubies, sapphires, opals, and topazes, to which she had helped herself out of the king's strong-box. All these came pelting down, like a shower of many-colored hailstones, upon the heads of grown people and children, who forthwith gathered them up and carried them back to the palace. But King Ægeus told them that they were welcome to the whole, and to twice as many more, if he had them, for the sake of his delight at finding his son, and losing the wicked Medea. And, indeed, if you had seen how hateful was her last look, as the flaming chariot flew upward, you would not have wondered that both king and people should think her departure a good riddance.

And now Prince Theseus was taken into great favor by his royal father. The old king was never weary of having him sit beside him on his throne (which was quite wide enough for two), and of hearing him tell about his dear mother, and his childhood, and his many boyish efforts to lift the ponderous stone. Theseus, however, was much too brave and active a young man to be willing to spend all his time in relating things which had already happened. His ambition was to perform other and more heroic deeds, which should be better worth telling in prose and verse. Nor had he been long in Athens before he caught and chained a terrible mad bull, and made a public show of him, greatly to the wonder and admiration of good King Ægeus and his subjects. But pretty soon, he undertook an affair that made all his foregone adventures seem like mere boy's play. The occasion of it was as follows : —

One morning, when Prince Theseus awoke, he fancied that he must have had a very sorrowful dream, and that it was still running in his mind, even now that his eyes were open. For it appeared as if the air was full of a melancholy wail; and when he listened more attentively, he could hear sobs and groans, and screams of woe, mingled with deep, quiet sighs, which came from the king's palace, and from the streets, and from the temples, and from every habitation in the city. And all these mournful noises, issuing out of thousands of separate hearts, united themselves into the one great sound of affliction, which had startled Theseus from slumber. He put on his clothes as quickly as he could (not forgetting his sandals and gold-hilted sword), and hastening to the king, inquired what it all meant.

" Alas ! my son," quoth King Ægeus, heaving a long sigh, " here is a very lamentable matter in hand ! This is the wofullest anniversary in the whole year. It is the day when we annually draw lots to see which of the youths and maidens of Athens shall go to be devoured by the horrible Minotaur ! "

" The Minotaur ! " exclaimed Prince Theseus; and,

like a brave young prince as he was, he put his hand to the hilt of his sword. " What kind of a monster may that be ? Is it not possible, at the risk of one's life, to slay him ? "

But King Ægeus shook his venerable head, and to convince Theseus that it was quite a hopeless case, he gave him an explanation of the whole affair. It seems that in the island of Crete there lived a certain dreadful monster, called a Minotaur, which was shaped partly like a man and partly like a bull, and was altogether such a hideous sort of a creature that it is really disagreeable to think of him. If he were suffered to exist at all, it should have been on some desert island, or in the duskiness of some deep cavern, where nobody would ever be tormented by his abominable aspect. But King Minos, who reigned over Crete, laid out a vast deal of money in building a habitation for the Minotaur, and took great care of his health and comfort, merely for mischief's sake. A few years before this time, there had been a war between the city of Athens and the island of Crete, in which the Athenians were beaten, and compelled to beg for peace. No peace could they obtain, however, except on condition that they should send seven young men and seven maidens, every year, to be devoured by the pet monster of the cruel King Minos. For three years past, this grievous calamity had been borne. And the sobs, and groans, and shrieks, with which the city was now filled, were caused by the people's woe, because the fatal day had come again, when the fourteen victims were to be chosen by lot ; and the old people feared lest their sons or daughters might be taken, and the youths and damsels dreaded lest they themselves might be destined to glut the ravenous maw of that detestable man-brute.

But when Theseus heard the story, he straightened himself up, so that he seemed taller than ever before ; and as for his face, it was indignant, despiteful, bold, tender, and compassionate, all in one look.

"Let the people of Athens, this year, draw lots for only six young men, instead of seven," said he. "I will myself be the seventh ; and let the Minotaur devour me, if he can ! "

"O my dear son," cried King Ægeus, "why should you expose yourself to this horrible fate ? You are a royal prince, and have a right to hold yourself above the destinies of common men."

"It is because I am a prince, your son, and the rightful heir of your kingdom, that I freely take upon me the calamity of your subjects," answered Theseus. "And you, my father, being king over this people, and answerable to Heaven for their welfare, are bound to sacrifice what is dearest to you, rather than that the son or daughter of the poorest citizen should come to any harm."

The old king shed tears, and besought Theseus not to leave him desolate in his old age, more especially as he had but just begun to know the happiness of possessing a good and valiant son. Theseus, however, felt that he was in the right, and therefore would not give up his resolution. But he assured his father that he did not intend to be eaten up, unresistingly, like a sheep, and that, if the Minotaur devoured him, it should not be without a battle for his dinner. And finally, since he could not help it, King Ægeus consented to let him go. So a vessel was got ready, and rigged with black sails ; and Theseus, with six other young men, and seven tender and beautiful damsels, came down to the harbor to embark. A sorrowful multitude accompanied them to the shore. There was the poor old king, too, leaning on his son's arm, and looking as if his single heart held all the grief of Athens.

Just as Prince Theseus was going on board, his father bethought himself of one last word to say.

" My beloved son," said he, grasping the prince's hand, " you observe that the sails of this vessel are black ; as indeed they ought to be, since it goes upon a voyage of sorrow and despair. Now, being weighed down with infirmities, I know not whether I can sur- vive till the vessel shall return. But, as long as I do live, I shall creep daily to the top of yonder cliff, to watch if there be a sail upon the sea. And, dearest Theseus, if by some happy chance you should escape the jaws of the Minotaur, then tear down those dismal sails, and hoist others that shall be bright as the sun- shine. Beholding them on the horizon, myself and all the people will know that you are coming back victo- rious, and will welcome you with such a festal uproar as Athens never heard before."

Theseus promised that he would do so. Then, going on board, the mariners trimmed the vessel's black sails to the wind, which blew faintly off the shore, be- ing pretty much made up of the sighs that everybody kept pouring forth on this melancholy occasion. But by and by, when they had got fairly out to sea, there came a stiff breeze from the northwest, and drove them along as merrily over the white-capped waves as if they had been going on the most delightful errand imaginable. And though it was a sad business enough, I rather question whether fourteen young people, with- out any old persons to keep them in order, could con- tinue to spend the whole time of the voyage in being miserable. There had been some few dances upon the undulating deck, I suspect, and some hearty bursts of laughter, and other such unseasonable merriment among the victims, before the high, blue mountains of Crete began to show themselves among the far-off clouds. That sight, to be sure, made them all very grave again.

Theseus stood among the sailors, gazing eagerly towards the land; although, as yet, it seemed hardly more substantial than the clouds, amidst which the mountains were looming up. Once or twice, he fancied that he saw a glare of some bright object, a long way off, flinging a gleam across the waves.

" Did you see that flash of light ? " he inquired of the master of the vessel.

" No, prince ; but I have seen it before," answered the master. " It came from Talus, I suppose."

As the breeze came fresher just then, the master was busy with trimming his sails, and had no more time to answer questions. But while the vessel flew faster and faster towards Crete, Theseus was astonished to behold a human figure, gigantic in size, which appeared to be striding with a measured movement, along the margin of the island. It stepped from cliff to cliff, and sometimes from one headland to another, while the sea foamed and thundered on the shore beneath, and dashed its jets of spray over the giant's feet. What was still more remarkable, whenever the sun shone on this huge figure, it flickered and glimmered ; its vast countenance, too, had a metallic lustre, and threw great flashes of splendor through the air. The folds of its garments, moreover, instead of waving in the wind, fell heavily over its limbs, as if woven of some kind of metal.

The nigher the vessel came, the more Theseus wondered what this immense giant could be, and whether it actually had life or no. For though it walked, and made other lifelike motions, there yet was a kind of jerk in its gait, which, together with its brazen aspect, caused the young prince to suspect that it was no true giant, but only a wonderful piece of machinery. The figure looked all the more terrible because it carried an enormous brass club on its shoulder.

" What is this wonder? " Theseus asked of the master of the vessel, who was now at leisure to answer him.

" It is Talus, the Man of Brass," said the master.

" And is he a live giant, or a brazen image? " asked Theseus.

" That, truly," replied the master, " is the point which has always perplexed me. Some say, indeed, that this Talus was hammered out for King Minos by Vulcan himself, the skilfullest of all workers in metal. But who ever saw a brazen image that had sense enough to walk round an island three times a day, as this giant walks round the island of Crete, challenging every vessel that comes nigh the shore? And, on the other hand, what living thing, unless his sinews were made of brass, would not be weary of marching eighteen hundred miles in the twenty-four hours, as Talus does, without ever sitting down to rest? He is a puzzler, take him how you will."

Still the vessel went bounding onward; and now Theseus could hear the brazen clangor of the giant's footsteps, as he trod heavily upon the sea-beaten rocks, some of which were seen to crack and crumble into the foamy waves beneath his weight. As they approached the entrance of the port, the giant straddled clear across it, with a foot firmly planted on each headland, and uplifting his club to such a height that its but-end was hidden in a cloud, he stood in that formidable posture, with the sun gleaming all over his metallic surface. There seemed nothing else to be expected but that, the next moment, he would fetch his great club down, slam bang, and smash the vessel into a thousand pieces, without heeding how many innocent people he might destroy; for there is seldom any mercy in a giant, you know, and quite as little in a piece of brass clockwork. But just when Theseus and his companions thought the blow was coming, the brazen lips unclosed themselves, and the figure spoke.

"Whence come you, strangers?"

And when the ringing voice ceased, there was just such a reverberation as you may have heard within a great church bell, for a moment or two after the stroke of the hammer.

"From Athens!" shouted the master in reply.

"On what errand?" thundered the Man of Brass.

And he whirled his club aloft more threateningly than ever, as if he were about to smite them with a thunder-stroke right amidships, because Athens, so little while ago, had been at war with Crete.

"We bring the seven youths and the seven maidens," answered the master, "to be devoured by the Minotaur!"

"Pass!" cried the brazen giant.

That one loud word rolled all about the sky, while again there was a booming reverberation within the figure's breast. The vessel glided between the headlands of the port, and the giant resumed his march. In a few moments, this wondrous sentinel was far away, flashing in the distant sunshine, and revolving with immense strides around the island of Crete, as it was his never-ceasing task to do.

No sooner had they entered the harbor than a party of the guards of King Minos came down to the water-side, and took charge of the fourteen young men and damsels. Surrounded by these armed warriors, Prince Theseus and his companions were led to the king's palace, and ushered into his presence. Now, Minos was a stern and pitiless king. If the figure that guarded Crete was made of brass, then the monarch, who ruled over it, might be thought to have a still harder metal in his breast, and might have been called a man of iron. He bent his shaggy brows upon the poor Athenian victims. Any other mortal, beholding their fresh and tender beauty, and their innocent looks, would have felt himself sitting on thorns until he had made every soul of them happy, by bidding them go free as the summer wind. But this immitigable Minos cared only to examine whether they were plump enough to satisfy the Minotaur's appetite. For my part, I wish he himself had been the only victim; and the monster would have found him a pretty tough one.

One after another, King Minos called these pale, frightened youths and sobbing maidens to his footstool, gave them each a poke in the ribs with his sceptre (to try whether they were in good flesh or no), and dismissed them with a nod to his guards. But when his eyes rested on Theseus, the king looked at him more attentively, because his face was calm and brave.

"Young man," asked he, with his stern voice, "are you not appalled at the certainty of being devoured by this terrible Minotaur?"

" I have offered my life in a good cause," answered
Theseus, "and therefore I give it freely and gladly.
But thou, King Minos, art thou not thyself appalled,
who, year after year, hast perpetrated this dreadful
wrong, by giving seven innocent youths and as many
maidens to be devoured by a monster ? Dost thou not
tremble, wicked king, to turn thine eyes inward on
thine own heart ? Sitting there on thy golden throne,
and in thy robes of majesty, I tell thee to thy face,
King Minos, thou art a more hideous monster than
the Minotaur himself ! "

" Aha! do you think me so ? " cried the king,
laughing in his cruel way. " To-morrow, at breakfast-
time, you shall have an opportunity of judging which
is the greater monster, the Minotaur or the king !
Take them away, guards ; and let this free-spoken
youth be the Minotaur's first morsel ! "

Near the king's throne (though I had no time to
tell you so before) stood his daughter Ariadne. She
was a beautiful and tender-hearted maiden, and looked
at these poor doomed captives with very different feelings from those of the iron-breasted King Minos. She
really wept, indeed, at the idea of how much human
happiness would be needlessly thrown away, by giving
so many young people, in the first bloom and rose
blossom of their lives, to be eaten up by a creature
who, no doubt, would have preferred a fat ox, or even
a large pig, to the plumpest of them. And when she
beheld the brave, spirited figure of Prince Theseus
bearing himself so calmly in his terrible peril, she
grew a hundred times more pitiful than before. As
the guards were taking him away, she flung herself at
the king's feet, and besought him to set all the captives free, and especially this one young man.

"Peace, foolish girl!" answered King Minos. "What hast thou to do with an affair like this? It is a matter of state policy, and therefore quite beyond thy weak comprehension. Go water thy flowers, and think no more of these Athenian caitiffs, whom the Minotaur shall as certainly eat up for breakfast as I will eat a partridge for my supper."

So saying, the king looked cruel enough to devour Theseus and all the rest of the captives, himself, had there been no Minotaur to save him the trouble. As he would hear not another word in their favor, the prisoners were now led away, and clapped into a dungeon, where the jailer advised them to go to sleep as soon as possible, because the Minotaur was in the habit of calling for breakfast early. The seven maidens and six of the young men soon sobbed themselves to slumber! But Theseus was not like them. He felt conscious that he was wiser and braver and stronger than his companions, and that therefore he had the responsibility of all their lives upon him, and must consider whether there was no way to save them, even in this last extremity. So he kept himself awake, and paced to and fro across the gloomy dungeon in which they were shut up.

Just before midnight, the door was softly unbarred, and the gentle Ariadne showed herself, with a torch in her hand.

"Are you awake, Prince Theseus?" she whispered.

"Yes," answered Theseus. "With so little time to live, I do not choose to waste any of it in sleep."

"Then follow me," said Ariadne, "and tread softly."

What had become of the jailer and the guards, Theseus never knew. But however that might be, Ariadne opened all the doors, and led him forth from the darksome prison into the pleasant moonlight.

"Theseus," said the maiden, "you can now get on board your vessel, and sail away for Athens."

"No," answered the young man; "I will never leave Crete unless I can first slay the Minotaur, and save my poor companions, and deliver Athens from this cruel tribute."

"I knew that this would be your resolution," said Ariadne. "Come, then, with me, brave Theseus. Here is your own sword, which the guards deprived you of. You will need it; and pray Heaven you may use it well."

Then she led Theseus along by the hand until they came to a dark, shadowy grove, where the moonlight wasted itself on the tops of the trees, without shedding hardly so much as a glimmering beam upon their pathway. After going a good way through this obscurity, they reached a high, marble wall, which was overgrown with creeping plants, that made it shaggy with their verdure. The wall seemed to have no door, nor any windows, but rose up, lofty, and massive, and mysterious, and was neither to be clambered over, nor, so far as Theseus could perceive, to be passed through. Nevertheless, Ariadne did but press one of her soft little fingers against a particular block of marble, and, though it looked as solid as any other part of the wall, it yielded to her touch, disclosing an entrance just wide enough to admit them. They crept through, and the marble stone swung back into its place.

"We are now," said Ariadne, "in the famous labyrinth which Dædalus built before he made himself a pair of wings, and flew away from our island like a bird. That Dædalus was a very cunning workman; but of all his artful contrivances, this labyrinth is the most wondrous. Were we to take but a few steps from the doorway, we might wander about all our lifetime, and never find it again. Yet in the very centre of this labyrinth is the Minotaur; and, Theseus, you must go thither to seek him."

" But how shall I ever find him," asked Theseus, " if the labyrinth so bewilders me as you say it will ? "

Just as he spoke they heard a rough and very disagreeable roar, which greatly resembled the lowing of a fierce bull, but yet had some sort of sound like the human voice. Theseus even fancied a rude articulation in it, as if the creature that uttered it were trying to shape his hoarse breath into words. It was at some distance, however, and he really could not tell whether it sounded most like a bull's roar or a man's harsh voice.

" That is the Minotaur's noise," whispered Ariadne, closely grasping the hand of Theseus, and pressing one of her own hands to her heart, which was all in a tremble. " You must follow that sound through the windings of the labyrinth, and, by and by, you will find him. Stay! take the end of this silken string; I will hold the other end; and then, if you win the victory, it will lead you again to this spot. Farewell, brave Theseus."

So the young man took the end of the silken string in his left hand, and his gold-hilted sword, ready drawn from its scabbard, in the other, and trod boldly into the inscrutable labyrinth. How this labyrinth was built is more than I can tell you. But so cunningly contrived a mizmaze was never seen in the world, before nor since. There can be nothing else so intricate, unless it were the brain of a man like Dædalus, who planned it, or the heart of any ordinary man; which last, to be sure, is ten times as great a mystery as the labyrinth of Crete. Theseus had not taken five steps before he lost sight of Ariadne ; and in five more his head was growing dizzy. But still he went on, now creeping through a low arch, now ascending a flight of steps, now in one crooked passage and now in another; with here a door opening before him, and there one banging behind, until it really seemed as if the walls spun round, and whirled him round along with them. And all the while, through these hollow avenues, now nearer, now farther off again, resounded the cry of the Minotaur ; and the sound was so fierce, so cruel, so ugly, so like a bull's roar, and withal so like a human voice, and yet like neither of them, that the brave heart of Theseus grew sterner and angrier at every step ; for he felt it an insult to the moon and sky, and to our affectionate and simple Mother Earth, that such a monster should have the audacity to exist.

As he passed onward, the clouds gathered over the moon, and the labyrinth grew so dusky that Theseus could no longer discern the bewilderment through which he was passing. He would have felt quite lost, and utterly hopeless of ever again walking in a straight path, if, every little while, he had not been conscious of a gentle twitch at the silken cord. Then he knew that the tender-hearted Ariadne was still holding the other end, and that she was fearing for him, and hoping for him, and giving him just as much of her sympathy as if she were close by his side. Oh, indeed, I can assure you, there was a vast deal of human sympathy running along that slender thread of silk. But still he followed the dreadful roar of the Minotaur, which now grew louder and louder, and finally so very loud that Theseus fully expected to come close upon him, at every new zigzag and wriggle of the path.

And at last, in an open space, at the very centre of the labyrinth, he did discern the hideous creature.

Sure enough, what an ugly monster it was! Only his horned head belonged to a bull; and yet, somehow or other, he looked like a bull all over, preposterously waddling on his hind legs; or, if you happened to view him in another way, he seemed wholly a man, and all the more monstrous for being so. And there he was, the wretched thing, with no society, no companion, no kind of a mate, living only to do mischief, and incapable of knowing what affection means. Theseus hated him, and shuddered at him, and yet could not but be sensible of some sort of pity; and all the more, the uglier and more detestable the creature was. For he kept striding to and fro in a solitary frenzy of rage, continually emitting a hoarse roar, which was oddly mixed up with half-shaped words; and, after listening awhile, Theseus understood that the Minotaur was saying to himself how miserable he was, and how hungry, and how he hated everybody, and how he longed to eat up the human race alive.

Ah, the bull-headed villain! And O, my good little people, you will perhaps see, one of these days, as I do now, that every human being who suffers anything evil to get into his nature, or to remain there, is a kind of Minotaur, an enemy of his fellow-creatures, and separated from all good companionship, as this poor monster was.

Was Theseus afraid? By no means, my dear auditors. What! a hero like Theseus afraid! Not had the Minotaur had twenty bull heads instead of one. Bold as he was, however, I rather fancy that it strengthened his valiant heart, just at this crisis, to feel a tremulous twitch at the silken cord, which he was still holding in his left hand. It was as if Ariadne were giving him all her might and courage ; and, much as he already had, and little as she had to give, it made his own seem twice as much. And to confess the honest truth, he needed the whole ; for now the Minotaur, turning suddenly about, caught sight of Theseus, and instantly lowered his horribly sharp horns, exactly as a mad bull does when he means to rush against an enemy. At the same time, he belched forth a tremendous roar, in which there was something like the words of human language, but all disjointed and shaken to pieces by passing through the gullet of a miserably enraged brute.

Theseus could only guess what the creature intended to say, and that rather by his gestures than his words ; for the Minotaur's horns were sharper than his wits, and of a great deal more service to him than his tongue. But probably this was the sense of what he uttered : —

"Ah, wretch of a human being ! I 'll stick my horns through you, and toss you fifty feet high, and eat you up the moment you come down."

"Come on, then, and try it ! " was all that Theseus deigned to reply ; for he was far too magnanimous to assault his enemy with insolent language.

Without more words on either side, there ensued the most awful fight between Theseus and the Minotaur that ever happened beneath the sun or moon. I really know not how it might have turned out, if the monster, in his first headlong rush against Theseus, had not missed him, by a hair's-breadth, and broken one of his horns short off against the stone wall. On this mishap, he bellowed so intolerably that a part of the labyrinth tumbled down, and all the inhabitants of Crete mistook the noise for an uncommonly heavy thunder-storm. Smarting with the pain, he galloped around the open space in so ridiculous a way that Theseus laughed at it. long afterwards, though not precisely at the moment. After this, the two antagonists stood valiantly up to one another, and fought sword to horn, for a long while. At last, the Minotaur made a run at Theseus, grazed his left side with his horn, and flung him down ; and thinking that he had stabbed him to the heart, he cut a great caper in the air, opened his bull mouth from ear to ear, and prepared to snap his head off. But Theseus by this time had leaped up, and caught the monster off his guard. Fetching a sword-stroke at him with all his force, he hit him fair upon the neck, and made his bull head skip six yards from his human body, which fell down flat upon the ground.

So now the battle was ended. Immediately the moon shone out as brightly as if all the troubles of the world, and all the wickedness and the ugliness that infest human life, were past and gone forever. And Theseus, as he leaned on his sword, taking breath, felt another twitch of the silken cord ; for all through the terrible encounter he had held it fast in his left hand. Eager to let Ariadne know of his success, he followed the guidance of the thread, and soon found himself at the entrance of the labyrinth.

" Thou hast slain the monster," cried Ariadne, clasping her hands.

" Thanks to thee, dear Ariadne," answered Theseus, " I return victorious."

" Then," said Ariadne, " we must quickly summon thy friends, and get them and thyself on board the vessel before dawn. If morning finds thee here, my father will avenge the Minotaur."

To make my story short, the poor captives were awakened, and, hardly knowing whether it was not a joyful dream, were told of what Theseus had done, and that they must set sail for Athens before daybreak. Hastening down to the vessel, they all clambered on board, except Prince Theseus, who lingered behind them, on the strand, holding Ariadne's hand clasped in his own.

" Dear maiden," said he, " thou wilt surely go with us. Thou art too gentle and sweet a child for such an iron-hearted father as King Minos. He cares no more for thee than a granite rock cares for the little flower that grows in one of its crevices. But my father, King Ægeus, and my dear mother, Æthra, and all the fathers and mothers in Athens, and all the sons and daughters too, will love and honor thee as their benefactress. Come with us, then ; for King Minos will be very angry when he knows what thou hast done."

Now, some low-minded people, who pretend to tell the story of Theseus and Ariadne, have the face to say that this royal and honorable maiden did really flee away, under cover of the night, with the young stranger whose life she had preserved. They say, too, that Prince Theseus (who would have died sooner than wrong the meanest creature in the world) ungratefully deserted Ariadne, on a solitary island, where the vessel touched on its voyage to Athens. But, had the noble Theseus heard these falsehoods, he would have served their slanderous authors as he served the Minotaur ! Here is what Ariadne answered, when the brave Prince of Athens besought her to accompany him : —

" No, Theseus," the maiden said, pressing his hand, and then drawing back a step or two, " I cannot go with you. My father is old, and has nobody but myself to love him. Hard as you think his heart is, it would break to lose me. At first King Minos will be angry; but he will soon forgive his only child; and, by and by, he will rejoice, I know, that no more youths and maidens must come from Athens to be devoured by the Minotaur. I have saved you, Theseus, as much for my father's sake as for your own. Farewell! Heaven bless you!"

All this was so true, and so maiden-like, and was spoken with so sweet a dignity, that Theseus would have blushed to urge her any longer. Nothing remained for him, therefore, but to bid Ariadne an affectionate farewell, and go on board the vessel, and set sail.

In a few moments the white foam was boiling up before their prow, as Prince Theseus and his companions sailed out of the harbor with a whistling breeze behind them. Talus, the brazen giant, on his never-ceasing sentinel's march, happened to be approaching that part of the coast; and they saw him, by the glimmering of the moonbeams on his polished surface, while he was yet a great way off. As the figure moved like clock-work, however, and could neither hasten his enormous strides nor retard them, he arrived at the port when they were just beyond the reach of his club. Nevertheless, straddling from headland to headland, as his custom was, Talus attempted to strike a blow at the vessel, and, overreaching himself, tumbled at full length into the sea, which splashed high over his gigantic shape, as when an iceberg turns a somerset. There he lies yet; and whoever desires to enrich himself by means of brass had better go thither with a diving-bell, and fish up Talus.

On the homeward voyage, the fourteen youths and damsels were in excellent spirits, as you will easily suppose. They spent most of their time in dancing, unless when the sidelong breeze made the deck slope too much. In due season, they came within sight of the coast of Attica, which was their native country. But here, I am grieved to tell you, happened a sad misfortune.

You will remember (what Theseus unfortunately forgot) that his father, King Ægeus, had enjoined it upon him to hoist sunshine sails, instead of black ones, in case he should overcome the Minotaur, and return victorious. In the joy of their success, however, and amidst the sports, dancing, and other merriment, with which these young folks wore away the time, they never once thought whether their sails were black, white, or rainbow colored, and, indeed, left it entirely to the mariners whether they had any sails at all. Thus the vessel returned, like a raven, with the same sable wings that had wafted her away. But poor King Ægeus, day after day, infirm as he was, had clambered to the summit of a cliff that overhung the sea, and there sat watching for Prince Theseus, homeward bound ; and no sooner did he behold the fatal blackness of the sails, than he concluded that his dear son, whom he loved so much, and felt so proud of, had been eaten by the Minotaur. He could not bear the thought of living any longer; so, first flinging his crown and sceptre into the sea, (useless bawbles that they were to him now !) King Ægeus merely stooped forward, and fell headlong over the cliff, and was drowned, poor soul, in the waves that foamed at its base !

This was melancholy news for Prince Theseus, who,

when he stepped ashore, found himself king of all the country, whether he would or no; and such a turn of fortune was enough to make any young man feel very much out of spirits. However, he sent for his dear mother to Athens, and, by taking her advice in matters of state, became a very excellent monarch, and was greatly beloved by his people.

THE PYGMIES.

A GREAT while ago, when the world was full of wonders, there lived an earth-born Giant named Antæus, and a million or more of curious little earth-born people, who were called Pygmies. This Giant and these Pygmies being children of the same mother (that is to say, our good old Grandmother Earth), were all brethren and dwelt together in a very friendly and affectionate manner, far, far off, in the middle of hot Africa. The Pygmies were so small, and there were so many sandy deserts and such high mountains between them and the rest of mankind, that nobody could get a peep at them oftener than once in a hundred years. As for the Giant, being of a very lofty stature, it was easy enough to see him, but safest to keep out of his sight.

Among the Pygmies, I suppose, if one of them grew to the height of six or eight inches, he was reckoned a prodigiously tall man. It must have been very pretty to behold their little cities, with streets two or three feet wide, paved with the smallest pebbles, and bordered by habitations about as big as a squirrel's cage. The king's palace attained to the stupendous magnitude of Periwinkle's baby-house, and stood in the centre of a spacious square, which could hardly have been covered by our hearth-rug. Their principal temple, or cathedral, was as lofty as yonder bureau, and was looked upon as a wonderfully sublime and magnificent edifice. All these structures were built

neither of stone nor wood. They were neatly plastered together by the Pygmy workmen, pretty much
like bird's-nests, out of straw, feathers, eggshells, and
other small bits of stuff, with stiff clay instead of mor-
tar ; and when the hot sun had dried them, they were
just as snug and comfortable as a Pygmy could desire.

The country round about was conveniently laid out
in fields, the largest of which was nearly of the same
extent as one of Sweet Fern's flower-beds. Here the
Pygmies used to plant wheat and other kinds of grain,
which, when it grew up and ripened, overshadowed
these tiny people, as the pines, and the oaks, and the
walnut and chestnut - trees overshadow you and me,
when we walk in our own tracts of woodland. At
harvest-time, they were forced to go with their little
axes and cut down the grain, exactly as a wood-cutter
makes a clearing in the forest ; and when a stalk of
wheat, with its overburdened top, chanced to come
crashing down upon an unfortunate Pygmy, it was
apt to be a very sad affair. If it did not smash him
all to pieces, at least, I am sure, it must have made the
poor little fellow's head ache. And oh, my stars ! if
the fathers and mothers were so small, what must
the children and babies have been? A whole family
of them might have been put to bed in a shoe, or have
crept into an old glove, and played at hide-and-seek
in its thumb and fingers. You might have hidden a
year-old baby under a thimble.

Now these funny Pygmies, as I told you before, had
a Giant for their neighbor and brother, who was bigger, if possible, than they were little. He was so very
tall that he carried a pine-tree, which was eight feet
through the but, for a walking-stick. It took a far-

sighted Pygmy, I can assure you, to discern his summit
without the help of a telescope; and sometimes, in
misty weather, they could not see his upper half, but
only his long legs, which seemed to be striding about
by themselves. But at noonday, in a clear atmosphere,
when the sun shone brightly over him, the Giant
Antæus presented a very grand spectacle. There he
used to stand, a perfect mountain of a man, with his
great countenance smiling down upon his little brothers, and his one vast eye (which was as big as a cart-
wheel, and placed right in the centre of his forehead)
giving a friendly wink to the whole nation at once.

The Pygmies loved to talk with Antæus; and fifty
times a day, one or another of them would turn up his
head, and shout through the hollow of his fists, "Halloo, brother Antæus! How are you, my good fellow?"
and when the small, distant squeak of their voices
reached his ear, the Giant would make answer, "Pretty
well, brother Pygmy, I thank you," in a thunderous
roar that would have shaken down the walls of their
strongest temple, only that it came from so far aloft.

It was a happy circumstance that Antæus was the
Pygmy people's friend; for there was more strength
in his little finger than in ten million of such bodies
as theirs. If he had been as ill-natured to them as he
was to everybody else, he might have beaten down
their biggest city at one kick, and hardly have known
that he did it. With the tornado of his breath, he
could have stripped the roofs from a hundred dwellings, and sent thousands of the inhabitants whirling
through the air. He might have set his immense foot
upon a multitude; and when he took it up again,
there would have been a pitiful sight, to be sure.
But, being the son of Mother Earth, as they likewise

were, the Giant gave them his brotherly kindness, and loved them with as big a love as it was possible to feel for creatures so very small. And, on their parts, the Pygmies loved Antæus with as much affection as their tiny hearts could hold. He was always ready to do them any good offices that lay in his power; as, for example, when they wanted a breeze to turn their windmills, the Giant would set all the sails a-going with the mere natural respiration of his lungs. When the sun was too hot, he often sat himself down, and let his shadow fall over the kingdom, from one frontier to the other; and as for matters in general, he was wise enough to let them alone, and leave the Pygmies to manage their own affairs, — which, after all, is about the best thing that great people can do for little ones.

In short, as I said before, Antæus loved the Pygmies, and the Pygmies loved Antæus. The Giant's life being as long as his body was large, while the lifetime of a Pygmy was but a span, this friendly intercourse had been going on for innumerable generations and ages. It was written about in the Pygmy histories, and talked about in their ancient traditions. The most venerable and white-bearded Pygmy had never heard of a time, even in his greatest of grandfather's days, when the Giant was not their enormous friend. Once, to be sure (as was recorded on an obelisk, three feet high, erected on the place of the catastrophe), Antæus sat down upon about five thousand Pygmies, who were assembled at a military review. But this was one of those unlucky accidents for which nobody is to blame; so that the small folks never took it to heart, and only requested the Giant to be careful forever afterwards to examine the acre of ground where he intended to squat himself.

It is a very pleasant picture to imagine Antæus standing among the Pygmies, like the spire of the tallest cathedral that ever was built, while they ran about like pismires at his feet; and to think that, in spite of their difference in size, there were affection and sympathy between them and him! Indeed, it has always seemed to me that the Giant needed the little people more than the Pygmies needed the Giant. For, unless they had been his neighbors and well-wishers, and, as we may say, his playfellows, Antæus would not have had a single friend in the world. No other being like himself had ever been created. No creature of his own size had ever talked with him, in thunder-like accents, face to face. When he stood with his head among the clouds, he was quite alone, and had been so for hundreds of years, and would be so forever. Even if he had met another Giant, Antæus would have fancied the world not big enough for two such vast personages, and, instead of being friends with him, would have fought him till one of the two was killed. But with the Pygmies he was the most sportive, and humorous, and merry-hearted, and sweet-tempered old Giant that ever washed his face in a wet cloud.

His little friends, like all other small people, had a great opinion of their own importance, and used to assume quite a patronizing air towards the Giant.

"Poor creature!" they said one to another. "He has a very dull time of it, all by himself; and we ought not to grudge wasting a little of our precious time to amuse him. He is not half so bright as we are, to be sure; and, for that reason, he needs us to look after his comfort and happiness. Let us be kind to the old fellow. Why, if Mother Earth had not been very kind to ourselves, we might all have been Giants too."

On all their holidays, the Pygmies had excellent sport with Antæus. He often stretched himself out at full length on the ground, where he looked like the long ridge of a hill; and it was a good hour's walk, no doubt, for a short-legged Pygmy to journey from head to foot of the Giant. He would lay down his great hand flat on the grass, and challenge the tallest of them to clamber upon it, and straddle from finger to finger. So fearless were they, that they made nothing of creeping in among the folds of his garments. When his head lay sidewise on the earth, they would march boldly up, and peep into the great cavern of his mouth, and take it all as a joke (as indeed it was meant) when Antæus gave a sudden snap with his jaws, as if he were going to swallow fifty of them at once. You would have laughed to see the children dodging in and out among his hair, or swinging from his beard. It is impossible to tell half of the funny tricks that they played with their huge comrade; but I do not know that anything was more curious than when a party of boys were seen running races on his forehead, to try which of them could get first round the circle of his one great eye. It was another favorite feat with them to march along the bridge of his nose, and jump down upon his upper lip.

If the truth must be told, they were sometimes as troublesome to the Giant as a swarm of ants or mosquitoes, especially as they had a fondness for mischief, and liked to prick his skin with their little swords and lances, to see how thick and tough it was. But Antæus took it all kindly enough; although, once in a

while, when he happened to be sleepy, he would grumble out a peevish word or two, like the muttering of a
tempest, and ask them to have done with their nonsense. A great deal oftener, however, he watched
their merriment and gambols until his huge, heavy,
clumsy wits were completely stirred up by them; and
then would he roar out such a tremendous volume of
immeasurable laughter, that the whole nation of Pygmies had to put their hands to their ears, else it would
certainly have deafened them.

"Ho! ho! ho!" quoth the Giant, shaking his
mountainous sides. "What a funny thing it is to be
little! If I were not Antæus, I should like to be a
pygmy, just for the joke's sake."

The Pygmies had but one thing to trouble them in
the world. They were constantly at war with the
cranes, and had always been so, ever since the long-
lived giant could remember. From time to time very
terrible battles had been fought, in which sometimes
the little men won the victory, and sometimes the
cranes. According to some historians, the Pygmies
used to go to the battle, mounted on the backs of goats
and rams; but such animals as these must have been
far too big for Pygmies to ride upon; so that, I rather
suppose, they rode on squirrel-back, or rabbit-back,
or rat-back, or perhaps got upon hedgehogs, whose
prickly quills would be very terrible to the enemy.
However this might be, and whatever creatures the
Pygmies rode upon, I do not doubt that they made a
formidable appearance, armed with sword and spear,
and bow and arrow, blowing their tiny trumpet, and
shouting their little war-cry. They never failed to
exhort one another to fight bravely, and recollect that
the world had its eyes upon them; although, in simple

truth, the only spectator was the Giant Antæus, with his one, great, stupid eye, in the middle of his forehead.

When the two armies joined battle, the cranes would rush forward, flapping their wings and stretching out their necks, and would perhaps snatch up some of the Pygmies crosswise in their beaks. Whenever this happened, it was truly an awful spectacle to see those little men of might kicking and sprawling in the air, and at last disappearing down the crane's long, crooked throat, swallowed up alive. A hero, you know, must hold himself in readiness for any kind of fate; and doubtless the glory of the thing was a consolation to him, even in the crane's gizzard. If Antæus observed that the battle was going hard against his little allies, he generally stopped laughing, and ran with mile-long strides to their assistance, flourishing his club aloft and shouting at the cranes, who quacked and croaked, and retreated as fast as they could. Then the Pygmy army would march homeward in triumph, attributing the victory entirely to their own valor, and to the warlike skill and strategy of whomsoever happened to be captain general; and for a tedious while afterwards, nothing would be heard of but grand processions, and public banquets, and brilliant illuminations, and shows of waxwork, with likenesses of the distinguished officers as small as life.

In the above-described warfare, if a Pygmy chanced to pluck out a crane's tail-feather, it proved a very great feather in his cap. Once or twice, if you will believe me, a little man was made chief ruler of the nation for no other merit in the world than bringing home such a feather.

But I have now said enough to let you see what a

gallant little people these were, and how happily they
and their forefathers, for nobody knows how many
generations, had lived with the immeasurable Giant
Antæus. In the remaining part of the story, I shall
tell you of a far more astonishing battle than any that
was fought between the Pygmies and the cranes.

One day the mighty Antæus was lolling at full
length among his little friends. His pine-tree walking-stick lay on the ground close by his side. His
head was in one part of the kingdom, and his feet extended across the boundaries of another part; and he
was taking whatever comfort he could get, while the
Pygmies scrambled over him, and peeped into his cavernous mouth, and played among his hair. Sometimes, for a minute or two, the Giant dropped asleep,
and snored like the rush of a whirlwind. During one
of these little bits of slumber, a Pygmy chanced to
climb upon his shoulder, and took a view around the
horizon, as from the summit of a hill; and he beheld
something, a long way off, which made him rub the
bright specks of his eyes, and look sharper than before. At first he mistook it for a mountain, and
wondered how it had grown up so suddenly out of the
earth. But soon he saw the mountain move. As it
came nearer and nearer, what should it turn out to be
but a human shape, not so big as Antæus, it is true,
although a very enormous figure, in comparison with
Pygmies, and a vast deal bigger than the men whom
we see nowadays.

When the Pygmy was quite satisfied that his eyes
had not deceived him, he scampered, as fast as his legs
would carry him, to the Giant's ear, and stooping over
its cavity, shouted lustily into it, —

"Halloo, brother Antæus! Get up this minute,

and take your pine-tree walking-stick in your hand.
Here comes another Giant to have a tussle with you."

"Poh, poh!" grumbled Antæus, only half awake,
"None of your nonsense, my little fellow! Don't you
see I 'm sleepy. There is not a Giant on earth for
whom I would take the trouble to get up."

But the Pygmy looked again, and now perceived
that the stranger was coming directly towards the
prostrate form of Antæus. With every step he looked
less like a blue mountain, and more like an immensely
large man. He was soon so nigh, that there could be
no possible mistake about the matter. There he was,
with the sun flaming on his golden helmet, and flashing from his polished breastplate ; he had a sword by
his side, and a lion's skin over his back, and on his
right shoulder he carried a club, which looked bulkier
and heavier than the pine-tree walking-stick of Antæus.

By this time, the whole nation of Pygmies had seen
the new wonder, and a million of them set up a shout,
all together ; so that it really made quite an audible
squeak.

"Get up, Antæus! Bestir yourself, you lazy old
Giant! Here comes another Giant, as strong as you
are, to fight with you."

"Nonsense, nonsense!" growled the sleepy Giant.
"I 'll have my nap out, come who may."

Still the stranger drew nearer ; and now the Pygmies could plainly discern that, if his stature were less
lofty than the Giant's, yet his shoulders were even
broader. And, in truth, what a pair of shoulders they
must have been! As I told you, a long while ago,
they once upheld the sky. The Pygmies, being ten
times as vivacious as their great numskull of a brother,

could not abide the Giant's slow movements, and were
determined to have him on his feet. So they kept
shouting to him, and even went so far as to prick him
with their swords.

"Get up, get up, get up!" they cried. "Up with
you, lazy bones! The strange Giant's club is bigger
than your own, his shoulders are the broadest, and we
think him the stronger of the two."

Antæus could not endure to have it said that any
mortal was half so mighty as himself. This latter remark of the Pygmies pricked him deeper than their
swords; and, sitting up, in rather a sulky humor, he
gave a gape of several yards wide, rubbed his eye, and
finally turned his stupid head in the direction whither
his little friends were eagerly pointing.

No sooner did he set eye on the stranger than, leaping on his feet, and seizing his walking-stick, he strode
a mile or two to meet him; all the while brandishing
the sturdy pine-tree, so that it whistled through the
air.

"Who are you?" thundered the Giant. "And
what do you want in my dominions?"

There was one strange thing about Antæus, of which
I have not yet told you, lest, hearing of so many wonders all in a lump, you might not believe much more
than half of them. You are to know, then, that whenever this redoubtable Giant touched the ground, either
with his hand, his foot, or any other part of his body,
he grew stronger than ever he had been before. The
Earth, you remember, was his mother, and was very
fond of him, as being almost the biggest of her children; and so she took this method of keeping him always in full vigor. Some persons affirm that he grew
ten times stronger at every touch; others say that it was

only twice as strong.   But only think of it! Whenever Antæus took a walk, supposing it were but ten
miles, and that he stepped a hundred yards at a stride,
you may try to cipher out how much mightier he was,
on sitting down again, than when he first started.
And whenever he flung himself on the earth to take a
little repose, even if he got up the very next instant,
he would be as strong as exactly ten just such giants
as his former self.   It was well for the world that
Antæus happened to be of a sluggish disposition, and
liked ease better than exercise; for, if he had frisked
about like the Pygmies, and touched the earth as often
as they did, he would long ago have been strong
enough to pull down the sky about people's ears.   But
these great lubberly fellows resemble mountains, not
only in bulk, but in their disinclination to move.

Any other mortal man, except the very one whom
Antæus had now encountered, would have been half
frightened to death by the Giant's ferocious aspect
and terrible voice. But the stranger did not seem at
all disturbed.   He carelessly lifted his club, and bal-
anced it in his hand, measuring Antæus with his eye
from head to foot, not as if wonder-smitten at his stature, but as if he had seen a great many Giants before,
and this was by no means the biggest of them.   In
fact, if the Giant had been no bigger than the Pygmies (who stood pricking up their ears, and looking
and listening to what was going forward), the stranger
could not have been less afraid of him.

"Who are you, I say?" roared Antæus again.
"What's your name?   Why do you come hither?
Speak, you vagabond, or I'll try the thickness of your
skull with my walking-stick."

"You are a very discourteous Giant," answered the

stranger, quietly, "and I shall probably have to teach
you a little civility, before we part. As for my name,
it is Hercules. I have come hither because this is my
most convenient road to the garden of the Hesperides,
whither I am going to get three of the golden apples
for King Eurystheus."

"Caitiff, you shall go no farther!" bellowed Antæus, putting on a grimmer look than before; for he
had heard of the mighty Hercules, and hated him because he was said to be so strong. "Neither shall
you go back whence you came!"

"How will you prevent me," asked Hercules,
"from going whither I please?"

"By hitting you a rap with this pine-tree here,"
shouted Antæus, scowling so that he made himself the
ugliest monster in Africa. "I am fifty times stronger
than you; and, now that I stamp my foot upon the
ground, I am five hundred times stronger! I am
ashamed to kill such a puny little dwarf as you seem
to be. I will make a slave of you, and you shall likewise be the slave of my brethren, here, the Pygmies.
So throw down your club and your other weapons;
and as for that lion's skin, I intend to have a pair of
gloves made of it."

"Come and take it off my shoulders, then," answered Hercules, lifting his club.

Then the Giant, grinning with rage, strode tower-
like towards the stranger (ten times strengthened at
every step), and fetched a monstrous blow at him
with his pine-tree, which Hercules caught upon his
club; and being more skilful than Antæus, he paid
him back such a rap upon the sconce, that down tumbled the great lumbering man-mountain, flat upon the
ground. The poor little Pygmies (who really never

dreamed that anybody in the world was half so strong as their brother Antæus) were a good deal dismayed at this. But no sooner was the Giant down, than up he bounced again, with tenfold might, and such a furious visage as was horrible to behold. He aimed another blow at Hercules, but struck awry, being blinded with wrath, and only hit his poor, innocent Mother Earth, who groaned and trembled at the stroke. His pine-tree went so deep into the ground, and stuck there so fast, that before Antæus could get it out, Hercules brought down his club across his shoulders with a mighty thwack, which made the Giant roar as if all sorts of intolerable noises had come screeching and rumbling out of his immeasurable lungs in that one cry. Away it went, over mountains and valleys, and, for aught I know, was heard on the other side of the African deserts.

As for the Pygmies, their capital city was laid in ruins by the concussion and vibration of the air; and, though there was uproar enough without their help, they all set up a shriek out of three millions of little throats, fancying, no doubt, that they swelled the Giant's bellow by at least ten times as much. Meanwhile, Antæus had scrambled upon his feet again, and pulled his pine-tree out of the earth; and, all a-flame with fury, and more outrageously strong than ever, he ran at Hercules, and brought down another blow.

"This time, rascal," shouted he, "you shall not escape me."

But once more Hercules warded off the stroke with his club, and the Giant's pine-tree was shattered into a thousand splinters, most of which flew among the Pygmies, and did them more mischief than I like to think about. Before Antæus could get out of the way, Hercules let drive again, and gave him another knock-down blow, which sent him heels over head, but served only to increase his already enormous and insufferable strength. As for his rage, there is no telling what a fiery furnace it had now got to be. His one eye was nothing but a circle of red flame. Having now no weapons but his fists, he doubled them up (each bigger than a hogshead), smote one against the other, and danced up and down with absolute frenzy, flourishing his immense arms about, as if he meant not merely to kill Hercules, but to smash the whole world to pieces.

" Come on ! " roared this thundering Giant. " Let me hit you but one box on the ear, and you 'll never have the headache again."

Now Hercules (though strong enough, as you already know, to hold the sky up) began to be sensible that he should never win the victory, if he kept on knocking Antæus down ; for, by and by, if he hit him such hard blows, the Giant would inevitably, by the help of his Mother Earth, become stronger than the mighty Hercules himself. So, throwing down his club, with which he had fought so many dreadful battles, the hero stood ready to receive his antagonist with naked arms.

" Step forward," cried he. " Since I 've broken your pine-tree, we 'll try which is the better man at a wrestling-match."

" Aha ! then I 'll soon satisfy you," shouted the Giant ; for, if there was one thing on which he prided himself more than another, it was his skill in wrestling. " Villain, I 'll fling you where you can never pick yourself up again."

On came Antæus, hopping and capering with the

scorching heat of his rage, and getting new vigor wherewith to wreak his passion, every time he hopped. But Hercules, you must understand, was wiser than this numskull of a Giant, and had thought of a way to fight him, — huge, earth-born monster that he was, — and to conquer him too, in spite of all that his Mother Earth could do for him. Watching his opportunity, as the mad Giant made a rush at him, Hercules caught him round the middle with both hands, lifted him high into the air, and held him aloft overhead.

Just imagine it, my dear little friends! What a spectacle it must have been, to see this monstrous fellow sprawling in the air, face downward, kicking out his long legs and wriggling his whole vast body, like a baby when its father holds it at arm's-length towards the ceiling.

But the most wonderful thing was, that, as soon as Antæus was fairly off the earth, he began to lose the vigor which he had gained by touching it. Hercules very soon perceived that his troublesome enemy was growing weaker, both because he struggled and kicked with less violence, and because the thunder of his big voice subsided into a grumble. The truth was, that, unless the Giant touched Mother Earth as often as once in five minutes, not only his overgrown strength, but the very breath of his life, would depart from him. Hercules had guessed this secret; and it may be well for us all to remember it, in case we should ever have to fight a battle with a fellow like Antæus. For these earth-born creatures are only difficult to conquer on their own ground, but may easily be managed if we can contrive to lift them into a loftier and purer region. So it proved with the poor Giant, whom I am really a little sorry for, notwithstanding his uncivil way of treating strangers who came to visit him.

When his strength and breath were quite gone, Hercules gave his huge body a toss, and flung it about a mile off, where it fell heavily, and lay with no more motion than a sand-hill. It was too late for the Giant's Mother Earth to help him now; and I should not wonder if his ponderous bones were lying on the same spot to this very day, and were mistaken for those of an uncommonly large elephant.

But, alas me! What a wailing did the poor little Pygmies set up when they saw their enormous brother treated in this terrible manner! If Hercules heard their shrieks, however, he took no notice, and perhaps fancied them only the shrill, plaintive twittering of small birds that had been frightened from their nests by the uproar of the battle between himself and Antæus. Indeed, his thoughts had been so much taken up with the Giant, that he had never once looked at the Pygmies, nor even knew that there was such a funny little nation in the world. And now, as he had travelled a good way, and was also rather weary with his exertions in the fight, he spread out his lion's skin on the ground, and reclining himself upon it, fell fast asleep.

As soon as the Pygmies saw Hercules preparing for a nap, they nodded their little heads at one another, and winked with their little eyes. And when his deep, regular breathing gave them notice that he was asleep, they assembled together in an immense crowd, spreading over a space of about twenty-seven feet square. One of their most eloquent orators (and a valiant warrior enough, besides, though hardly so good at any other weapon as he was with his tongue) climbed upon a toadstool, and, from that elevated position, addressed the multitude. His sentiments were pretty much as follows ; or, at all events, something like this was probably the upshot of his speech : —

"Tall Pygmies and mighty little men! You and all of us have seen what a public calamity has been brought to pass, and what an insult has here been offered to the majesty of our nation. Yonder lies Antæus, our great friend and brother, slain, within our territory, by a miscreant who took him at disadvantage, and fought him (if fighting it can be called) in a way that neither man, nor Giant, nor Pygmy ever dreamed of fighting until this hour. And, adding a grievous contumely to the wrong already done us, the miscreant has now fallen asleep as quietly as if nothing were to be dreaded from our wrath! It behooves you, fellow-countrymen, to consider in what aspect we shall stand before the world, and what will be the verdict of impartial history, should we suffer these accumulated outrages to go unavenged.

"Antæus was our. brother, born of that same beloved parent to whom we owe the thews and sinews, as well as the courageous hearts, which made him proud of our relationship. He was our faithful ally, and fell fighting as much for our national rights and immunities as for his own personal ones. We and our forefathers have dwelt in friendship with him, and held affectionate intercourse, as man to man, through immemorial generations. You remember how often our entire people have reposed in his great shadow, and how our little ones have played at hide-and-seek in the tangles of his hair, and how his mighty footsteps have familiarly gone to and fro among us, and never trodden upon any of our toes. And there lies this dear brother, — this sweet and amiable friend, — this brave and faithful ally, — this virtuous Giant, — this

blameless and excellent Antæus, — dead! Dead!
Silent! Powerless! A mere mountain of clay! Forgive my tears! Nay, I behold your own! Were we
to drown the world with them, could the world blame
us?

"But to resume : Shall we, my countrymen, suffer
this wicked stranger to depart unharmed, and triumph
in his treacherous victory, among distant communities
of the earth? Shall we not rather compel him to
leave his bones here on our soil, by the side of our
slain brother's bones, so that, while one skeleton shall
remain as the everlasting monument of our sorrow,
the other shall endure as long, exhibiting to the whole
human race a terrible example of Pygmy vengeance?
Such is the question. I put it to you in full confidence of a response that shall be worthy of our national character, and calculated to increase, rather
than diminish, the glory which our ancestors have
transmitted to us, and which we ourselves have proudly
vindicated in our warfare with the cranes."

The orator was here interrupted by a burst of irrepressible enthusiasm ; every individual Pygmy crying
out that the national honor must be preserved at all
hazards. He bowed, and making a gesture for silence,
wound up his harangue in the following admirable
manner : —

"It only remains for us, then, to decide whether we
shall carry on the war in our national capacity, — one
united people against a common enemy, — or whether
some champion, famous in former fights, shall be se-
lected to defy the slayer of our brother Antæus to
single combat. In the latter case, though not unconscious that there may be taller men among you, I
hereby offer myself for that enviable duty. And, be-

lieve me, dear countrymen, whether I live or die, the
honor of this great country, and the fame bequeathed
us by our heroic progenitors, shall suffer no diminu-
tion in my hands. Never, while I can wield this
sword, of which I now fling away the scabbard, —
never, never, never, even if the crimson hand that
slew the great Antæus shall lay me prostrate, like him,
on the soil which I give my life to defend."

So saying, this valiant Pygmy drew out his weapon
(which was terrible to behold, being as long as the
blade of a penknife), and sent the scabbard whirling
over the heads of the multitude. His speech was followed by an uproar of applause, as its patriotism and
self-devotion unquestionably deserved; and the shouts
and clapping of hands would have been greatly pro-
longed had they not been rendered quite inaudible by
a deep respiration, vulgarly called a snore, from the
sleeping Hercules.

It was finally decided that the whole nation of Pygmies should set to work to destroy Hercules; not, be
it understood, from any doubt that a single champion
would be capable of putting him to the sword, but because he was a public enemy, and all were desirous of
sharing in the glory of his defeat. There was a de-
bate whether the national honor did not demand that
a herald should be sent with a trumpet, to stand over
the ear of Hercules, and, after blowing a blast right
into it, to defy him to the combat by formal proclamation. But two or three venerable and sagacious Pygmies, well versed in state affairs, gave it as their opinion that war already existed, and that it was their
rightful privilege to take the enemy by surprise.
Moreover, if awakened, and allowed to get upon his
feet, Hercules might happen to do them a mischief

before he could be beaten down again. For, as these sage counsellors remarked, the stranger's club was really very big, and had rattled like a thunderbolt against the skull of Antæus. So the Pygmies resolved to set aside all foolish punctilios, and assail their antagonist at once.

Accordingly, all the fighting men of the nation took their weapons, and went boldly up to Hercules, who still lay fast asleep, little dreaming of the harm which the Pygmies meant to do him. A body of twenty thousand archers marched in front, with their little bows all ready, and the arrows on the string. The same number were ordered to clamber upon Hercules, some with spades to dig his eyes out, and others with bundles of hay, and all manner of rubbish, with which they intended to plug up his mouth and nostrils, so that he might perish for lack of breath. These last, however, could by no means perform their appointed duty; inasmuch as the enemy's breath rushed out of his nose in an obstreperous hurricane and whirlwind, which blew the Pygmies away as fast as they came nigh. It was found necessary, therefore, to hit upon some other method of carrying on the war.

After holding a council, the captains ordered their troops to collect sticks, straws, dry weeds, and whatever combustible stuff they could find, and make a pile of it, heaping it high around the head of Hercules. As a great many thousand Pygmies were employed in this task, they soon brought together several bushels of inflammatory matter, and raised so tall a heap, that, mounting on its summit, they were quite upon a level with the sleeper's face. The archers, meanwhile, were stationed within bow-shot, with orders to let fly at Hercules the instant that he stirred. Everything being in readiness, a torch was applied to the pile, which immediately burst into flames, and soon waxed hot enough to roast the enemy, had he but chosen to lie still. A Pygmy, you know, though so very small, might set the world on fire, just as easily as a Giant could; so that this was certainly the very best way of dealing with their foe, provided they could have kept him quiet while the conflagration was going forward.

But no sooner did Hercules begin to be scorched, than up he started, with his hair in a red blaze.

" What's all this?" he cried, bewildered with sleep, and staring about him as if he expected to see another Giant.

At that moment the twenty thousand archers twanged their bowstrings, and the arrows came whizzing, like so many winged mosquitoes, right into the face of Hercules. But I doubt whether more than half a dozen of them punctured the skin, which was remarkably tough, as you know the skin of a hero has good need to be.

" Villain! " shouted all the Pygmies at once. " You have killed the Giant Antæus, our great brother, and the ally of our nation. We declare bloody war against you and will slay you on the spot."

Surprised at the shrill piping of so many little voices, Hercules, after putting out the conflagration of his hair, gazed all round about, but could see nothing. At last, however, looking narrowly on the ground, he espied the innumerable assemblage of Pygmies at his feet. He stooped down, and taking up the nearest one between his thumb and finger, set him on the palm of his left hand, and held him at a proper distance for examination. It chanced to be the very identical Pygmy who had spoken from the top of the toadstool, and had offered himself as a champion to meet Hercules in single combat.

"What in the world, my little fellow," ejaculated Hercules, "may you be?"

"I am your enemy," answered the valiant Pygmy, in his mightiest squeak. "You have slain the enormous Antæus, our brother by the mother's side, and for ages the faithful ally of our illustrious nation. We are determined to put you to death; and for my own part, I challenge you to instant battle, on equal ground."

Hercules was so tickled with the Pygmy's big words and warlike gestures, that he burst into a great explosion of laughter, and almost dropped the poor little mite of a creature off the palm of his hand, through the ecstasy and convulsion of his merriment.

"Upon my word," cried he, "I thought I had seen wonders before to-day, — hydras with nine heads, stags with golden horns, six-legged men, three-headed dogs, giants with furnaces in their stomachs, and nobody knows what besides. But here, on the palm of my hand, stands a wonder that outdoes them all! Your body, my little friend, is about the size of an ordinary man's finger. Pray, how big may your soul be?"

"As big as your own!" said the Pygmy.

Hercules was touched with the little man's dauntless courage, and could not help acknowledging such a brotherhood with him as one hero feels for another.

"My good little people," said he, making a low obeisance to the grand nation, "not for all the world would I do an intentional injury to such brave fellows as you! Your hearts seem to me so exceedingly great, that, upon my honor, I marvel how your small bodies can contain them. I sue for peace, and, as a condi-

tion of it, will take five strides, and be out of your
kingdom at the sixth. Good-by. I shall pick my steps
carefully, for fear of treading upon some fifty of you,
without knowing it. Ha, ha, ha! Ho, ho, ho! For
once, Hercules acknowledges himself vanquished."

Some writers say, that Hercules gathered up the
whole race of Pygmies in his lion's skin, and carried
them home to Greece, for the children of King Eurystheus to play with. But this is a mistake. He left
them, one and all, within their own territory, where,
for aught I can tell, their descendants are alive to the
present day, building their little houses, cultivating
their little fields, spanking their little children, wag-
ing their little warfare with the cranes, doing their
little business, whatever it may be, and reading their
little histories of ancient times. In those histories,
perhaps, it stands recorded, that, a great many centuries ago, the valiant Pygmies avenged the death of the
Giant Antæus by scaring away the mighty Hercules.

THE DRAGON'S TEETH.

CADMUS, Phœnix, and Cilix, the three sons of King Agenor, and their little sister Europa (who was a very beautiful child) were at play together, near the sea-shore, in their father's kingdom of Phœnicia. They had rambled to some distance from the palace where their parents dwelt, and were now in a verdant mead-ow, on one side of which lay the sea, all sparkling and dimpling in the sunshine, and murmuring gently against the beach. The three boys were very happy, gathering flowers, and twining them into garlands, with which they adorned the little Europa. Seated on the grass, the child was almost hidden under an abundance of buds and blossoms, whence her rosy face peeped merrily out, and, as Cadmus said, was the pret-tiest of all the flowers.

Just then, there came a splendid butterfly, fluttering along the meadow; and Cadmus, Phœnix, and Cilix set off in pursuit of it, crying out that it was a flower with wings. Europa, who was a little wearied with playing all day long, did not chase the butterfly with her brothers, but sat still where they had left her, and closed her eyes. For a while, she listened to the pleas-ant murmur of the sea, which was like a voice say-ing "Hush!" and bidding her go to sleep. But the pretty child, if she slept at all, could not have slept more than a moment, when she heard something tram-ple on the grass, not far from her, and peeping out from the heap of flowers, beheld a snow-white bull.

And whence could this bull have come? Europa and her brothers had been a long time playing in the meadow, and had seen no cattle, nor other living thing, either there or on the neighboring hills.

"Brother Cadmus!" cried Europa, starting up out of the midst of the roses and lilies. "Phœnix! Cilix! Where are you all? Help! Help! Come and drive away this bull!"

But her brothers were too far off to hear; especially as the fright took away Europa's voice, and hindered her from calling very loudly. So there she stood, with her pretty mouth wide open, as pale as the white lilies that were twisted among the other flowers in her garlands.

Nevertheless, it was the suddenness with which she had perceived the bull, rather than anything frightful in his appearance, that caused Europa so much alarm. On looking at him more attentively, she began to see that he was a beautiful animal, and even fancied a particularly amiable expression in his face. As for his breath, — the breath of cattle, you know, is always sweet, — it was as fragrant as if he had been grazing on no other food than rosebuds, or, at least, the most delicate of clover-blossoms. Never before did a bull have such bright and tender eyes, and such smooth horns of ivory, as this one. And the bull ran little races, and capered sportively around the child; so that she quite forgot how big and strong he was, and, from the gentleness and playfulness of his actions, soon came to consider him as innocent a creature as a pet lamb.

Thus, frightened as she at first was, you might by and by have seen Europa stroking the bull's forehead with her small white hand, and taking the garlands off her own head to hang them on his neck and ivory horns. Then she pulled up some blades of grass, and he ate them out of her hand, not as if he were hungry, but because he wanted to be friends with the child, and took pleasure in eating what she had touched. Well, my stars! was there ever such a gentle, sweet, pretty, and amiable creature as this bull, and ever such a nice playmate for a little girl?

When the animal saw (for the bull had so much intelligence that it is really wonderful to think of), when he saw that Europa was no longer afraid of him, he grew overjoyed, and could hardly contain himself for delight. He frisked about the meadow, now here, now there, making sprightly leaps, with as little effort as a bird expends in hopping from twig to twig. Indeed, his motion was as light as if he were flying through the air, and his hoofs seemed hardly to leave their print in the grassy soil over which he trod. With his spotless hue, he resembled a snow-drift, wafted along by the wind. Once he galloped so far away that Europa feared lest she might never see him again; so, setting up her childish voice, she called him back.

"Come back, pretty creature!" she cried. "Here is a nice clover-blossom."

And then it was delightful to witness the gratitude of this amiable bull, and how he was so full of joy and thankfulness that he capered higher than ever. He came running, and bowed his head before Europa, as if he knew her to be a king's daughter, or else recognized the important truth that a little girl is everybody's queen. And not only did the bull bend his neck, he absolutely knelt down at her feet, and made such intelligent nods, and other inviting gestures, that

Europa understood what he meant just as well as if he had put it in so many words.

" Come, dear child," was what he wanted to say, " let me give you a ride on my back."

At the first thought of such a thing, Europa drew back. But then she considered in her wise little head that there could be no possible harm in taking just one gallop on the back of this docile and friendly animal, who would certainly set her down the very instant she desired it. And how it would surprise her brothers to see her riding across the green meadow! And what merry times they might have, either taking turns for a gallop, or clambering on the gentle creature, all four children together, and careering round the field with shouts of laughter that would be heard as far off as King Agenor's palace!

" I think I will do it," said the child to herself.

And, indeed, why not? She cast a glance around, and caught a glimpse of Cadmus, Phœnix, and Cilix, who were still in pursuit of the butterfly, almost at the other end of the meadow. It would be the quickest way of rejoining them, to get upon the white bull's back. She came a step nearer to him, therefore; and — sociable creature that he was — he showed so much joy at this mark of her confidence, that the child could not find it in her heart to hesitate any longer. Making one bound (for this little princess was as active as a squirrel), there sat Europa on the beautiful bull, holding an ivory horn in each hand, lest she should fall off.

" Softly, pretty bull, softly ! " she said, rather frightened at what she had done. " Do not gallop too fast."

Having got the child on his back, the animal gave

a leap into the air, and came down so like a feather that Europa did not know when his hoofs touched the ground. He then began a race to that part of the flowery plain where her three brothers were, and where they had just caught their splendid butterfly. Europa screamed with delight; and Phœnix, Cilix, and Cadmus stood gaping at the spectacle of their sister mounted on a white bull, not knowing whether to be frightened or to wish the same good luck for themselves. The gentle and innocent creature (for who could possibly doubt that he was so?) pranced round among the children as sportively as a kitten. Europa all the while looked down upon her brothers, nodding and laughing, but yet with a sort of stateliness in her rosy little face. As the bull wheeled about to take another gallop across the meadow, the child waved her hand, and said, " Good-by," playfully pretending that she was now bound on a distant journey, and might not see her brothers again for nobody could tell how long.

"Good-by," shouted Cadmus, Phœnix, and Cilix, all in one breath.

But, together with her enjoyment of the sport, there was still a little remnant of fear in the child's heart; so that her last look at the three boys was a troubled one, and made them feel as if their dear sister were really leaving them forever. And what do you think the snowy bull did next? Why, he set off, as swift as the wind, straight down to the sea-shore, scampered across the sand, took an airy leap, and plunged right in among the foaming billows. The white spray rose in a shower over him and little Europa, and fell spattering down upon the water.

Then what a scream of terror did the poor child

send forth! The three brothers screamed manfully,
likewise, and ran to the shore as fast as their legs
would carry them, with Cadmus at their head. But
it was too late. When they reached the margin of
the sand, the treacherous animal was already far away
in the wide blue sea, with only his snowy head and
tail emerging, and poor little Europa between them,
stretching out one hand towards her dear brothers,
while she grasped the bull's ivory horn with the other.
And there stood Cadmus, Phœnix, and Cilix, gazing
at this sad spectacle, through their tears, until they
could no longer distinguish the bull's snowy head from
the white-capped billows that seemed to boil up out of
the sea's depths around him. Nothing more was ever
seen of the white bull, — nothing more of the beautiful child.

This was a mournful story, as you may well think,
for the three boys to carry home to their parents.
King Agenor, their father, was the ruler of the whole
country; but he loved his little daughter Europa better than his kingdom, or than all his other children,
or than anything else in the world. Therefore, when
Cadmus and his two brothers came crying home, and
told him how that a white bull had carried off their
sister, and swam with her over the sea, the king was
quite beside himself with grief and rage. Although
it was now twilight, and fast growing dark, he bade
them set out instantly in search of her.

"Never shall you see my face again," he cried,
"unless you bring me back my little Europa, to glad-
den me with her smiles and her pretty ways. Begone,
and enter my presence no more, till you come leading
her by the hand."

As King Agenor said this, his eyes flashed fire (for

he was a very passionate king), and he looked so terribly angry that the poor boys did not even venture to ask for their suppers, but slunk away out of the palace, and only paused on the steps a moment to consult whither they should go first. While they were standing there, all in dismay, their mother, Queen Telephassa (who happened not to be by when they told the story to the king), came hurrying after them, and said that she too would go in quest of her daughter.

"Oh no, mother!" cried the boys. "The night is dark, and there is no knowing what troubles and perils we may meet with."

"Alas! my dear children," answered poor Queen Telephassa, weeping bitterly, "that is only another reason why I should go with you. If I should lose you, too, as well as my little Europa, what would become of me?"

"And let me go likewise!" said their playfellow Thasus, who came running to join them.

Thasus was the son of a seafaring person in the neighborhood; he had been brought up with the young princes, and was their intimate friend, and loved Europa very much; so they consented that he should accompany them. The whole party, therefore, set forth together; Cadmus, Phœnix, Cilix, and Thasus clustered round Queen Telephassa, grasping her skirts, and begging her to lean upon their shoulders whenever she felt weary. In this manner they went down the palace steps, and began a journey which turned out to be a great deal longer than they dreamed of. The last that they saw of King Agenor, he came to the door, with a servant holding a torch beside him, and called after them into the gathering darkness: —

"Remember! Never ascend these steps again without the child!"

"Never!" sobbed Queen Telephassa; and the three brothers and Thasus answered, "Never! Never! Never! Never!"

And they kept their word. Year after year King Agenor sat in the solitude of his beautiful palace, listening in vain for their returning footsteps, hoping to hear the familiar voice of the queen, and the cheerful talk of his sons and their playfellow Thasus, entering the door together, and the sweet, childish accents of little Europa in the midst of them. But so long a time went by, that, at last, if they had really come, the king would not have known that this was the voice of Telephassa, and these the younger voices that used to make such joyful echoes when the children were playing about the palace. We must now leave King Agenor to sit on his throne, and must go along with Queen Telephassa and her four youthful companions.

They went on and on, and travelled a long way, and passed over mountains and rivers, and sailed over seas. Here, and there, and everywhere, they made continual inquiry if any person could tell them what had become of Europa. The rustic people, of whom they asked this question, paused a little while from their labors in the field, and looked very much surprised. They thought it strange to behold a woman in the garb of a queen (for Telephassa, in her haste, had forgotten to take off her crown and her royal robes), roaming about the country, with four lads around her, on such an errand as this seemed to be. But nobody could give them any tidings of Europa; nobody had seen a little girl dressed like a princess, and mounted on a snow-white bull, which galloped as swiftly as the wind.

I cannot tell you how long Queen Telephassa, and
Cadmus, Phœnix, and Cilix, her three sons, and
Thasus, their playfellow, went wandering along the
highways and bypaths, or through the pathless wilder-
nesses of the earth, in this manner. But certain it is,
that, before they reached any place of rest, their splendid garments were quite worn out. They all looked
very much travel-stained, and would have had the dust
of many countries on their shoes, if the streams,
through which they waded, had not washed it all
away. When they had been gone a year, Telephassa
threw away her crown, because it chafed her forehead.

"It has given me many a headache," said the poor
queen, "and it cannot cure my heartache."

As fast as their princely robes got torn and tattered, they exchanged them for such mean attire as
ordinary people wore. By and by they came to have
a wild and homeless aspect; so that you would much
sooner have taken them for a gypsy family than a
queen and three princes, and a young nobleman, who
had once a palace for their home, and a train of servants to do their bidding. The four boys grew up
to be tall young men, with sunburnt faces. Each of
them girded on a sword, to defend themselves against
the perils of the way. When the husbandmen, at
whose farm-houses they sought hospitality, needed
their assistance in the harvest-field, they gave it willingly; and Queen Telephassa (who had done no work
in her palace, save to braid silk threads with golden
ones) came behind them to bind the sheaves. If payment was offered, they shook their heads, and only
asked for tidings of Europa.

"There are bulls enough in my pasture," the old
farmers would reply; "but I never heard of one like

this you tell me of. A snow-white bull with a little princess on his back! Ho! ho! I ask your pardon, good folks; but there never was such a sight seen hereabouts."

At last, when his upper lip began to have the down on it, Phœnix grew weary of rambling hither and thither to no purpose. So, one day, when they happened to be passing through a pleasant and solitary tract of country, he sat himself down on a heap of moss.

" I can go no farther," said Phœnix. " It is a mere foolish waste of life, to spend it, as we do, in always wandering up and down, and never coming to any home at nightfall. Our sister is lost, and never will be found. She probably perished in the sea ; or, to whatever shore the white bull may have carried her, it is now so many years ago, that there would be neither love nor acquaintance between us should we meet again. My father has forbidden us to return to his palace ; so I shall build me a hut of branches, and dwell here."

" Well, son Phœnix," said Telephassa, sorrowfully, " you have grown to be a man, and must do as you judge best. But, for my part, I will still go in quest of my poor child."

" And we three will go along with you ! " cried Cadmus and Cilix, and their faithful friend Thasus.

But, before setting out, they all helped Phœnix to build a habitation. When completed, it was a sweet rural bower, roofed overhead with an arch of living boughs. Inside there were two pleasant rooms, one of which had a soft heap of moss for a bed, while the other was furnished with a rustic seat or two, curiously fashioned out of the crooked roots of trees. So comfortable and homelike did it seem, that Telephassa and her three companions could not help sighing, to think that they must still roam about the world, instead of spending the remainder of their lives in some such cheerful abode as they had here built for Phœnix. But, when they bade him farewell, Phœnix shed tears, and probably regretted that he was no longer to keep them company.

However, he had fixed upon an admirable place to dwell in. And by and by there came other people, who chanced to have no homes; and, seeing how pleasant a spot it was, they built themselves huts in the neighborhood of Phœnix's habitation. Thus, before many years went by, a city had grown up there, in the centre of which was seen a stately palace of marble, wherein dwelt Phœnix, clothed in a purple robe, and wearing a golden crown upon his head. For the inhabitants of the new city, finding that he had royal blood in his veins, had chosen him to be their king. The very first decree of state which King Phœnix issued was, that if a maiden happened to arrive in the kingdom, mounted on a snow-white bull, and calling herself Europa, his subjects should treat her with the greatest kindness and respect, and immediately bring her to the palace. You may see, by this, that Phœnix's conscience never quite ceased to trouble him, for giving up the quest of his dear sister, and sitting himself down to be comfortable, while his mother and her companions went onward.

But often and often, at the close of a weary day's journey, did Telephassa and Cadmus, Cilix and Thasus, remember the pleasant spot in which they had left Phœnix. It was a sorrowful prospect for these wanderers, that on the morrow they must again set forth, and that, after many nightfalls, they would perhaps be no nearer the close of their toilsome pilgrimage than now. These thoughts made them all melancholy at times, but appeared to torment Cilix more than the rest of the party. At length, one morning, when they were taking their staffs in hand to set out, he thus addressed them : —

" My dear mother, and you good brother Cadmus, and my friend Thasus, methinks we are like people in a dream. There is no substance in the life which we are leading. It is such a dreary length of time since the white bull carried off my sister Europa, that I have quite forgotten how she looked, and the tones of her voice, and, indeed, almost doubt whether such a little girl ever lived in the world. And whether she once lived or no, I am convinced that she no longer survives, and that therefore it is the merest folly to waste our own lives and happiness in seeking her. Were we to find her, she would now be a woman grown, and would look upon us all as strangers. So, to tell you the truth, I have resolved to take up my abode here ; and I entreat you, mother, brother, and friend, to follow my example."

" Not I, for one," said Telephassa ; although the poor queen, firmly as she spoke, was so travel-worn that she could hardly put her foot to the ground, — " not I, for one ! In the depths of my heart, little Europa is still the rosy child who ran to gather flowers so many years ago. She has not grown to womanhood, nor forgotten me. At noon, at night, journeying onward, sitting down to rest, her childish voice is always in my ears, calling, ' Mother ! mother !' Stop here who may, there is no repose for me."

" Nor for me," said Cadmus, " while my dear mother pleases to go onward."

And the faithful Thasus, too, was resolved to bear them company. They remained with Cilix a few days, however, and helped him to build a rustic bower, resembling the one which they had formerly built for Phœnix.

When they were bidding him farewell, Cilix burst into tears, and told his mother that it seemed just as melancholy a dream to stay there, in solitude, as to go onward. If she really believed that they would ever find Europa, he was willing to continue the search with them, even now. But Telephassa bade him remain there, and be happy, if his own heart would let him. So the pilgrims took their leave of him, and departed, and were hardly out of sight before some other wandering people came along that way, and saw Cilix's habitation, and were greatly delighted with the appearance of the place. There being abundance of unoccupied ground in the neighborhood, these strangers built huts for themselves, and were soon joined by a multitude of new settlers, who quickly formed a city. In the middle of it was seen a magnificent palace of colored marble, on the balcony of which, every noontide, appeared Cilix, in a long purple robe, and with a jewelled crown upon his head; for the inhabitants, when they found out that he was a king's son, had considered him the fittest of all men to be a king himself.

One of the first acts of King Cilix's government was to send out an expedition, consisting of a grave ambassador and an escort of bold and hardy young men, with orders to visit the principal kingdoms of the earth, and inquire whether a young maiden had passed through those regions, galloping swiftly on a white bull. It is, therefore, plain to my mind, that

Cilix secretly blamed himself for giving up the search for Europa, as long as he was able to put one foot before the other.

As for Telephassa, and Cadmus, and the good Thasus, it grieves me to think of them, still keeping up that weary pilgrimage. The two young men did their best for the poor queen, helping her over the rough places, often carrying her across rivulets in their faithful arms, and seeking to shelter her at nightfall, even when they themselves lay on the ground. Sad, sad it was to hear them asking of every passer-by if he had seen Europa, so long after the white bull had carried her away. But, though the gray years thrust themselves between, and made the child's figure dim in their remembrance, neither of these true-hearted three ever dreamed of giving up the search.

One morning, however, poor Thasus found that he had sprained his ankle, and could not possibly go a step farther.

"After a few days, to be sure," said he, mournfully, "I might make shift to hobble along with a stick. But that would only delay you, and perhaps hinder you from finding dear little Europa, after all your pains and trouble. Do you go forward, therefore, my beloved companions, and leave me to follow as I may."

"Thou hast been a true friend, dear Thasus," said Queen Telephassa, kissing his forehead. "Being neither my son, nor the brother of our lost Europa, thou hast shown thyself truer to me and her than Phœnix and Cilix did, whom we have left behind us. Without thy loving help, and that of my son Cadmus, my limbs could not have borne me half so far as this. Now, take thy rest, and be at peace. For — and it is the first time I have owned it to myself — I begin to question whether we shall ever find my beloved daughter in this world."

Saying this, the poor queen shed tears, because it was a grievous trial to the mother's heart to confess that her hopes were growing faint. From that day forward, Cadmus noticed that she never travelled with the same alacrity of spirit that had heretofore supported her. Her weight was heavier upon his arm.

Before setting out, Cadmus helped Thasus build a bower; while Telephassa, being too infirm to give any great assistance, advised them how to fit it up and furnish it, so that it might be as comfortable as a hut of branches could. Thasus, however, did not spend all his days in this green bower. For it happened to him, as to Phœnix and Cilix, that other homeless people visited the spot and liked it, and built themselves habitations in the neighborhood. So here, in the course of a few years, was another thriving city with a red freestone palace in the centre of it, where Thasus sat upon a throne, doing justice to the people, with a purple robe over his shoulders, a sceptre in his hand, and a crown upon his head. The inhabitants had made him king, not for the sake of any royal blood (for none was in his veins), but because Thasus was an upright, true-hearted, and courageous man, and therefore fit to rule.

But, when the affairs of his kingdom were all settled, King Thasus laid aside his purple robe, and crown, and sceptre, and bade his worthiest subject distribute justice to the people in his stead. Then, grasping the pilgrim's staff that had supported him so long, he set forth again, hoping still to discover some hoof-mark of the snow-white bull, some trace of the vanished child. He returned, after a lengthened absence, and sat down wearily upon his throne. To his latest hour, nevertheless, King Thasus showed his true-hearted remembrance of Europa, by ordering that a fire should always be kept burning in his palace, and a bath steaming hot, and food ready to be served up, and a bed with snow-white sheets, in case the maiden should arrive, and require immediate refreshment. And though Europa never came, the good Thasus had the blessings of many a poor traveller, who profited by the food and lodging which were meant for the little playmate of the king's boyhood.

Telephassa and Cadmus were now pursuing their weary way, with no companion but each other. The queen leaned heavily upon her son's arm, and could walk only a few miles a day. But for all her weakness and weariness, she would not be persuaded to give up the search. It was enough to bring tears into the eyes of bearded men to hear the melancholy tone with which she inquired of every stranger whether he could tell her any news of the lost child.

"Have you seen a little girl — no, no, I mean a young maiden of full growth — passing by this way, mounted on a snow-white bull, which gallops as swiftly as the wind?"

"We have seen no such wondrous sight," the people would reply; and very often, taking Cadmus aside, they whispered to him, "Is this stately and sad-looking woman your mother? Surely she is not in her right mind; and you ought to take her home, and make her comfortable, and do your best to get this dream out of her fancy."

"It is no dream," said Cadmus. "Everything else is a dream, save that."

But, one day, Talephassa seemed feebler than usual,

and leaned almost her whole weight on the arm of Cadmus, and walked more slowly than ever before. At last they reached a solitary spot, where she told her son that she must needs lie down, and take a good, long rest.

" A good, long rest ! " she repeated, looking Cadmus tenderly in the face, — " a good, long rest, thou dearest one ! "

" As long as you please, dear mother," answered Cadmus.

Telephassa bade him sit down on the turf beside her, and then she took his hand.

" My son," said she, fixing her dim eyes most lovingly upon him, " this rest that I speak of will be very long indeed ! You must not wait till it is finished. Dear Cadmus, you do not comprehend me. You must make a grave here, and lay your mother's weary frame into it. My pilgrimage is over."

Cadmus burst into tears, and, for a long time, refused to believe that his dear mother was now to be taken from him. But Telephassa reasoned with him, and kissed him, and at length made him discern that it was better for her spirit to pass away out of the toil, the weariness, the grief, and disappointment which had burdened her on earth, ever since the child was lost. He therefore repressed his sorrow, and listened to her last words.

" Dearest Cadmus," said she, " thou hast been the truest son that ever mother had, and faithful to the very last. Who else would have borne with my infirmities as thou hast ! It is owing to thy care, thou tenderest child, that my grave was not dug long years ago, in some valley, or on some hill-side, that lies far, far behind us. It is enough. Thou shalt wander no more on this hopeless search. But when thou hast laid thy mother in the earth, then go, my son, to Delphi, and inquire of the oracle what thou shalt do next."

" O mother, mother," cried Cadmus, " couldst thou but have seen my sister before this hour ! "

" It matters little now," answered Telephassa, and there was a smile upon her face. " I go now to the better world, and, sooner or later, shall find my daughter there."

I will not sadden you, my little hearers, with telling how Telephassa died and was buried, but will only say, that her dying smile grew brighter, instead of vanishing from her dead face ; so that Cadmus felt convinced that, at her very first step into the better world, she had caught Europa in her arms. He planted some flowers on his mother's grave, and left them to grow there, and make the place beautiful, when he should be far away.

After performing this last sorrowful duty, he set forth alone, and took the road towards the famous oracle of Delphi, as Telephassa had advised him. On his way thither, he still inquired of most people whom he met whether they had seen Europa ; for, to say the truth, Cadmus had grown so accustomed to ask the question, that it came to his lips as readily as a remark about the weather. He received various answers. Some told him one thing, and some another. Among the rest, a mariner affirmed, that, many years before, in a distant country, he had heard a rumor about a white bull, which came swimming across the sea with a child on his back, dressed up in flowers that were blighted by the sea-water. He did not know what had become of the child or the bull ; and Cadmus suspected, indeed, by a queer twinkle in the mari-

ner's eyes, that he was putting a joke upon him, and
had never really heard anything about the matter.

Poor Cadmus found it more wearisome to travel
alone than to bear all his dear mother's weight while
she had kept him company. His heart, you will understand, was now so heavy that it seemed impossible,
sometimes, to carry it any farther. But his limbs
were strong and active, and well accustomed to exercise. He walked swiftly along, thinking of King
Agenor and Queen Telephassa, and his brothers, and
the friendly Thasus, all of whom he had left behind
him, at one point of his pilgrimage or another, and
never expected to see them any more. Full of these
remembrances, he came within sight of a lofty mountain, which the people thereabouts told him was called
Parnassus. On the slope of Mount Parnassus was the
famous Delphi, whither Cadmus was going.

This Delphi was supposed to be the very midmost
spot of the whole world. The place of the oracle was
a certain cavity in the mountain-side, over which,
when Cadmus came thither, he found a rude bower of
branches. It reminded him of those which he had
helped to build for Phœnix and Cilix, and afterwards
for Thasus. In later times, when multitudes of people
came from great distances to put questions to the oracle, a spacious temple of marble was erected over the
spot. But in the days of Cadmus, as I have told you,
there was only this rustic bower, with its abundance
of green foliage, and a tuft of shrubbery, that ran wild
over the mysterious hole in the hill-side.

When Cadmus had thrust a passage through the
tangled boughs, and made his way into the bower, he
did not at first discern the half-hidden cavity. But
soon he felt a cold stream of air rushing out of it, with

so much force that it shook the ringlets on his cheek.
Pulling away the shrubbery which clustered over the
hole, he bent forward, and spoke in a distinct but rev-
erential tone, as if addressing some unseen personage
inside of the mountain.

" Sacred oracle of Delphi," said he, " whither shall
I go next in quest of my dear sister Europa? "

There was at first a deep silence, and then a rushing
sound, or a noise like a long sigh, proceeding out of
the interior of the earth. This cavity, you must know,
was looked upon as a sort of fountain of truth, which
sometimes gushed out in audible words; although, for
the most part, these words were such a riddle that
they might just as well have stayed at the bottom of
the hole. But Cadmus was more fortunate than many
others who went to Delphi in search of truth. By and
by, the rushing noise began to sound like articulate
language. It repeated, over and over again, the following sentence, which, after all, was so like the vague
whistle of a blast of air, that Cadmus really did not
quite know whether it meant anything or not : —

" Seek her no more! Seek her no more! Seek her
no more ! "

" What, then, shall I do? " asked Cadmus.

For, ever since he was a child, you know, it had
been the great object of his life to find his sister.
From the very hour that he left following the butterfly
in the meadow, near his father's palace, he had done
his best to follow Europa, over land and sea. And
now, if he must give up the search, he seemed to have
no more business in the world.

But again the sighing gust of air grew into something like a hoarse voice.

" Follow the cow ! " it said. " Follow the cow!
Follow the cow ! "

And when these words had been repeated until Cadmus was tired of hearing them (especially as he could not imagine what cow it was, or why he was to follow her), the gusty hole gave vent to another sentence.

"Where the stray cow lies down, there is your home."

These words were pronounced but a single time, and died away into a whisper before Cadmus was fully satisfied that he had caught the meaning. He put other questions, but received no answer; only the gust of wind sighed continually out of the cavity, and blew the withered leaves rustling along the ground before it.

"Did there really come any words out of the hole?" thought Cadmus; "or have I been dreaming all this while?"

He turned away from the oracle, and thought himself no wiser than when he came thither. Caring little what might happen to him, he took the first path that offered itself, and went along at a sluggish pace; for, having no object in view, nor any reason to go one way more than another, it would certainly have been foolish to make haste. Whenever he met anybody, the old question was at his tongue's end: —

"Have you seen a beautiful maiden, dressed like a king's daughter, and mounted on a snow-white bull, that gallops as swiftly as the wind?"

But, remembering what the oracle had said, he only half uttered the words, and then mumbled the rest indistinctly; and from his confusion, people must have imagined that this handsome young man had lost his wits.

I know not how far Cadmus had gone, nor could he himself have told you, when, at no great distance before him, he beheld a brindled cow. She was lying down by the wayside, and quietly chewing her cud; nor did she take any notice of the young man until he had approached pretty nigh. Then, getting leisurely upon her feet, and giving her head a gentle toss, she began to move along at a moderate pace, often pausing just long enough to crop a mouthful of grass. Cadmus loitered behind, whistling idly to himself, and scarcely noticing the cow; until the thought occurred to him, whether this could possibly be the animal which, according to the oracle's response, was to serve him for a guide. But he smiled at himself for fancying such a thing. He could not seriously think that this was the cow, because she went along so quietly, behaving just like any other cow. Evidently she neither knew nor cared so much as a wisp of hay about Cadmus, and was only thinking how to get her living along the wayside, where the herbage was green and fresh. Perhaps she was going home to be milked.

"Cow, cow, cow!" cried Cadmus. "Hey, Brindle, hey! Stop, my good cow."

He wanted to come up with the cow, so as to examine her, and see if she would appear to know him, or whether there were any peculiarities to distinguish her from a thousand other cows, whose only business is to fill the milk-pail, and sometimes kick it over. But still the brindled cow trudged on, whisking her tail to keep the flies away, and taking as little notice of Cadmus as she well could. If he walked slowly, so did the cow, and seized the opportunity to graze. If he quickened his pace, the cow went just so much the faster; and once, when Cadmus tried to catch her by running, she threw out her heels, stuck her tail straight on end, and set off at a gallop, looking as

queerly as cows generally do, while putting themselves
to their speed.

When Cadmus saw that it was impossible to come
up with her, he walked on moderately, as before. The
cow, too, went leisurely on, without looking behind.
Wherever the grass was greenest, there she nibbled a
mouthful or two. Where a brook glistened brightly
across the path, there the cow drank, and breathed a
comfortable sigh, and drank again, and trudged onward at the pace that best suited herself and Cadmus.

"I do believe," thought Cadmus, "that this may
be the cow that was foretold me. If it be the one, I
suppose she will lie down somewhere hereabouts."

Whether it were the oracular cow or some other
one, it did not seem reasonable that she should travel
a great way farther. So, whenever they reached a
particularly pleasant spot on a breezy hill-side, or in
a sheltered vale, or flowery meadow, on the shore of
a calm lake, or along the bank of a clear stream, Cadmus looked eagerly around to see if the situation would
suit him for a home. But still, whether he liked the
place or no, the brindled cow never offered to lie down.
On she went at the quiet pace of a cow going homeward to the barn-yard; and, every moment, Cadmus
expected to see a milkmaid approaching with a pail,
or a herdsman running to head the stray animal, and
turn her back towards the pasture. But no milkmaid
came; no herdsman drove her back; and Cadmus followed the stray Brindle till he was almost ready to
drop down with fatigue.

"O brindled cow," cried he, in a tone of despair,
"do you never mean to stop?"

He had now grown too intent on following her to
think of lagging behind, however long the way, and

whatever might be his fatigue. Indeed, it seemed as if there were something about the animal that bewitched people. Several persons who happened to see the brindled cow, and Cadmus following behind, began to trudge after her, precisely as he did. Cadmus was glad of somebody to converse with, and therefore talked very freely to these good people. He told them all his adventures, and how he had left King Agenor in his palace, and Phœnix at one place, and Cilix at another, and Thasus at a third, and his dear mother, Queen Telephassa, under a flowery sod; so that now he was quite alone, both friendless and homeless. He mentioned, likewise, that the oracle had bidden him be guided by a cow, and inquired of the strangers whether they supposed that this brindled animal could be the one.

" Why, 't is a very wonderful affair," answered one of his new companions. " I am pretty well acquainted with the ways of cattle, and I never knew a cow, of her own accord, to go so far without stopping. If my legs will let me, I 'll never leave following the beast till she lies down."

" Nor I ! " said a second.

" Nor I ! " cried a third. " If she goes a hundred miles farther, I 'm determined to see the end of it."

The secret of it was, you must know, that the cow was an enchanted cow, and that, without their being conscious of it, she threw some of her enchantment over everybody that took so much as half a dozen steps behind her. They could not possibly help following her, though, all the time, they fancied themselves doing it of their own accord. The cow was by no means very nice in choosing her path; so that sometimes they had to scramble over rocks, or wade

through mud and mire, and were all in a terribly be-
draggled condition, and tired to death, and very hungry, into the bargain. What a weary business it was!

But still they kept trudging stoutly forward, and
talking as they went. The strangers grew very fond
of Cadmus, and resolved never to leave him, but to
help him build a city wherever the cow might lie down.
In the centre of it there should be a noble palace, in
which Cadmus might dwell, and be their king, with a
throne, a crown and sceptre, a purple robe, and everything else that a king ought to have ; for in him there
was the royal blood, and the royal heart, and the head
that knew how to rule.

While they were talking of these schemes, and be-
guiling the tediousness of the way with laying out the
plan of the new city, one of the company happened to
look at the cow.

"Joy! joy!" cried he, clapping his hands. "Brindle is going to lie down."

They all looked; and, sure enough, the cow had
stopped, and was staring leisurely about her, as other
cows do when on the point of lying down. And slowly,
slowly did she recline herself on the soft grass, first
bending her fore legs, and then crouching her hind
ones. When Cadmus and his companions came up
with her, there was the brindled cow taking her ease,
chewing her cud, and looking them quietly in the face;
as if this was just the spot she had been seeking for,
and as if it were all a matter of course.

"This, then," said Cadmus, gazing around him,
"this is to be my home."

It was a fertile and lovely plain, with great trees
flinging their sun-speckled shadows over it, and hills
fencing it in from the rough weather. At no great

distance, they beheld a river gleaming in the sunshine.
A home feeling stole into the heart of poor Cadmus.
He was very glad to know that here he might awake
in the morning, without the necessity of putting on
his dusty sandals to travel farther and farther. The
days and the years would pass over him, and find him
still in this pleasant spot. If he could have had his
brothers with him, and his friend Thasus, and could
have seen his dear mother under a roof of his own, he
might here have been happy, after all their disappointments. Some day or other, too, his sister Europa
might have come quietly to the door of his home, and
smiled round upon the familiar faces. But, indeed,
since there was no hope of regaining the friends of his
boyhood, or ever seeing his dear sister again, Cadmus
resolved to make himself happy with these new companions, who had grown so fond of him while following the cow.

"Yes, my friends," said he to them, "this is to be
our home. Here we will build our habitations. The
brindled cow, which has led us hither, will supply us
with milk. We will cultivate the neighboring soil,
and lead an innocent and happy life."

His companions joyfully assented to this plan; and,
in the first place, being very hungry and thirsty, they
looked about them for the means of providing a comfortable meal. Not far off, they saw a tuft of trees,
which appeared as if there might be a spring of water
beneath them. They went thither to fetch some, leaving Cadmus stretched on the ground along with the
brindled cow; for, now that he had found a place of
rest, it seemed as if all the weariness of his pilgrimage,
ever since he left King Agenor's palace, had fallen
upon him at once. But his new friends had not long

been gone, when he was suddenly startled by cries, shouts, and screams, and the noise of a terrible struggle, and in the midst of it all, a most awful hissing, which went right through his ears like a rough saw.

Running towards the tuft of trees, he beheld the head and fiery eyes of an immense serpent or dragon, with the widest jaws that ever a dragon had, and a vast many rows of horribly sharp teeth. Before Cadmus could reach the spot, this pitiless reptile had killed his poor companions, and was busily devouring them, making but a mouthful of each man.

It appears that the fountain of water was enchanted, and that the dragon had been set to guard it, so that no mortal might ever quench his thirst there. As the neighboring inhabitants carefully avoided the spot, it was now a long time (not less than a hundred years, or thereabouts) since the monster had broken his fast; and, as was natural enough, his appetite had grown to be enormous, and was not half satisfied by the poor people whom he had just eaten up. When he caught sight of Cadmus, therefore, he set up another abominable hiss, and flung back his immense jaws, until his mouth looked like a great red cavern, at the farther end of which were seen the legs of his last victim, whom he had hardly had time to swallow.

But Cadmus was so enraged at the destruction of his friends, that he cared neither for the size of the dragon's jaws nor for his hundreds of sharp teeth. Drawing his sword, he rushed at the monster, and flung himself right into his cavernous mouth. This bold method of attacking him took the dragon by surprise; for, in fact, Cadmus had leaped so far down into his throat, that the rows of terrible teeth could not close upon him, nor do him the least harm in the world. Thus, though the struggle was a tremendous one, and though the dragon shattered the tuft of trees into small splinters by the lashing of his tail, yet, as Cadmus was all the while slashing and stabbing at his very vitals, it was not long before the scaly wretch bethought himself of slipping away. He had not gone his length, however, when the brave Cadmus gave him a sword-thrust that finished the battle ; and, creeping out of the gateway of the creature's jaws, there he beheld him still wriggling his vast bulk, although there was no longer life enough in him to harm a little child.

But do not you suppose that it made Cadmus sorrowful to think of the melancholy fate which had befallen those poor, friendly people, who had followed the cow along with him ? It seemed as if he were doomed to lose everybody whom he loved, or to see them perish in one way or another. And here he was, after all his toils and troubles, in a solitary place, with not a single human being to help him build a hut.

" What shall I do ? " cried he aloud. " It were better for me to have been devoured by the dragon, as my poor companions were."

" Cadmus," said a voice, — but whether it came from above or below him, or whether it spoke within his own breast, the young man could not tell, —" Cadmus, pluck out the dragon's teeth, and plant them in the earth."

This was a strange thing to do ; nor was it very easy, I should imagine, to dig out all those deep-rooted fangs from the dead dragon's jaws. But Cadmus toiled and tugged, and after pounding the monstrous head almost to pieces with a great stone, he at last collected as many teeth as might have filled a bushel or two. The next thing was to plant them. This, likewise, was a tedious piece of work, especially as Cadmus was already exhausted with killing the dragon and knocking his head to pieces, and had nothing to dig the earth with, that I know of, unless it were his sword-blade. Finally, however, a sufficiently large tract of ground was turned up, and sown with this new kind of seed; although half of the dragon's teeth still remained to be planted some other day.

Cadmus, quite out of breath, stood leaning upon his sword, and wondering what was to happen next. He had waited but a few moments, when he began to see a sight, which was as great a marvel as the most marvellous thing I ever told you about.

The sun was shining slantwise over the field, and showed all the moist, dark soil just like any other newly planted piece of ground. All at once, Cadmus fancied he saw something glisten very brightly, first at one spot, then at another, and then at a hundred and a thousand spots together. Soon he perceived them to be the steel heads of spears, sprouting up everywhere like so many stalks of grain, and continually growing taller and taller. Next appeared a vast number of bright sword-blades, thrusting themselves up in the same way. A moment afterwards, the whole surface of the ground was broken up by a multitude of polished brass helmets, coming up like a crop of enormous beans. So rapidly did they grow, that Cadmus now discerned the fierce countenance of a man beneath every one. In short, before he had time to think what a wonderful affair it was, he beheld an abundant harvest of what looked like human beings, armed with helmets and breastplates, shields, swords and spears; and before they were well out of the earth, they brandished their weapons, and clashed them one against another, seeming to think, little while as they had yet lived, that they had wasted too much of life without a battle. Every tooth of the dragon had produced one of these sons of deadly mischief.

Up sprouted, also, a great many trumpeters; and with the first breath that they drew, they put their brazen trumpets to their lips, and sounded a tremendous and ear-shattering blast; so that the whole space, just now so quiet and solitary, reverberated with the clash and clang of arms, the bray of warlike music, and the shouts of angry men. So enraged did they all look, that Cadmus fully expected them to put the whole world to the sword. How fortunate would it be for a great conqueror, if he could get a bushel of the dragon's teeth to sow!

" Cadmus," said the same voice which he had before heard, " throw a stone into the midst of the armed men."

So Cadmus seized a large stone, and, flinging it into the middle of the earth army, saw it strike the breast-plate of a gigantic and fierce-looking warrior. Immediately on feeling the blow, he seemed to take it for granted that somebody had struck him; and, uplifting his weapon, he smote his next neighbor a blow that cleft his helmet asunder, and stretched him on the ground. In an instant, those nearest the fallen warrior began to strike at one another with their swords and stab with their spears. The confusion spread wider and wider. Each man smote down his brother, and was himself smitten down before he had time to exult in his victory. The trumpeters, all the while, blew their blasts shriller and shriller; each soldier shouted a battle-cry and often fell with it on his lips. It was the strangest spectacle of causeless wrath, and of mischief for no good end, that had ever been witnessed ; but, after all, it was neither more foolish nor more wicked than a thousand battles that have since been fought, in which men have slain their brothers with just as little reason as these children of the dragon's teeth. It ought to be considered, too, that the dragon people were made for nothing else ; whereas other mortals were born to love and help one another.

Well, this memorable battle continued to rage until the ground was strewn with helmeted heads that had been cut off. Of all the thousands that began the fight, there were only five left standing. These now rushed from different parts of the field, and, meeting in the middle of it, clashed their swords, and struck at each other's hearts as fiercely as ever.

" Cadmus," said the voice again, " bid those five warriors sheathe their swords. They will help you to build the city."

Without hesitating an instant, Cadmus stepped forward, with the aspect of a king and a leader, and extending his drawn sword amongst them, spoke to the warriors in a stern and commanding voice.

" Sheathe your weapons ! " said he.

And forthwith, feeling themselves bound to obey him, the five remaining sons of the dragon's teeth made him a military salute with their swords, returned them to the scabbards, and stood before Cadmus in a rank, eyeing him as soldiers eye their captain, while awaiting the word of command.

These five men had probably sprung from the biggest of the dragon's teeth, and were the boldest and strongest of the whole army. They were almost giants, indeed, and had good need to be so, else they never could have lived through so terrible a fight. They still had a very furious look, and, if Cadmus happened to glance aside, would glare at one another, with fire flashing out of their eyes. It was strange, too, to observe how the earth, out of which they had so lately grown, was incrusted, here and there, on their bright breastplates, and even begrimed their faces, just as you may have seen it clinging to beets and carrots when pulled out of their native soil. Cadmus hardly knew whether to consider them as men, or some odd kind of vegetable; although, on the whole, he concluded that there was human nature in them, because they were so fond of trumpets and weapons, and so ready to shed blood.

They looked him earnestly in the face, waiting for his next order, and evidently desiring no other employment than to follow him from one battle-field to another, all over the wide world. But Cadmus was wiser than these earth-born creatures, with the dragon's fierceness in them, and knew better how to use their strength and hardihood.

"Come!" said he. "You are sturdy fellows. Make yourselves useful! Quarry some stones with those great swords of yours, and help me to build a city."

The five soldiers grumbled a little, and muttered that it was their business to overthrow cities, not to build them up. But Cadmus looked at them with a stern eye, and spoke to them in a tone of authority, so that they knew him for their master, and never again thought of disobeying his commands. They set to work in good earnest, and toiled so diligently, that, in a very short time, a city began to make its appearance. At first, to be sure, the workmen showed a quarrelsome disposition. Like savage beasts, they would doubtless have done one another a mischief, if Cadmus had not kept watch over them and quelled the fierce old serpent that lurked in their hearts, when he saw it gleaming out of their wild eyes. But, in course of time, they got accustomed to honest labor, and had sense enough to feel that there was more true enjoyment in living at peace, and doing good to one's neighbor, than in striking at him with a two-edged sword. It may not be too much to hope that the rest of mankind will by and by grow as wise and peaceable as these five earth-begrimed warriors, who sprang from the dragon's teeth.

And now the city was built, and there was a home in it for each of the workmen. But the palace of Cadmus was not yet erected, because they had left it till the last, meaning to introduce all the new improvements of architecture, and make it very commodious, as well as stately and beautiful. After finishing the rest of their labors, they all went to bed betimes, in order to rise in the gray of the morning, and get at least the foundation of the edifice laid before nightfall. But, when Cadmus arose, and took his way towards the site where the palace was to be built, followed by his five sturdy workmen marching all in a row, what do you think he saw?

What should it be but the most magnificent palace that had ever been seen in the world? It was built of marble and other beautiful kinds of stone, and rose high into the air, with a splendid dome and a portico along the front, and carved pillars, and everything else that befitted the habitation of a mighty king. It had

grown up out of the earth in almost as short a time as
it had taken the armed host to spring from the dragon's teeth; and what made the matter more strange,
no seed of this stately edifice had ever been planted.

When the five workmen beheld the dome, with the
morning sunshine making it look golden and glorious,
they gave a great shout.

"Long live King Cadmus," they cried, "in his
beautiful palace."

And the new king, with his five faithful followers at
his heels, shouldering their pickaxes and marching in
a rank (for they still had a soldier-like sort of behavior, as their nature was), ascended the palace steps.
Halting at the entrance, they gazed through a long
vista of lofty pillars that were ranged from end to end
of a great hall. At the farther extremity of this hall,
approaching slowly towards him, Cadmus beheld a
female figure, wonderfully beautiful, and adorned with
a royal robe, and a crown of diamonds over her golden
ringlets, and the richest necklace that ever a queen
wore. His heart thrilled with delight. He fancied it
his long-lost sister Europa, now grown to womanhood,
coming to make him happy, and to repay him, with
her sweet sisterly affection, for all those weary wanderings in quest of her since he left King Agenor's
palace, — for the tears that he had shed, on parting
with Phœnix, and Cilix, and Thasus, — for the heart-
breakings that had made the whole world seem dismal
to him over his dear mother's grave.

But, as Cadmus advanced to meet the beautiful
stranger, he saw that her features were unknown to
him, although, in the little time that it required to
tread along the hall, he had already felt a sympathy
betwixt himself and her.

"No, Cadmus," said the same voice that had spoken to him in the field of the armed men, "this is not that dear sister Europa whom you have sought so faithfully all over the wide world. This is Harmonia, a daughter of the sky, who is given you instead of sister, and brothers, and friend, and mother. You will find all those dear ones in her alone."

So King Cadmus dwelt in the palace, with his new friend Harmonia, and found a great deal of comfort in his magnificent abode, but would doubtless have found as much, if not more, in the humblest cottage by the wayside. Before many years went by, there was a group of rosy little children (but how they came thither has always been a mystery to me) sporting in the great hall, and on the marble steps of the palace, and running joyfully to meet King Cadmus when affairs of state left him at leisure to play with them. They called him father, and Queen Harmonia mother. The five old soldiers of the dragon's teeth grew very fond of these small urchins, and were never weary of showing them how to shoulder sticks, flourish wooden swords, and march in military order, blowing a penny trumpet, or beating an abominable rub-a-dub upon a little drum.

But King Cadmus, lest there should be too much of the dragon's tooth in his children's disposition, used to find time from his kingly duties to teach them their A B C, — which he invented for their benefit, and for which many little people, I am afraid, are not half so grateful to him as they ought to be.

CIRCE'S PALACE.

SOME of you have heard, no doubt, of the wise King Ulysses, and how he went to the siege of Troy, and how, after that famous city was taken and burned, he spent ten long years in trying to get back again to his own little kingdom of Ithaca. At one time in the course of this weary voyage, he arrived at an island that looked very green and pleasant, but the name of which was unknown to him. For, only a little while before he came thither, he had met with a terrible hurricane, or rather a great many hurricanes at once, which drove his fleet of vessels into a strange part of the sea, where neither himself nor any of his mariners had ever sailed. This misfortune was entirely owing to the foolish curiosity of his shipmates, who, while Ulysses lay asleep, had untied some very bulky leathern bags, in which they supposed a valuable treasure to be concealed. But in each of these stout bags, King Æolus, the ruler of the winds, had tied up a tempest, and had given it to Ulysses to keep, in order that he might be sure of a favorable passage homeward to Ithaca; and when the strings were loosened, forth rushed the whistling blasts, like air out of a blown bladder, whitening the sea with foam, and scattering the vessels nobody could tell whither.

Immediately after escaping from this peril, a still greater one had befallen him. Scudding before the hurricane, he reached a place, which, as he afterwards found, was called Læstrygonia, where some monstrous giants had eaten up many of his companions, and had sunk every one of his vessels, except that in which he himself sailed, by flinging great masses of rock at them, from the cliffs along the shore. After going through such troubles as these, you cannot wonder that King Ulysses was glad to moor his tempest-beaten bark in a quiet cove of the green island, which I began with telling you about. But he had encountered so many dangers from giants, and one-eyed Cyclopes, and monsters of the sea and land, that he could not help dreading some mischief, even in this pleasant and seemingly solitary spot. For two days, therefore, the poor weather-worn voyagers kept quiet, and either stayed on board of their vessel, or merely crept along under cliffs that bordered the shore ; and to keep themselves alive, they dug shell-fish out of the sand, and sought for any little rill of fresh water that might be running towards the sea.

Before the two days were spent, they grew very weary of this kind of life; for the followers of King Ulysses, as you will find it important to remember, were terrible gormandizers, and pretty sure to grumble if they missed their regular meals, and their irregular ones besides. Their stock of provisions was quite exhausted, and even the shell-fish began to get scarce, so that they had now to choose between starving to death or venturing into the interior of the island, where, perhaps, some huge three-headed dragon, or other horrible monster, had his den. Such misshapen creatures were very numerous in those days ; and nobody ever expected to make a voyage, or take a journey, without running more or less risk of being devoured by them.

But King Ulysses was a bold man as well as a pru

dent one ; and on the third morning he determined
to discover what sort of a place the island was, and
whether it were possible to obtain a supply of food for
the hungry mouths of his companions. So, taking a
spear in his hand, he clambered to the summit of a
cliff, and gazed round about him. At a distance, towards the centre of the island, he beheld the stately
towers of what seemed to be a palace, built of snow-
white marble, and rising in the midst of a grove
of lofty trees. The thick branches of these trees
stretched across the front of the edifice, and more
than half concealed it, although, from the portion
which he saw, Ulysses judged it to be spacious and
exceedingly beautiful, and probably the residence of
some great nobleman or prince. A blue smoke went
curling up from the chimney, and was almost the
pleasantest part of the spectacle to Ulysses. For,
from the abundance of this smoke, it was reasonable
to conclude that there was a good fire in the kitchen,
and that, at dinner-time, a plentiful banquet would be
served up to the inhabitants of the palace, and to
whatever guests might happen to drop in.

With so agreeable a prospect before him, Ulysses
fancied that he could not do better than to go straight
to the palace gate, and tell the master of it that there
was a crew of poor shipwrecked mariners, not far off,
who had eaten nothing for a day or two save a few
clams and oysters, and would therefore be thankful
for a little food. And the prince or nobleman must
be a very stingy curmudgeon, to be sure, if, at least,
when his own dinner was over, he would not bid them
welcome to the broken victuals from the table.

Pleasing himself with this idea, King Ulysses had
made a few steps in the direction of the palace, when

there was a great twittering and chirping from the branch of a neighboring tree. A moment afterwards, a bird came flying towards him, and hovered in the air, so as almost to brush his face with its wings. It was a very pretty little bird, with purple wings and body, and yellow legs, and a circle of golden feathers round its neck, and on its head a golden tuft, which looked like a king's crown in miniature. Ulysses tried to catch the bird. But it fluttered nimbly out of his reach, still chirping in a piteous tone, as if it could have told a lamentable story, had it only been gifted with human language. And when he attempted to drive it away, the bird flew no farther than the bough of the next tree, and again came fluttering about his head, with its doleful chirp, as soon as he showed a purpose of going forward.

"Have you anything to tell me, little bird?" asked Ulysses.

And he was ready to listen attentively to whatever the bird might communicate; for at the siege of Troy, and elsewhere, he had known such odd things to happen, that he would not have considered it much out of the common run had this little feathered creature talked as plainly as himself.

"Peep!" said the bird, "peep, peep, pe — weep!" And nothing else would it say, but only, "Peep, peep, pe — weep!" in a melancholy cadence, and over and over and over again. As often as Ulysses moved forward, however, the bird showed the greatest alarm, and did its best to drive him back, with the anxious flutter of its purple wings. Its unaccountable behavior made him conclude, at last, that the bird knew of some danger that awaited him, and which must needs be very terrible, beyond all question, since it moved even a little fowl to feel compassion for a human being. So he resolved, for the present, to return to the vessel, and tell his companions what he had seen.

This appeared to satisfy the bird. As soon as Ulysses turned back, it ran up the trunk of a tree, and began to pick insects out of the bark with its long, sharp bill; for it was a kind of woodpecker, you must know, and had to get its living in the same manner as other birds of that species. But every little while, as it pecked at the bark of the tree, the purple bird bethought itself of some secret sorrow, and repeated its plaintive note of " Peep, peep, pe — weep ! "

On his way to the shore, Ulysses had the good luck to kill a large stag by thrusting his spear into its back. Taking it on his shoulders (for he was a remarkably strong man), he lugged it along with him, and flung it down before his hungry companions. I have already hinted to you what gormandizers some of the comrades of King Ulysses were. From what is related of them, I reckon that their favorite diet was pork, and that they had lived upon it until a good part of their physical substance was swine's flesh, and their tempers and dispositions were very much akin to the hog. A dish of venison, however, was no unacceptable meal to them, especially after feeding so long on oysters and clams. So, beholding the dead stag, they felt of its ribs in a knowing way, and lost no time in kindling a fire, of drift-wood, to cook it. The rest of the day was spent in feasting ; and if these enormous eaters got up from table at sunset, it was only because they could not scrape another morsel off the poor animal's bones.

The next morning their appetites were as sharp as ever. They looked at Ulysses, as if they expected him to clamber up the cliff again, and come back with another fat deer upon his shoulders. Instead of setting out, however, he summoned the whole crew together, and told them it was in vain to hope that he could kill a stag every day for their dinner, and therefore it was advisable to think of some other mode of satisfying their hunger.

"Now," said he, "when I was on the cliff yesterday, I discovered that this island is inhabited. At a considerable distance from the shore stood a marble palace, which appeared to be very spacious, and had a great deal of smoke curling out of one of its chimneys."

"Aha!" muttered some of his companions, smacking their lips. "That smoke must have come from the kitchen fire. There was a good dinner on the spit; and no doubt there will be as good a one to-day."

"But," continued the wise Ulysses, "you must remember, my good friends, our misadventure in the cavern of one-eyed Polyphemus, the Cyclops! Instead of his ordinary milk diet, did he not eat up two of our comrades for his supper, and a couple more for breakfast, and two at his supper again? Methinks I see him yet, the hideous monster, scanning us with that great red eye, in the middle of his forehead, to single out the fattest. And then again only a few days ago, did we not fall into the hands of the king of the Læstrygons, and those other horrible giants, his subjects, who devoured a great many more of us than are now left? To tell you the truth, if we go to yonder palace, there can be no question that we shall make our appearance at the dinner-table ; but whether seated as guests, or served up as food, is a point to be seriously considered."

" Either way," murmured some of the hungriest of the crew, " it will be better than starvation; particularly if one could be sure of being well fattened beforehand, and daintily cooked afterwards."

"That is a matter of taste," said King Ulysses, " and, for my own part, neither the most careful fattening nor the daintiest of cookery would reconcile me to being dished at last. My proposal is, therefore, that we divide ourselves into two equal parties, and ascertain, by drawing lots, which of the two shall go to the palace, and beg for food and assistance. If these can be obtained, all is well. If not, and if the inhabitants prove as inhospitable as Polyphemus, or the Læstrygons, then there will but half of us perish, and the remainder may set sail and escape."

As nobody objected to this scheme, Ulysses proceeded to count the whole band, and found that there were forty-six men including himself. He then numbered off twenty - two of them, and put Eurylochus (who was one of his chief officers, and second only to himself in sagacity) at their head. Ulysses took command of the remaining twenty-two men, in person. Then, taking off his helmet, he put two shells into it, on one of which was written, " Go," and on the other " Stay." Another person now held the helmet, while Ulysses and Eurylochus drew out each a shell; and the word " Go " was found written on that which Eurylochus had drawn. In this manner, it was decided that Ulysses and his twenty-two men were to remain at the seaside until the other party should have found out what sort of treatment they might expect at the mysterious palace. As there was no help for it, Eurylochus immediately set forth at the head of his twenty-two followers, who went off in a very melancholy state of mind, leaving their friends in hardly better spirits than themselves.

No sooner had they clambered up the cliff, than they discerned the tall marble towers of the palace, ascending, as white as snow, out of the lovely green shadow of the trees which surrounded it. A gush of smoke came from a chimney in the rear of the edifice. This vapor rose high in the air, and, meeting with a breeze, was wafted seaward, and made to pass over the heads of the hungry mariners. When people's appetites are keen, they have a very quick scent for anything savory in the wind.

" That smoke comes from the kitchen ! " cried one of them, turning up his nose as high as he could, and snuffing eagerly. " And, as sure as I'm a half-starved vagabond, I smell roast meat in it."

" Pig, roast pig ! " said another. " Ah, the dainty little porker ! My mouth waters for him."

" Let us make haste," cried the others, " or we shall be too late for the good cheer ! "

But scarcely had they made half a dozen steps from the edge of the cliff, when a bird came fluttering to meet them. It was the same pretty little bird, with the purple wings and body, the yellow legs, the golden collar round its neck, and the crown-like tuft upon its head, whose behavior had so much surprised Ulysses. It hovered about Eurylochus, and almost brushed his face with its wings.

" Peep, peep, pe — weep ! " chirped the bird.

So plaintively intelligent was the sound, that it seemed as if the little creature were going to break its

heart with some mighty secret that it had to tell, and
only this one poor note to tell it with.

" My pretty bird," said Eurylochus, — for he was a
wary person, and let no token of harm escape his notice, — " my pretty bird, who sent you hither ? And
what is the message which you bring ? "

" Peep, peep, pe — weep ! " replied the bird, very
sorrowfully.

Then it flew towards the edge of the cliff, and looked
round at them, as if exceedingly anxious that they
should return whence they came. Eurylochus and a
few of the others were inclined to turn back. They
could not help suspecting that the purple bird must
be aware of something mischievous that would befall
them at the palace, and the knowledge of which affected its airy spirit with a human sympathy and sorrow. But the rest of the voyagers, snuffing up the
smoke from the palace kitchen, ridiculed the idea of
returning to the vessel. One of them (more brutal
than his fellows, and the most notorious gormandizer
in the whole crew) said such a cruel and wicked thing,
that I wonder the mere thought did not turn him into
a wild beast in shape, as he already was in his nature.

" This troublesome and impertinent little fowl,"
said he, "would make a delicate titbit to begin dinner
with. Just one plump morsel, melting away between
the teeth. If he comes within my reach, I 'll catch
him, and give him to the palace cook to be roasted on
a skewer."

The words were hardly out of his mouth, before the
purple bird flew away, crying " Peep, peep, pe —
weep," more dolorously than ever.

" That bird," remarked Eurylochus, " knows more
than we do about what awaits us at the palace."

"Come on, then," cried his comrades, "and we'll soon know as much as he does."

The party, accordingly, went onward through the green and pleasant wood. Every little while they caught new glimpses of the marble palace, which looked more and more beautiful the nearer they approached it. They soon entered a broad pathway, which seemed to be very neatly kept, and which went winding along with streaks of sunshine falling across it, and specks of light quivering among the deepest shadows that fell from the lofty trees. It was bordered, too, with a great many sweet-smelling flowers, such as the mariners had never seen before. So rich and beautiful they were, that, if the shrubs grew wild here, and were native in the soil, then this island was surely the flower-garden of the whole earth; or, if transplanted from some other clime, it must have been from the Happy Islands that lay towards the golden sunset.

"There has been a great deal of pains foolishly wasted on these flowers," observed one of the company; and I tell you what he said, that you may keep in mind what gormandizers they were. "For my part, if I were the owner of the palace, I would bid my gardener cultivate nothing but savory potherbs to make a stuffing for roast meat, or to flavor a stew with."

"Well said!" cried the others. "But I'll warrant you there's a kitchen-garden in the rear of the palace."

At one place they came to a crystal spring, and paused to drink at it for want of liquor which they liked better. Looking into its bosom, they beheld their own faces dimly reflected, but so extravagantly distorted by the gush and motion of the water, that each one of them appeared to be laughing at himself and all his companions. So ridiculous were these images of themselves, indeed, that they did really laugh aloud, and could hardly be grave again as soon as they wished. And after they had drank, they grew still merrier than before.

"It has a twang of the wine-cask in it," said one, smacking his lips.

"Make haste!" cried his fellows; "we'll find the wine-cask itself at the palace; and that will be better than a hundred crystal fountains."

Then they quickened their pace, and capered for joy at the thought of the savory banquet at which they hoped to be guests. But Eurylochus told them that he felt as if he were walking in a dream.

"If I am really awake," continued he, "then, in my opinion, we are on the point of meeting with some stranger adventure than any that befell us in the cave of Polyphemus, or among the gigantic man-eating Læstrygons, or in the windy palace of King Æolus, which stands on a brazen-walled island. This kind of dreamy feeling always comes over me before any wonderful occurrence. If you take my advice, you will turn back."

"No, no," answered his comrades, snuffing the air, in which the scent from the palace kitchen was now very perceptible. "We would not turn back, though we were certain that the king of the Læstrygons, as big as a mountain, would sit at the head of the table, and huge Polyphemus, the one-eyed Cyclops, at its foot."

At length they came within full sight of the palace, which proved to be very large and lofty, with a great number of airy pinnacles upon its roof. Though it was now midday, and the sun shone brightly over the marble front, yet its snowy whiteness, and its fantastic style of architecture, made it look unreal, like the frostwork on a window-pane, or like the shapes of castles which one sees among the clouds by moonlight. But, just then, a puff of wind brought down the smoke of the kitchen chimney among them, and caused each man to smell the odor of the dish that he liked best; and, after scenting it, they thought everything else moonshine, and nothing real save this palace, and save the banquet that was evidently ready to be served up in it.

So they hastened their steps towards the portal, but had not got half-way across the wide lawn, when a pack of lions, tigers, and wolves came bounding to meet them. The terrified mariners started back, expecting no better fate than to be torn to pieces and devoured. To their surprise and joy, however, these wild beasts merely capered around them, wagging their tails, offering their heads to be stroked and patted, and behaving just like so many well-bred housedogs, when they wish to express their delight at meeting their master, or their master's friends. The biggest lion licked the feet of Eurylochus; and every other lion, and every wolf and tiger, singled out one of his two-and-twenty followers, whom the beast fondled as if he loved him better than a beef-bone.

But, for all that, Eurylochus imagined that he saw something fierce and savage in their eyes; nor would he have been surprised, at any moment, to feel the big lion's terrible claws, or to see each of the tigers make a deadly spring, or each wolf leap at the throat of the man whom he had fondled. Their mildness seemed unreal, and a mere freak; but their savage nature was as true as their teeth and claws.

Nevertheless, the men went safely across the lawn with the wild beasts frisking about them, and doing no manner of harm; although, as they mounted the steps of the palace, you might possibly have heard a low growl, particularly from the wolves; as if they thought it a pity, after all, to let the strangers pass without so much as tasting what they were made of.

Eurylochus and his followers now passed under a lofty portal, and looked through the open doorway into the interior of the palace. The first thing that they saw was a spacious hall, and a fountain in the middle of it, gushing up towards the ceiling out of a marble basin, and falling back into it with a continual plash. The water of this fountain, as it spouted upward, was constantly taking new shapes, not very distinctly, but plainly enough for a nimble fancy to recognize what they were. Now it was the shape of a man in a long robe, the fleecy whiteness of which was made out of the fountain's spray; now it was a lion, or a tiger, or a wolf, or an ass, or, as often as anything else, a hog, wallowing in the marble basin as if it were his sty. It was either magic or some very curious machinery that caused the gushing waterspout to assume all these forms. But, before the strangers had time to look closely at this wonderful sight, their attention was drawn off by a very sweet and agreeable sound. A woman's voice was singing melodiously in another room of the palace, and with her voice was mingled the noise of a loom, at which she was probably seated, weaving a rich texture of cloth, and intertwining the high and low sweetness of her voice into a rich tissue of harmony.

By and by, the song came to an end; and then, all at once, there were several feminine voices, talking airily and cheerfully, with now and then a merry burst of laughter, such as you may always hear when three or four young women sit at work together.

"What a sweet song that was!" exclaimed one of the voyagers.

"Too sweet, indeed," answered Eurylochus, shaking his head. "Yet it was not so sweet as the song of the Sirens, those birdlike damsels who wanted to tempt us on the rocks, so that our vessel might be wrecked, and our bones left whitening along the shore."

"But just listen to the pleasant voices of those maidens, and that buzz of the loom, as the shuttle passes to and fro," said another comrade. "What a domestic, household, homelike sound it is! Ah, before that weary siege of Troy, I used to hear the buzzing loom and the women's voices under my own roof. Shall I never hear them again? nor taste those nice little savory dishes which my dearest wife knew how to serve up?"

"Tush! we shall fare better here," said another. "But how innocently those women are babbling together, without guessing that we overhear them! And mark that richest voice of all, so pleasant and familiar, but which yet seems to have the authority of a mistress among them. Let us show ourselves at once. What harm can the lady of the palace and her maidens do to mariners and warriors like us?"

"Remember," said Eurylochus, "that it was a young maiden who beguiled three of our friends into the palace of the king of the Læstrygons, who ate up one of them in the twinkling of an eye."

No warning or persuasion, however, had any effect on his companions. They went up to a pair of folding-doors at the farther end of the hall, and, throwing them wide open, passed into the next room. Eurylochus, meanwhile, had stepped behind a pillar. In the short moment while the folding-doors opened and closed again, he caught a glimpse of a very beautiful woman rising from the loom, and coming to meet the poor weather-beaten wanderers, with a hospitable smile, and her hand stretched out in welcome. There were four other young women, who joined their hands and danced merrily forward, making gestures of obeisance to the strangers. They were only less beautiful than the lady who seemed to be their mistress. Yet Eurylochus fancied that one of them had sea-green hair, and that the close-fitting bodice of a second looked like the bark of a tree, and that both the others had something odd in their aspect, although he could not quite determine what it was, in the little while that he had to examine them.

The folding-doors swung quickly back, and left him standing behind the pillar, in the solitude of the outer hall. There Eurylochus waited until he was quite weary, and listened eagerly to every sound, but without hearing anything that could help him to guess what had become of his friends. Footsteps, it is true, seemed to be passing and repassing in other parts of the palace. Then there was a clatter of silver dishes, or golden ones, which made him imagine a rich feast in a splendid banqueting-hall. But by and by he heard a tremendous grunting and squealing, and then a sudden scampering, like that of small, hard hoofs over a marble floor, while the voices of the mistress and her four handmaidens were screaming all together, in tones of anger and derision. Eurylochus could not conceive what had happened, unless a drove of swine had broken into the palace, attracted by the smell of the feast. Chancing to cast his eyes at the fountain, he saw that it did not shift its shape, as formerly, nor looked either like a long-robed man, or a lion, a tiger, a wolf, or an ass. It looked like nothing but a hog, which lay wallowing in the marble basin, and filled it from brim to brim.

But we must leave the prudent Eurylochus waiting in the outer hall, and follow his friends into the inner secrecy of the palace. As soon as the beautiful woman saw them, she arose from the loom, as I have told you, and came forward, smiling, and stretching out her hand. She took the hand of the foremost among them, and bade him and the whole party welcome.

"You have been long expected, my good friends," said she. "I and my maidens are well acquainted with you, although you do not appear to recognize us. Look at this piece of tapestry, and judge if your faces must not have been familiar to us."

So the voyagers examined the web of cloth which the beautiful woman had been weaving in her loom; and, to their vast astonishment they saw their own figures perfectly represented in different colored threads. It was a lifelike picture of their recent adventures, showing them in the cave of Polyphemus, and how they had put out his one great moony eye; while in another part of the tapestry they were untying the leathern bags, puffed out with contrary winds; and farther on, they beheld themselves scampering away from the gigantic king of the Læstrygons, who had caught one of them by the leg. Lastly, there they were, sitting on the desolate shore of this very island, hungry and downcast, and looking ruefully at the bare bones of the stag which they devoured yesterday.

This was as far as the work had yet proceeded; but when the beautiful woman should again sit down at her loom, she would probably make a picture of what had since happened to the strangers, and of what was now going to happen.

"You see," she said, "that I know all about your troubles; and you cannot doubt that I desire to make you happy for as long a time as you may remain with me. For this purpose, my honored guests, I have ordered a banquet to be prepared. Fish, fowl, and flesh, roasted, and in luscious stews, and seasoned, I trust, to all your tastes, are ready to be served up. If your appetites tell you it is dinner-time, then come with me to the festal saloon."

At this kind invitation, the hungry mariners were quite overjoyed; and one of them, taking upon himself to be spokesman, assured their hospitable hostess that any hour of the day was dinner-time with them, whenever they could get flesh to put in the pot, and fire to boil it with. So the beautiful woman led the way; and the four maidens (one of them had sea-green hair, another a bodice of oak bark, a third sprinkled a shower of water-drops from her fingers' ends, and the fourth had some other oddity, which I have forgotten), all these followed behind, and hurried the guests along, until they entered a magnificent saloon. It was built in a perfect oval, and lighted from a crystal dome above. Around the walls were ranged two-and-twenty thrones, overhung by canopies of crimson and gold, and provided with the softest of cushions, which were tasselled and fringed with gold cord. Each of the strangers was invited to sit down; and there they were, two-and-twenty storm-beaten mariners, in worn and tattered garb, sitting on two-and-twenty cushioned and canopied thrones, so rich and gorgeous that the proudest monarch had nothing more splendid in his stateliest hall.

Then you might have seen the guests nodding, winking with one eye, and leaning from one throne to another, to communicate their satisfaction in hoarse whispers.

" Our good hostess has made kings of us all," said one. " Ha! do you smell the feast? I 'll engage it will be fit to set before two-and-twenty kings."

" I hope," said another, " it will be, mainly, good substantial joints, sirloins, spareribs, and hinder quarters, without too many kickshaws. If I thought the good lady would not take it amiss, I should call for a fat slice of fried bacon to begin with."

Ah, the gluttons and gormandizers! You see how it was with them. In the loftiest seats of dignity, on royal thrones, they could think of nothing but their greedy appetite, which was the portion of their nature that they shared with wolves and swine; so that they resembled those vilest of animals far more than they did kings, — if, indeed, kings were what they ought to be.

But the beautiful woman now clapped her hands; and immediately there entered a train of two-and-twenty serving-men, bringing dishes of the richest food, all hot from the kitchen fire, and sending up such a steam that it hung like a cloud below the crystal dome of the saloon. An equal number of attendants brought great flagons of wine, of various kinds, some of which sparkled as it was poured out, and went bubbling down the throat; while, of other sorts, the purple liquor was so clear that you could see the wrought figures at the bottom of the goblet. While the servants supplied the two-and-twenty guests with food and drink, the hostess and her four maidens went from one throne to another, exhorting them to eat their fill, and to quaff wine abundantly, and thus to recompense themselves, at this one banquet, for the many days when they had gone without a dinner. But, whenever the mariners were not looking at them (which was pretty often, as they looked chiefly into the basins and platters), the beautiful woman and her damsels turned aside and laughed. Even the servants, as they knelt down to present the dishes, might be seen to grin and sneer, while the guests were helping themselves to the offered dainties.

And, once in a while, the strangers seemed to taste something that they did not like.

"Here is an odd kind of a spice in this dish," said one. "I can't say it quite suits my palate. Down it goes, however."

"Send a good draught of wine down your throat," said his comrade on the next throne. "That is the stuff to make this sort of cookery relish well. Though I must needs say, the wine has a queer taste too. But the more I drink of it the better I like the flavor."

Whatever little fault they might find with the dishes, they sat at dinner a prodigiously long while; and it would really have made you ashamed to see how they swilled down the liquor and gobbled up the food. They sat on golden thrones, to be sure; but they behaved like pigs in a sty; and, if they had had their wits about them, they might have guessed that this was the opinion of their beautiful hostess and her maidens. It brings a blush into my face to reckon up, in my own mind, what mountains of meat and pudding, and what gallons of wine, these two-and-twenty guzzlers and gormandizers ate and drank. They forgot all about their homes, and their wives and children, and all about Ulysses, and everything else, except this banquet, at which they wanted to keep feasting forever. But at length they began to give over, from mere incapacity to hold any more.

" That last bit of fat is too much for me," said one.

" And I have not room for another morsel," said his next neighbor, heaving a sigh. " What a pity! My appetite is as sharp as ever."

In short, they all left off eating, and leaned back on their thrones, with such a stupid and helpless aspect as made them ridiculous to behold. When their hostess saw this, she laughed aloud; so did her four damsels; so did the two-and-twenty serving men that bore the dishes, and their two-and-twenty fellows that poured out the wine. And the louder they all laughed, the more stupid and helpless did the two-and-twenty gor-mandizers look. Then the beautiful woman took her stand in the middle of the saloon, and stretching out a slender rod (it had been all the while in her hand, al-though they never noticed it till this moment), she turned it from one guest to another, until each had felt it pointed at himself. Beautiful as her face was, and though there was a smile on it, it looked just as wicked and mischievous as the ugliest serpent that ever was seen; and fat-witted as the voyagers had made them-selves, they began to suspect that they had fallen into the power of an evil-minded enchantress.

" Wretches," cried she, " you have abused a lady's hospitality; and in this princely saloon your behavior has been suited to a hogpen. You are already swine in everything but the human form, which you disgrace, and which I myself should be ashamed to keep a mo-

ment longer, were you to share it with me. But it
will require only the slightest exercise of magic to
make the exterior conform to the hoggish disposition.
Assume your proper shapes, gormandizers, and begone
to the sty ! "

Uttering these last words, she waved her wand ; and
stamping her foot imperiously, each of the guests was
struck aghast at beholding, instead of his comrades in
human shape, one-and-twenty hogs sitting on the same
number of golden thrones. Each man (as he still supposed himself to be) essayed to give a cry of surprise,
but found that he could merely grunt, and that, in a
word, he was just such another beast as his companions. It looked so intolerably absurd to see hogs on
cushioned thrones, that they made haste to wallow
down upon all fours, like other swine. They tried to
groan and beg for mercy, but forthwith emitted the
most awful grunting and squealing that ever came out
of swinish throats. They would have wrung their
hands in despair, but, attempting to do so, grew all
the more desperate for seeing themselves squatted on
their hams, and pawing the air with their fore trotters.
Dear me ! what pendulous ears they had ! what little
red eyes, half buried in fat ! and what long snouts,
instead of Grecian noses !

But brutes as they certainly were, they yet had
enough of human nature in them to be shocked at their
own hideousness ; and, still intending to groan, they
uttered a viler grunt and squeal than before. · So
harsh and ear-piercing it was, that you would have
fancied a butcher was sticking his knife into each of
their throats, or, at the very least, that somebody was
pulling every hog by his funny little twist of a tail.

"Begone to your sty ! " cried the enchantress, giving them some smart strokes with her wand ; and then she turned to the serving-men, " Drive out these swine, and throw down some acorns for them to eat."

The door of the saloon being flung open, the drove of hogs ran in all directions save the right one, in accordance with their hoggish perversity, but were finally driven into the back yard of the palace. It was a sight to bring tears into one's eyes (and I hope none of you will be cruel enough to laugh at it), to see the poor creatures go snuffing along, picking up here a cabbage leaf and there a turnip-top, and rooting their noses in the earth for whatever they could find. In their sty, moreover, they behaved more piggishly than the pigs that had been born so ; for they bit and snorted at one another, put their feet in the trough, and gobbled up their victuals in a ridiculous hurry ; and, when there was nothing more to be had, they made a great pile of themselves among some unclean straw, and fell fast asleep. If they had any human reason left, it was just enough to keep them wondering when they should be slaughtered, and what quality of bacon they should make.

Meantime, as I told you before, Eurylochus had waited, and waited, and waited, in the entrance-hall of the palace, without being able to comprehend what had befallen his friends. At last, when the swinish uproar resounded through the palace, and when he saw the image of a hog in the marble basin, he thought it best to hasten back to the vessel, and inform the wise Ulysses of these marvellous occurrences. So he ran as fast as he could down the steps, and never stopped to draw breath till he reached the shore.

" Why do you come alone ? " asked King Ulysses, as soon as he saw him. " Where are your two-and-twenty comrades ? "

At these questions, Eurylochus burst into tears.

"Alas!" cried he, "I greatly fear that we shall never see one of their faces again."

Then he told Ulysses all that had happened, as far as he knew it, and added that he suspected the beautiful woman to be a vile enchantress, and the marble palace, magnificent as it looked, to be only a dismal cavern in reality. As for his companions, he could not imagine what had become of them, unless they had been given to the swine to be devoured alive. At this intelligence all the voyagers were greatly affrighted. But Ulysses lost no time in girding on his sword, and hanging his bow and quiver over his shoulders, and taking a spear in his right hand. When his followers saw their wise leader making these preparations, they inquired whither he was going, and earnestly besought him not to leave them.

"You are our king," cried they; "and what is more, you are the wisest man in the whole world, and nothing but your wisdom and courage can get us out of this danger. If you desert us, and go to the enchanted palace, you will suffer the same fate as our poor companions, and not a soul of us will ever see our dear Ithaca again."

"As I am your king," answered Ulysses, "and wiser than any of you, it is therefore the more my duty to see what has befallen our comrades, and whether anything can yet be done to rescue them. Wait for me here until to-morrow. If I do not then return, you must hoist sail, and endeavor to find your way to our native land. For my part, I am answerable for the fate of these poor mariners, who have stood by my side in battle, and been so often drenched to the skin, along with me, by the same tempestuous surges. I will either bring them back with me or perish."

Had his followers dared, they would have detained him by force. But King Ulysses frowned sternly on them, and shook his spear, and bade them stop him at their peril. Seeing him so determined, they let him go, and sat down on the sand, as disconsolate a set of people as could be, waiting and praying for his return.

It happened to Ulysses, just as before, that, when he had gone a few steps from the edge of the cliff, the purple bird came fluttering towards him, crying, " Peep, peep, pe — weep ! " and using all the art it could to persuade him to go no farther.

" What mean you, little bird ? " cried Ulysses. " You are arrayed like a king in purple and gold, and wear a golden crown upon your head. Is it because I too am a king, that you desire so earnestly to speak with me ? If you can talk in human language, say what you would have me do."

" Peep ! " answered the purple bird, very dolorously. " Peep, peep, pe — we — ep ! "

Certainly there lay some heavy anguish at the little bird's heart ; and it was a sorrowful predicament that he could not, at least, have the consolation of telling what it was. But Ulysses had no time to waste in trying to get at the mystery. He therefore quickened his pace, and had gone a good way along the pleasant wood-path, when there met him a young man of very brisk and intelligent aspect, and clad in a rather singular garb. He wore a short cloak, and a sort of cap that seemed to be furnished with a pair of wings ; and from the lightness of his step, you would have supposed that there might likewise be wings on his feet. To enable him to walk still better (for he was always on one journey or another), he carried a winged staff,

around which two serpents were wriggling and twisting. In short, I have said enough to make you guess
that it was Quicksilver; and Ulysses (who knew him
of old, and had learned a great deal of his wisdom
from him) recognized him in a moment.

" Whither are you going in such a hurry, wise Ulysses ? " asked Quicksilver. " Do you not know that
this island is enchanted ? The wicked enchantress
(whose name is Circe, the sister of King Æetes)
dwells in the marble palace which you see yonder
among the trees. By her magic arts, she changes
every human being into the brute, beast, or fowl whom
he happens most to resemble."

" That little bird, which met me at the edge of the
cliff," exclaimed Ulysses; " was he a human being
once ? "

" Yes," answered Quicksilver. " He was once a
king, named Picus, and a pretty good sort of a king
too, only rather too proud of his purple robe, and his
crown, and the golden chain about his neck; so he
was forced to take the shape of a gaudy-feathered
bird. The lions, and wolves, and tigers, who will
come running to meet you, in front of the palace, were
formerly fierce and cruel men, resembling in their dispositions the wild beasts whose forms they now right-
fully wear."

" And my poor companions," said Ulysses. " Have
they undergone a similar change, through the arts of
this wicked Circe ? "

" You well know what gormandizers they were,"
replied Quicksilver; and, rogue that he was, he could
not help laughing at the joke. " So you will not be
surprised to hear that they have all taken the shapes
of swine! If Circe had never done anything worse,
I really should not think her so very much to blame."

"But can I do nothing to help them?" inquired Ulysses.

"It will require all your wisdom," said Quicksilver, "and a little of my own into the bargain, to keep your royal and sagacious self from being transformed into a fox. But do as I bid you; and the matter may end better than it has begun."

While he was speaking, Quicksilver seemed to be in search of something; he went stooping along the ground, and soon laid his hand on a little plant with a snow-white flower, which he plucked and smelt of. Ulysses had been looking at that very spot only just before; and it appeared to him that the plant had burst into full flower the instant when Quicksilver touched it with his fingers.

"Take this flower, King Ulysses," said he. "Guard it as you do your eyesight; for I can assure you it is exceedingly rare and precious, and you might seek the whole earth over without ever finding another like it. Keep it in your hand, and smell of it frequently after you enter the palace, and while you are talking with the enchantress. Especially when she offers you food, or a draught of wine out of her goblet, be careful to fill your nostrils with the flower's fragrance. Follow these directions, and you may defy her magic arts to change you into a fox."

Quicksilver then gave him some further advice how to behave, and, bidding him be bold and prudent, again assured him that, powerful as Circe was, he would have a fair prospect of coming safely out of her enchanted palace. After listening attentively, Ulysses thanked his good friend, and resumed his way. But he had taken only a few steps, when, recollecting some other questions which he wished to ask, he turned round again, and beheld nobody on the spot where Quicksilver had stood; for that winged cap of his, and those winged shoes, with the help of the winged staff, had carried him quickly out of sight.

When Ulysses reached the lawn, in front of the palace, the lions and other savage animals came bounding to meet him, and would have fawned upon him and licked his feet. But the wise king struck at them with his long spear, and sternly bade them begone out of his path; for he knew that they had once been bloodthirsty men, and would now tear him limb from limb, instead of fawning upon him, could they do the mischief that was in their hearts. The wild beasts yelped and glared at him, and stood at a distance while he ascended the palace steps.

On entering the hall, Ulysses saw the magic fountain in the centre of it. The up-gushing water had now again taken the shape of a man in a long, white, fleecy robe, who appeared to be making gestures of welcome. The king likewise heard the noise of the shuttle in the loom, and the sweet melody of the beautiful woman's song, and then the pleasant voices of herself and the four maidens talking together, with peals of merry laughter intermixed. But Ulysses did not waste much time in listening to the laughter or the song. He leaned his spear against one of the pillars of the hall, and then, after loosening his sword in the scabbard, stepped boldly forward, and threw the folding-doors wide open. The moment she beheld his stately figure standing in the doorway, the beautiful woman rose from the loom, and ran to meet him with a glad smile throwing its sunshine over her face, and both her hands extended.

" Welcome, brave stranger! " cried she. " We were expecting you."

And the nymph with the sea-green hair made a courtesy down to the ground, and likewise bade him welcome; so did her sister with the bodice of oaken bark, and she that sprinkled dew-drops from her fingers' ends, and the fourth one with some oddity which I cannot remember. And Circe, as the beautiful enchantress was called (who had deluded so many persons that she did not doubt of being able to delude Ulysses, not imagining how wise he was), again addressed him.

"Your companions," said she, "have already been received into my palace, and have enjoyed the hospitable treatment to which the propriety of their behavior so well entitles them. If such be your pleasure, you shall first take some refreshment, and then join them in the elegant apartment which they now occupy. See, I and my maidens have been weaving their figures into this piece of tapestry."

She pointed to the web of beautifully woven cloth in the loom. Circe and the four nymphs must have been very diligently at work since the arrival of the mariners; for a great many yards of tapestry had now been wrought, in addition to what I before described. In this new part, Ulysses saw his two-and-twenty friends represented as sitting on cushioned and canopied thrones, greedily devouring dainties and quaffing deep draughts of wine. The work had not yet gone any further. Oh no, indeed. The enchantress was far too cunning to let Ulysses see the mischief which her magic arts had since brought upon the gormandizers.

"As for yourself, valiant sir," said Circe, "judging by the dignity of your aspect, I take you to be nothing less than a king. Deign to follow me, and you shall be treated as befits your rank."

So Ulysses followed her into the oval saloon, where his two-and-twenty comrades had devoured the banquet, which ended so disastrously for themselves. But, all this while, he had held the snow-white flower in his hand, and had constantly smelt of it while Circe was speaking; and as he crossed the threshold of the saloon, he took good care to inhale several long and deep snuffs of its fragrance. Instead of two-and-twenty thrones, which had before been ranged around the wall, there was now only a single throne, in the centre of the apartment. But this was surely the most magnificent seat that ever a king or an emperor reposed himself upon, all made of chased gold, studded with precious stones, with a cushion that looked like a soft heap of living roses, and overhung by a canopy of sunlight which Circe knew how to weave into drapery. The enchantress took Ulysses by the hand, and made him sit down upon this dazzling throne. Then, clapping her hands, she summoned the chief butler.

"Bring hither," said she, "the goblet that is set apart for kings to drink out of. And fill it with the same delicious wine which my royal brother, King Æetes, praised so highly, when he last visited me with my fair daughter Medea. That good and amiable child! Were she now here, it would delight her to see me offering this wine to my honored guest."

But Ulysses, while the butler was gone for the wine, held the snow-white flower to his nose.

"Is it a wholesome wine?" he asked.

At this the four maidens tittered; whereupon the enchantress looked round at them, with an aspect of severity.

"It is the wholesomest juice that ever was squeezed

out of the grape," said she ; " for, instead of disguis-
ing a man, as other liquor is apt to do, it brings him
to his true self, and shows him as he ought to be."

The chief butler liked nothing better than to see
people turned into swine, or making any kind of a
beast of themselves ; so he made haste to bring the
royal goblet, filled with a liquid as bright as gold, and
which kept sparkling upward, and throwing a sunny
spray over the brim. But, delightfully as the wine
looked, it was mingled with the most potent enchantments that Circe knew how to concoct. For every
drop of the pure grape-juice there were two drops of
the pure mischief ; and the danger of the thing was,
that the mischief made it taste all the better. The
mere smell of the bubbles, which effervesced at the
brim, was enough to turn a man's beard into pig's
bristles, or make a lion's claws grow out of his fingers,
or a fox's brush behind him.

" Drink, my noble guest," said Circe, smiling as
she presented him with the goblet. " You will find
in this draught a solace for all your troubles."

King Ulysses took the goblet with his right hand,
while with his left he held the snow-white flower to his
nostrils, and drew in so long a breath that his lungs
were quite filled with its pure and simple fragrance.
Then, drinking off all the wine, he looked the enchantress calmly in the face.

" Wretch," cried Circe, giving him a smart stroke
with her wand, " how dare you keep your human shape
a moment longer ? Take the form of the brute whom
you most resemble. If a hog, go join your fellow-
swine in the sty ; if a lion, a wolf, a tiger, go howl
with the wild beasts on the lawn ; if a fox, go exercise
your craft in stealing poultry. Thou hast quaffed off
my wine, and canst be man no longer."

But, such was the virtue of the snow-white flower, instead of wallowing down from his throne in swinish shape, or taking any other brutal form, Ulysses looked even more manly and king-like than before. He gave the magic goblet a toss, and sent it clashing over the marble floor, to the farthest end of the saloon. Then, drawing his sword, he seized the enchantress by her beautiful ringlets, and made a gesture as if he meant to strike off her head at one blow.

"Wicked Circe," cried he, in a terrible voice, "this sword shall put an end to thy enchantments. Thou shalt die, vile wretch, and do no more mischief in the world, by tempting human beings into the vices which make beasts of them."

The tone and countenance of Ulysses were so awful, and his sword gleamed so brightly, and seemed to have so intolerably keen an edge, that Circe was almost killed by the mere fright, without waiting for a blow. The chief butler scrambled out of the saloon, picking up the golden goblet as he went; and the enchantress and the four maidens fell on their knees, wringing their hands, and screaming for mercy.

"Spare me!" cried Circe, — "spare me, royal and wise Ulysses. For now I know that thou art he of whom Quicksilver forewarned me, the most prudent of mortals, against whom no enchantments can prevail. Thou only couldst have conquered Circe. Spare me, wisest of men. I will show thee true hospitality, and even give myself to be thy slave, and this magnificent palace to be henceforth thy home."

The four nymphs, meanwhile, were making a most piteous ado; and especially the ocean-nymph, with the sea-green hair, wept a great deal of salt water, and the fountain-nymph, besides scattering dew-drops from her finger's ends, nearly melted away into tears. But Ulysses would not be pacified until Circe had taken a solemn oath to change back his companions, and as many others as he should direct, from their present forms of beast or bird into their former shapes of men.

" On these conditions," said he, " I consent to spare your life. Otherwise you must die upon the spot."

With a drawn sword hanging over her, the enchantress would readily have consented to do as much good as she had hitherto done mischief, however little she might like such employment. She therefore led Ulysses out of the back entrance of the palace, and showed him the swine in their sty. There were about fifty of these unclean beasts in the whole herd ; and though the greater part were hogs by birth and education, there was wonderfully little difference to be seen betwixt them and their new brethren who had so recently worn the human shape. To speak critically, indeed, the latter rather carried the thing to excess, and seemed to make it a point to wallow in the miriest part of the sty, and otherwise to outdo the original swine in their own natural vocation. When men once turn to brutes, the trifle of man's wit that remains in them adds tenfold to their brutality.

The comrades of Ulysses, however, had not quite lost the remembrance of having formerly stood erect. When he approached the sty, two-and-twenty enormous swine separated themselves from the herd, and scampered towards him, with such a chorus of horrible squealing as made him clap both hands to his ears. And yet they did not seem to know what they wanted, nor whether they were merely hungry, or miserable from some other cause. It was curious, in the midst of their distress, to observe them thrusting their noses into the mire, in quest of something to eat. The nymph with the bodice of oaken bark (she was the hamadryad of an oak) threw a handful of acorns among them ; and the two-and-twenty hogs scrambled and fought for the prize, as if they had tasted not so much as a noggin of sour milk for a twelvemonth.

"These must certainly be my comrades," said Ulysses. "I recognize their dispositions. They are hardly worth the trouble of changing them into the human form again. Nevertheless, we will have it done, lest their bad example should corrupt the other hogs. Let them take their original shapes, therefore, Dame Circe, if your skill is equal to the task. It will require greater magic, I trow, than it did to make swine of them."

So Circe waved her wand again, and repeated a few magic words, at the sound of which the two-and-twenty hogs pricked up their pendulous ears. It was a wonder to behold how their snouts grew shorter and shorter, and their mouths (which they seemed to be sorry for, because they could not gobble so expeditiously) smaller and smaller, and how one and another began to stand upon his hind legs, and scratch his nose with his fore trotters. At first the spectators hardly knew whether to call them hogs or men, but by and by came to the conclusion that they rather resembled the latter. Finally, there stood the twenty-two comrades of Ulysses, looking pretty much the same as when they left the vessel.

You must not imagine, however, that the swinish quality had entirely gone out of them. When once it fastens itself into a person's character, it is very difficult getting rid of it. This was proved by the hamadryad, who, being exceedingly fond of mischief, threw another handful of acorns before the twenty-two newly restored people ; whereupon down they wallowed, in a moment, and gobbled them up in a very shameful way. Then, recollecting themselves, they scrambled to their feet, and looked more than commonly foolish.

"Thanks, noble Ulysses!" they cried. "From brute beasts you have restored us to the condition of men again."

"Do not put yourselves to the trouble of thanking me," said the wise king. "I fear I have done but little for you."

To say the truth, there was a suspicious kind of a grunt in their voices, and for a long time afterwards they spoke gruffly, and were apt to set up a squeal.

"It must depend on your own future behavior," added Ulysses, "whether you do not find your way back to the sty."

At this moment, the note of a bird sounded from the branch of a neighboring tree.

"Peep, peep, pe — wee — ep!"

It was the purple bird, who, all this while, had been sitting over their heads, watching what was going forward, and hoping that Ulysses would remember how he had done his utmost to keep him and his followers out of harm's way. Ulysses ordered Circe instantly to make a king of this good little fowl, and leave him exactly as she found him. Hardly were the words spoken, and before the bird had time to utter another "Pe — weep," King Picus leaped down from the bough of the tree, as majestic a sovereign as any in the world, dressed in a long purple robe and gorgeous yellow stockings, with a splendidly wrought collar about his neck, and a golden crown upon his head. He and King Ulysses exchanged with one another the

courtesies which belong to their elevated rank.   But
from that time forth, King Picus was no longer proud
of his crown and his trappings of royalty, nor of the
fact of his being a king; he felt himself merely the
upper servant of his people, and that it must be his
lifelong labor to make them better and happier.

As for the lions, tigers, and wolves (though Circe
would have restored them to their former shapes at his
slightest word), Ulysses thought it advisable that they
should remain as they now were, and thus give warning of their cruel dispositions, instead of going about
under the guise of men, and pretending to human
sympathies, while their hearts had the blood-thirstiness
of wild beasts.   So he let them howl as much as they
liked, but never troubled his head about them.   And,
when everything was settled according to his pleasure,
he sent to summon the remainder of his comrades,
whom he had left at the sea-shore.   These being arrived, with the prudent Eurylochus at their head, they
all made themselves comfortable in Circe's enchanted
palace, until quite rested and refreshed from the toils
and hardships of their voyage.

THE POMEGRANATE SEEDS.

MOTHER CERES was exceedingly fond of her daughter Proserpina, and seldom let her go alone into the fields. But, just at the time when my story begins, the good lady was very busy, because she had the care of the wheat, and the Indian corn, and the rye and barley, and, in short, of the crops of every kind, all over the earth; and as the season had thus far been uncommonly backward, it was necessary to make the harvest ripen more speedily than usual. So she put on her turban, made of poppies (a kind of flower which she was always noted for wearing), and got into her car drawn by a pair of winged dragons, and was just ready to set off.

"Dear mother," said Proserpina, "I shall be very lonely while you are away. May I not run down to the shore, and ask some of the sea-nymphs to come up out of the waves and play with me?"

"Yes, child," answered Mother Ceres. "The sea-nymphs are good creatures, and will never lead you into any harm. But you must take care not to stray away from them, nor go wandering about the fields by yourself. Young girls, without their mothers to take care of them, are very apt to get into mischief."

The child promised to be as prudent as if she were a grown-up woman, and, by the time the winged dragons had whirled the car out of sight, she was already on the shore, calling to the sea-nymphs to come and play with her. They knew Proserpina's voice, and were not long in showing their glistening faces and sea-green hair above the water, at the bottom of which was their home. They brought along with them a great many beautiful shells; and, sitting down on the moist sand, where the surf wave broke over them, they busied themselves in making a necklace, which they hung round Proserpina's neck. By way of showing her gratitude, the child besought them to go with her a little way into the fields, so that they might gather abundance of flowers, with which she would make each of her kind playmates a wreath.

"Oh no, dear Proserpina," cried the sea-nymphs; "we dare not go with you upon the dry land. We are apt to grow faint, unless at every breath we can snuff up the salt breeze of the ocean. And don't you see how careful we are to let the surf wave break over us every moment or two, so as to keep ourselves comfortably moist? If it were not for that, we should soon look like bunches of uprooted sea-weed dried in the sun."

"It is a great pity," said Proserpina. "But do you wait for me here, and I will run and gather my apron full of flowers, and be back again before the surf wave has broken ten times over you. I long to make you some wreaths that shall be as lovely as this necklace of many-colored shells."

"We will wait, then," answered the sea-nymphs. "But while you are gone, we may as well lie down on a bank of soft sponge, under the water. The air to-day is a little too dry for our comfort. But we will pop up our heads every few minutes to see if you are coming."

The young Proserpina ran quickly to a spot where only the day before, she had seen a great many flow-

ers. These, however, were now a little past their
bloom; and wishing to give her friends the freshest
and loveliest blossoms, she strayed farther into the
fields, and found some that made her scream with delight. Never had she met with such exquisite flowers
before, — violets, so large and fragrant, — roses, with
so rich and delicate a blush, — such superb hyacinths
and such aromatic pinks, — and many others, some of
which seemed to be of new shapes and colors. Two
or three times, moreover, she could not help thinking
that a tuft of most splendid flowers had suddenly
sprouted out of the earth before her very eyes, as if
on purpose to tempt her a few steps farther. Proserpina's apron was soon filled and brimming over with
delightful blossoms. She was on the point of turning
back in order to rejoin the sea-nymphs, and sit with
them on the moist sands, all twining wreaths together.
But, a little farther on, what should she behold? It
was a large shrub, completely covered with the most
magnificent flowers in the world.

"The darlings!" cried Proserpina; and then she
thought to herself, "I was looking at that spot only
a moment ago. How strange it is that I did not see
the flowers!"

The nearer she approached the shrub, the more at-
tractive it looked, until she came quite close to it; and
then, although its beauty was richer than words can
tell, she hardly knew whether to like it or not. It
bore above a hundred flowers of the most brilliant
hues, and each different from the others, but all having a kind of resemblance among themselves, which
showed them to be sister blossoms. But there was a
deep, glossy lustre on the leaves of the shrub, and on
the petals of the flowers, that made Proserpina doubt

whether they might not be poisonous. To tell you the truth, foolish as it may seem, she was half inclined to turn round and run away.

"What a silly child I am!" thought she, taking courage. "It is really the most beautiful shrub that ever sprang out of the earth. I will pull it up by the roots, and carry it home, and plant it in my mother's garden."

Holding up her apron full of flowers with her left hand, Proserpina seized the large shrub with the other, and pulled and pulled, but was hardly able to loosen the soil about its roots. What a deep-rooted plant it was! Again the girl pulled with all her might, and observed that the earth began to stir and crack to some distance around the stem. She gave another pull, but relaxed her hold, fancying that there was a rumbling sound right beneath her feet. Did the roots extend down into some enchanted cavern? Then, laughing at herself for so childish a notion, she made another effort; up came the shrub, and Proserpina staggered back, holding the stem triumphantly in her hand, and gazing at the deep hole which its roots had left in the soil.

Much to her astonishment, this hole kept spreading wider and wider, and growing deeper and deeper, until it really seemed to have no bottom; and all the while, there came a rumbling noise out of its depths, louder and louder, and nearer and nearer, and sounding like the tramp of horses' hoofs and the rattling of wheels. Too much frightened to run away, she stood straining her eyes into this wonderful cavity, and soon saw a team of four sable horses, snorting smoke out of their nostrils, and tearing their way out of the earth with a splendid golden chariot whirling at their heels. They

leaped out of the bottomless hole, chariot and all; and
there they were, tossing their black manes, flourishing
their black tails, and curvetting with every one of
their hoofs off the ground at once, close by the spot
where Proserpina stood. In the chariot sat the figure
of a man, richly dressed, with a crown on his head, all
flaming with diamonds. He was of a noble aspect,
and rather handsome, but looked sullen and discontented; and he kept rubbing his eyes and shading
them with his hand, as if he did not live enough in
the sunshine to be very fond of its light.

As soon as this personage saw the affrighted Proserpina, he beckoned her to come a little nearer.

"Do not be afraid," said he, with as cheerful a
smile as he knew how to put on. "Come! Will not
you like to ride a little way with me, in my beautiful
chariot?"

But Proserpina was so alarmed, that she wished for
nothing but to get out of his reach. And no wonder.
The stranger did not look remarkably good-natured, in
spite of his smile; and as for his voice, its tones were
deep and stern, and sounded as much like the rumbling of an earthquake under ground as anything else.
As is always the case with children in trouble, Proserpina's first thought was to call for her mother.

"Mother, Mother Ceres!" cried she, all in a tremble. "Come quickly and save me."

But her voice was too faint for her mother to hear.
Indeed, it is most probable that Ceres was then a thousand miles off, making the corn grow in some far-dis-
tant country. Nor could it have availed her poor
daughter, even had she been within hearing; for no
sooner did Proserpina begin to cry out, than the
stranger leaped to the ground, caught the child in his

arms, and again mounting the chariot, shook the reins, and shouted to the four black horses to set off. They immediately broke into so swift a gallop that it seemed rather like flying through the air than running along the earth. In a moment, Proserpina lost sight of the pleasant vale of Enna, in which she had always dwelt. Another instant, and even the summit of Mount Ætna had become so blue in the distance, that she could scarcely distinguish it from the smoke that gushed out of its crater. But still the poor child screamed, and scattered her apron full of flowers along the way, and left a long cry trailing behind the chariot; and many mothers, to whose ears it came, ran quickly to see if any mischief had befallen their children. But Mother Ceres was a great way off, and could not hear the cry.

As they rode on, the stranger did his best to soothe her.

" Why should you be so frightened, my pretty child ? " said he, trying to soften his rough voice. " I promise not to do you any harm. What! You have been gathering flowers? Wait till we come to my palace, and I will give you a garden full of prettier flowers than those, all made of pearls, and diamonds, and rubies. Can you guess who I am ? They call my name Pluto, and I am the king of diamonds and all other precious stones. Every atom of the gold and silver that lies under the earth belongs to me, to say nothing of the copper and iron, and of the coal-mines, which supply me with abundance of fuel. Do you see this splendid crown upon my head ? You may have it for a plaything. Oh, we shall be very good friends, and you will find me more agreeable than you expect, when once we get out of this troublesome sunshine."

" Let me go home !" cried Proserpina, — " let me go home !"

" My home is better than your mother's," answered King Pluto. " It is a palace, all made of gold, with crystal windows ; and because there is little or no sunshine thereabouts, the apartments are illuminated with diamond lamps. You never saw anything half so magnificent as my throne. If you like, you may sit down on it, and be my little queen, and I will sit on the footstool."

" I don't care for golden palaces and thrones," sobbed Proserpina. " Oh, my mother, my mother ! Carry me back to my mother ! "

But King Pluto, as he called himself, only shouted to his steeds to go faster.

" Pray do not be foolish, Proserpina," said he, in rather a sullen tone. " I offer you my palace and my crown, and all the riches that are under the earth ; and you treat me as if I were doing you an injury. The one thing which my palace needs is a merry little maid, to run up stairs and down, and cheer up the rooms with her smile. And this is what you must do for King Pluto."

" Never ! " answered Proserpina, looking as miserable as she could. " I shall never smile again till you set me down at my mother's door."

But she might just as well have talked to the wind that whistled past them ; for Pluto urged on his horses, and went faster than ever. Proserpina continued to cry out, and screamed so long and so loudly, that her poor little voice was almost screamed away ; and when it was nothing but a whisper, she happened to cast her eyes over a great, broad field of waving grain — and whom do you think she saw ? Who, but Mother Ceres, making the corn grow, and too busy to notice the golden chariot as it went rattling along. The child mustered all her strength, and gave one more scream, but was out of sight before Ceres had time to turn her head.

King Pluto had taken a road which now began to grow excessively gloomy. It was bordered on each side with rocks and precipices, between which the rumbling of the chariot-wheels was reverberated with a noise like rolling thunder. The trees and bushes that grew in the crevices of the rocks had very dismal foliage; and by and by, although it was hardly noon, the air became obscured with a gray twilight. The black horses had rushed along so swiftly, that they were already beyond the limits of the sunshine. But the duskier it grew, the more did Pluto's visage assume an air of satisfaction. After all, he was not an ill-looking person, especially when he left off twisting his features into a smile that did not belong to them. Proserpina peeped at his face through the gathering dusk, and hoped that he might not be so very wicked as she at first thought him.

" Ah, this twilight is truly refreshing," said King Pluto, " after being so tormented with that ugly and impertinent glare of the sun. How much more agreeable is lamplight or torchlight, more particularly when reflected from diamonds! It will be a magnificent sight when we get to my palace."

" Is it much farther? " asked Proserpina. " And will you carry me back when I have seen it? "

" We will talk of that by and by," answered Pluto. " We are just entering my dominions. Do you see that tall gateway before us? When we pass those gates, we are at home. And there lies my faithful

mastiff at the threshold. Cerberus! Cerberus! Come
hither, my good dog!"

So saying, Pluto pulled at the reins, and stopped
the chariot right between the tall, massive pillars of
the gateway. The mastiff of which he had spoken got
up from the threshold, and stood on his hinder legs,
so as to put his fore paws on the chariot-wheel. But,
my stars, what a strange dog it was! Why, he was a
big, rough, ugly-looking monster, with three separate
heads, and each of them fiercer than the two others;
but, fierce as they were, King Pluto patted them all.
He seemed as fond of his three-headed dog as if it had
been a sweet little spaniel, with silken ears and curly
hair. Cerberus, on the other hand, was evidently rejoiced to see his master, and expressed his attachment,
as other dogs do, by wagging his tail at a great rate.
Proserpina's eyes being drawn to it by its brisk motion, she saw that this tail was neither more nor less
than a live dragon, with fiery eyes, and fangs that had
a very poisonous aspect. And while the three-headed
Cerberus was fawning so lovingly on King Pluto, there
was the dragon tail wagging against its will, and looking as cross and ill-natured as you can imagine, on its
own separate account.

"Will the dog bite me?" asked Proserpina, shrink-
ing closer to Pluto. "What an ugly creature he is!"

"Oh, never fear," answered her companion. "He
never harms people, unless they try to enter my dominions without being sent for, or to get away when I
wish to keep them here. Down Cerberus! Now, my
pretty Proserpina, we will drive on."

On went the chariot, and King Pluto seemed greatly
pleased to find himself once more in his own kingdom.
He drew Proserpina's attention to the rich veins of

gold that were to be seen among the rocks, and pointed to several places where one stroke of a pick-axe would loosen a bushel of diamonds. All along the road, indeed, there were sparkling gems, which would have been of inestimable value above ground, but which were here reckoned of the meaner sort, and hardly worth a beggar's stooping for.

Not far from the gateway, they came to a bridge, which seemed to be built of iron. Pluto stopped the chariot, and bade Proserpina look at the stream which was gliding so lazily beneath it. Never in her life had she beheld so torpid, so black, so muddy-looking a stream: its waters reflected no images of anything that was on the banks, and it moved as sluggishly as if it had quite forgotten which way it ought to flow, and had rather stagnate than flow either one way or the other.

"This is the river Lethe," observed King Pluto. "Is it not a very pleasant stream?"

"I think it a very dismal one," said Proserpina.

"It suits my taste, however," answered Pluto, who was apt to be sullen when anybody disagreed with him. "At all events, its water has one very excellent quality; for a single draught of its makes people forget every care and sorrow that has hitherto tormented them. Only sip a little of it, my dear Proserpina, and you will instantly cease to grieve for your mother, and will have nothing in your memory that can prevent your being perfectly happy in my palace. I will send for some, in a golden goblet, the moment we arrive."

"Oh no, no, no!" cried Proserpina, weeping afresh. "I had a thousand times rather be miserable with remembering my mother, than be happy in forgetting

her. That dear, dear mother! I never, never will
forget her."

"We shall see," said King Pluto. "You do not
know what fine times we will have in my palace.
Here we are just at the portal. These pillars are
solid gold, I assure you."

He alighted from the chariot, and taking Proserpina
in his arms, carried her up a lofty flight of steps into
the great hall of the palace. It was splendidly illuminated by means of large precious stones, of various
hues, which seemed to burn like so many lamps, and
glowed with a hundred-fold radiance all through the
vast apartment. And yet there was a kind of gloom
in the midst of this enchanted light; nor was there a
single object in the hall that was really agreeable to
behold, except the little Proserpina herself, a lovely
child, with one earthly flower which she had not let
fall from her hand. It is my opinion that even King
Pluto had never been happy in his palace, and that
this was the true reason why he had stolen away Proserpina, in order that he might have something to love,
instead of cheating his heart any longer with this tiresome magnificence. And, though he pretended to dislike the sunshine of the upper world, yet the effect of
the child's presence, bedimmed as she was by her
tears, was as if a faint and watery sunbeam had somehow or other found its way into the enchanted hall.

Pluto now summoned his domestics, and bade them
lose no time in preparing a most sumptuous banquet,
and above all things, not to fail of setting a golden
beaker of the water of Lethe by Proserpina's plate.

"I will neither drink that nor anything else," said
Proserpina. "Nor will I taste a morsel of food, even
if you keep me forever in your palace."

" I should be sorry for that," replied King Pluto, patting her cheek; for he really wished to be kind, if he had only known how. " You are a spoiled child, I perceive, my little Proserpina; but when you see the nice things which my cook will make for you, your appetite will quickly come again."

Then, sending for the head cook, he gave strict orders that all sorts of delicacies, such as young people are usually fond of, should be set before Proserpina. He had a secret motive in this; for, you are to understand, it is a fixed law, that, when persons are carried off to the land of magic, if they once taste any food there, they can never get back to their friends. Now, if King Pluto had been cunning enough to offer Proserpina some fruit, or bread and milk (which was the simple fare to which the child had always been accustomed), it is very probable that she would soon have been tempted to eat it. But he left the matter entirely to his cook, who, like all other cooks, considered nothing fit to eat unless it were rich pastry, or highly seasoned meat, or spiced sweet cakes, — things which Proserpina's mother had never given her, and the smell of which quite took away her appetite, instead of sharpening it.

But my story must now clamber out of King Pluto's dominions, and see what Mother Ceres has been about, since she was bereft of her daughter. We had a glimpse of her, as you remember, half hidden among the waving grain, while the four black steeds were swiftly whirling along the chariot in which her beloved Proserpina was so unwillingly borne away. You recollect, too, the loud scream which Proserpina gave just when the chariot was out of sight.

Of all the child's outcries, this last shriek was the

only one that reached the ears of Mother Ceres. She
had mistaken the rumbling of the chariot-wheels for a
peal of thunder, and imagined that a shower was coming up, and that it would assist her in making the
corn grow. But, at the sound of Proserpina's shriek,
she started, and looked about in every direction, not
knowing whence it came, but feeling almost certain
that it was her daughter's voice. It seemed so unaccountable, however, that the girl should have strayed
over so many lands and seas (which she herself could
not have traversed without the aid of her winged dragons), that the good Ceres tried to believe that it must
be the child of some other parent, and not her own
darling Proserpina, who had uttered this lamentable
cry. Nevertheless, it troubled her with a vast many
tender fears, such as are ready to bestir themselves in
every mother's heart, when she finds it necessary to
go away from her dear children without leaving them
under the care of some maiden aunt, or other such
faithful guardian. So she quickly left the field in
which she had been so busy; and, as her work was not
half done, the grain looked, next day, as if it needed
both sun and rain, and as if it were blighted in the
ear, and had something the matter with its roots.

The pair of dragons must have had very nimble
wings; for, in less than an hour, Mother Ceres had
alighted at the door of her home, and found it empty.
Knowing, however, that the child was fond of sporting
on the sea-shore, she hastened thither as fast as she
could, and there beheld the wet faces of the poor sea-
nymphs peeping over a wave. All this while, the good
creatures had been waiting on the bank of sponge, and,
once every half-minute or so, had popped up their four
heads above water, to see if their playmate were yet

coming back. When they saw Mother Ceres, they sat down on the crest of the surf wave, and let it toss them ashore at her feet.

"Where is Proserpina?" cried Ceres. "Where is my child? Tell me, you naughty sea-nymphs, have you enticed her under the sea?"

"Oh no, good Mother Ceres," said the innocent sea-nymphs, tossing back their green ringlets, and looking her in the face. "We never should dream of such a thing. Proserpina has been at play with us, it is true; but she left us a long while ago, meaning only to run a little way upon the dry land, and gather some flowers for a wreath. This was early in the day, and we have seen nothing of her since."

Ceres scarcely waited to hear what the nymphs had to say, before she hurried off to make inquiries all through the neighborhood. But nobody told her anything that could enable the poor mother to guess what had become of Proserpina. A fisherman, it is true, had noticed her little footprints in the sand, as he went homeward along the beach with a basket of fish; a rustic had seen the child stooping to gather flowers; several persons had heard either the rattling of chariot-wheels, or the rumbling of distant thunder; and one old woman, while plucking vervain and catnip, had heard a scream, but supposed it to be some childish nonsense, and therefore did not take the trouble to look up. The stupid people! It took them such a tedious while to tell the nothing that they knew, that it was dark night before Mother Ceres found out that she must seek her daughter elsewhere. So she lighted a torch, and set forth, resolving never to come back until Proserpina was discovered.

In her haste and trouble of mind, she quite forgot

her car and the winged dragons; or, it may be, she thought that she could follow up the search more thoroughly on foot. At all events, this was the way in which she began her sorrowful journey, holding her torch before her, and looking carefully at every object along the path. And as it happened, she had not gone far before she found one of the magnificent flowers which grew on the shrub that Proserpina had pulled up.

" Ha! " thought Mother Ceres, examining it by torchlight. " Here is mischief in this flower ! The earth did not produce it by any help of mine, nor of its own accord. It is the work of enchantment, and is therefore poisonous ; and perhaps it has poisoned my poor child."

But she put the poisonous flower in her bosom, not knowing whether she might ever find any other memorial of Proserpina.

All night long, at the door of every cottage and farm-house, Ceres knocked, and called up the weary laborers to inquire if they had seen her child ; and they stood, gaping and half asleep, at the threshold, and answered her pityingly, and besought her to come in and rest. At the portal of every palace, too, she made so loud a summons that the menials hurried to throw open the gate, thinking that it must be some great king or queen, who would demand a banquet for supper and a stately chamber to repose in. And when they saw only a sad and anxious woman, with a torch in her hand and a wreath of withered poppies on her head, they spoke rudely, and sometimes threatened to set the dogs upon her. But nobody had seen Proserpina, nor could give Mother Ceres the least hint which way to seek her. Thus passed the night ; and

still she continued her search without sitting down to
rest, or stopping to take food, or even remembering to
put out the torch; although first the rosy dawn, and
then the glad light of the morning sun, made its red
flame look thin and pale. But I wonder what sort of
stuff this torch was made of; for it burned dimly
through the day, and, at night, was as bright as ever,
and never was extinguished by the rain or wind, in
all the weary days and nights while Ceres was seeking
for Proserpina.

It was not merely of human beings that she asked
tidings of her daughter. In the woods and by the
streams, she met creatures of another nature, who
used, in those old times, to haunt the pleasant and
solitary places, and were very sociable with persons
who understood their language and customs, as Mother
Ceres did. Sometimes, for instance, she tapped with
her finger against the knotted trunk of a majestic oak;
and immediately its rude bark would cleave asunder,
and forth would step a beautiful maiden, who was the
hamadryad of the oak, dwelling inside of it, and sharing its long life, and rejoicing when its green leaves
sported with the breeze. But not one of these leafy
damsels had seen Proserpina. Then, going a little
farther, Ceres would, perhaps, come to a fountain,
gushing out of a pebbly hollow in the earth, and
would dabble with her hand in the water. Behold, up
through its sandy and pebbly bed, along with the fountain's gush, a young woman with dripping hair would
arise, and stand gazing at Mother Ceres, half out of
the water, and undulating up and down with its ever-
restless motion. But when the mother asked whether
her poor lost child had stopped to drink out of the
fountain, the naiad, with weeping eyes (for these

water-nymphs had tears to spare for everybody's grief), would answer, "No!" in a murmuring voice, which was just like the murmur of the stream.

Often, likewise, she encountered fauns, who looked like sunburnt country people, except that they had hairy ears, and little horns upon their foreheads, and the hinder legs of goats, on which they gambolled merrily about the woods and fields. They were a frolicsome kind of creature, but grew as sad as their cheerful dispositions would allow when Ceres inquired for her daughter, and they had no good news to tell. But sometimes she came suddenly upon a rude gang of satyrs, who had faces like monkeys and horses' tails behind them, and who were generally dancing in a very boisterous manner, with shouts of noisy laughter. When she stopped to question them, they would only laugh the louder, and make new merriment out of the lone woman's distress. How unkind of those ugly satyrs! And once, while crossing a solitary sheep-pasture, she saw a personage named Pan, seated at the foot of a tall rock, and making music on a shepherd's flute. He, too, had horns, and hairy ears, and goat's feet; but, being acquainted with Mother Ceres, he answered her question as civilly as he knew how, and invited her to taste some milk and honey out of a wooden bowl. But neither could Pan tell her what had become of Proserpina, any better than the rest of these wild people.

And thus Mother Ceres went wandering about for nine long days and nights, finding no trace of Proserpina, unless it were now and then a withered flower; and these she picked up and put in her bosom, because she fancied that they might have fallen from her poor child's hand. All day she travelled onward through

the hot sun ; and at night, again, the flame of the
torch would redden and gleam along the pathway, and
she continued her search by its light, without ever sitting down to rest.

On the tenth day, she chanced to espy the mouth of
a cavern, within which (though it was bright noon
everywhere else) there would have been only a dusky
twilight ; but it so happened that a torch was burning there.   It flickered, and struggled with the duskiness, but could not half light up the gloomy cavern
with all its melancholy glimmer.   Ceres was resolved
to leave no spot without a search ; so she peeped into
the entrance of the cave, and lighted it up a little
more, by holding her own torch before her.   In so
doing, she caught a glimpse of what seemed to be a
woman, sitting on the brown leaves of the last autumn,
a great heap of which had been swept into the cave by
the wind.   This woman (if woman it were) was by
no means so beautiful as many of her sex ; for her
head, they tell me, was shaped very much like a dog's,
and, by way of ornament, she wore a wreath of snakes
around it.   But Mother Ceres, the moment she saw
her, knew that this was an odd kind of a person, who
put all her enjoyment in being miserable, and never
would have a word to say to other people, unless they
were as melancholy and wretched as she herself delighted to be.

" I am wretched enough now," thought poor Ceres,
" to talk with this melancholy Hecate, were she ten
times sadder than ever she was yet."

So she stepped into the cave, and sat down on the
withered leaves by the dog-headed woman's side.   In
all the world, since her daughter's loss, she had found
no other companion.

"O Hecate," said she, "if ever you lose a daughter, you will know what sorrow is. Tell me, for pity's sake, have you seen my poor child Proserpina pass by the mouth of your cavern?"

"No," answered Hecate, in a cracked voice, and sighing betwixt every word or two, — "no, Mother Ceres, I have seen nothing of your daughter. But my ears, you must know, are made in such a way that all cries of distress and affright, all over the world are pretty sure to find their way to them; and nine days ago, as I sat in my cave, making myself very miserable, I heard the voice of a young girl, shrieking as if in great distress. Something terrible has happened to the child, you may rest assured. As well as I could judge, a dragon, or some other cruel monster, was carrying her away."

"You kill me by saying so," cried Ceres, almost ready to faint. "Where was the sound, and which way did it seem to go?"

"It passed very swiftly along," said Hecate, "and, at the same time, there was a heavy rumbling of wheels towards the eastward. I can tell you nothing more, except that, in my honest opinion, you will never see your daughter again. The best advice I can give you is, to take up your abode in this cavern, where we will be the two most wretched women in the world."

"Not yet, dark Hecate," replied Ceres. "But do you first come with your torch, and help me to seek for my lost child. And when there shall be no more hope of finding her (if that black day is ordained to come), then, if you will give me room to fling myself down, either on these withered leaves or on the naked rock, I will show you what it is to be miserable. But, until I know that she has perished from the face of the earth, I will not allow myself space even to grieve."

The dismal Hecate did not much like the idea of going abroad into the sunny world. But then she reflected that the sorrow of the disconsolate Ceres would be like a gloomy twilight round about them both, let the sun shine ever so brightly, and that therefore she might enjoy her bad spirits quite as well as if she were to stay in the cave. So she finally consented to go, and they set out together, both carrying torches, although it was broad daylight and clear sunshine. The torchlight seemed to make a gloom; so that the people whom they met along the road could not very distinctly see their figures; and, indeed, if they once caught a glimpse of Hecate, with the wreath of snakes round her forehead, they generally thought it prudent to run away, without waiting for a second glance.

As the pair travelled along in this woe-begone manner, a thought struck Ceres.

"There is one person," she exclaimed, "who must have seen my poor child, and can doubtless tell what has become of her. Why did not I think of him before? It is Phœbus."

"What," said Hecate, "the young man that always sits in the sunshine? Oh, pray do not think of going near him. He is a gay, light, frivolous young fellow, and will only smile in your face. And besides, there is such a glare of the sun about him, that he will quite blind my poor eyes, which I have almost wept away already."

"You have promised to be my companion," answered Ceres. "Come, let us make haste, or the sunshine will be gone, and Phœbus along with it."

Accordingly, they went along in quest of Phœbus,

both of them sighing grievously, and Hecate, to say the truth, making a great deal worse lamentation than Ceres; for all the pleasure she had, you know, lay in being miserable, and therefore she made the most of it. By and by, after a pretty long journey, they arrived at the sunniest spot in the whole world. There they beheld a beautiful young man, with long, curling ringlets, which seemed to be made of golden sunbeams; his garments were like light summer clouds; and the expression of his face was so exceedingly vivid, that Hecate held her hands before her eyes, muttering that he ought to wear a black veil. Phœbus (for this was the very person whom they were seeking) had a lyre in his hands, and was making its chords tremble with sweet music; at the same time singing a most exquisite song, which he had recently composed. For, besides a great many other accomplishments, this young man was renowned for his admirable poetry.

As Ceres and her dismal companion approached him, Phœbus smiled on them so cheerfully that Hecate's wreath of snakes gave a spiteful hiss, and Hecate heartily wished herself back in her cave. But as for Ceres, she was too earnest in her grief either to know or care whether Phœbus smiled or frowned.

"Phœbus!" exclaimed she, "I am in great trouble, and have come to you for assistance. Can you tell me what has become of my dear child Proserpina?"

"Proserpina! Proserpina, did you call her name?" answered Phœbus, endeavoring to recollect; for there was such a continual flow of pleasant ideas in his mind that he was apt to forget what had happened no longer ago than yesterday. "Ah, yes, I remember her now. A very lovely child, indeed. I am happy to tell you, my dear madam, that I did see the little Proserpina not many days ago. You may make yourself perfectly easy about her. She is safe, and in excellent hands."

" Oh, where is my dear child?" cried Ceres, clasping her hands and flinging herself at his feet.

" Why," said Phœbus, — and as he spoke, he kept touching his lyre so as to make a thread of music run in and out among his words, — " as the little damsel was gathering flowers (and she has really a very exquisite taste for flowers) she was suddenly snatched up by King Pluto, and carried off to his dominions. I have never been in that part of the universe; but the royal palace, I am told, is built in a very noble style of architecture, and of the most splendid and costly materials. Gold, diamonds, pearls, and all manner of precious stones will be your daughter's ordinary playthings. I recommend to you, my dear lady, to give yourself no uneasiness. Proserpina's sense of beauty will be duly gratified, and, even in spite of the lack of sunshine, she will lead a very enviable life."

" Hush! Say not such a word!" answered Ceres, indignantly. "What is there to gratify her heart? What are all the splendors you speak of, without affection? I must have her back again. Will you go with me, Phœbus, to demand my daughter of this wicked Pluto?"

" Pray excuse me," replied Phœbus, with an elegant obeisance. "I certainly wish you success, and regret that my own affairs are so immediately pressing that I cannot have the pleasure of attending you. Besides, I am not upon the best of terms with King Pluto. To tell you the truth, his three-headed mastiff would never let me pass the gateway; for I should be compelled to take a sheaf of sunbeams along with me, and those, you know, are forbidden things in Pluto's kingdom."

" Ah, Phœbus," said Ceres, with bitter meaning in her words, " you have a harp instead of a heart. Farewell."

" Will not you stay a moment," asked Phœbus, " and hear me turn the pretty and touching story of Proserpina into extemporary verses ? "

But Ceres shook her head, and hastened away, along with Hecate. Phœbus (who, as I have told you, was an exquisite poet) forthwith began to make an ode about the poor mother's grief; and, if we were to judge of his sensibility by this beautiful production, he must have been endowed with a very tender heart. But when a poet gets into the habit of using his heart-strings to make chords for his lyre, he may thrum upon them as much as he will, without any great pain to himself. Accordingly, though Phœbus sang a very sad song, he was as merry all the while as were the sunbeams amid which he dwelt.

Poor Mother Ceres had now found out what had become of her daughter, but was not a whit happier than before. Her case, on the contrary, looked more desperate than ever. As long as Proserpina was above ground there might have been hopes of regaining her. But now, that the poor child was shut up within the iron gates of the king of the mines, at the threshold of which lay the three-headed Cerberus, there seemed no possibility of her ever making her escape. The dismal Hecate, who loved to take the darkest view of things, told Ceres that she had better come with her to the cavern, and spend the rest of her life in being miserable. Ceres answered that Hecate was welcome to go back thither herself, but that, for her part, she would wander about the earth in quest of the entrance to King Pluto's dominions. And Hecate took her at

her word, and hurried back to her beloved cave,
frightening a great many little children with a glimpse
of her dog's face, as she went.

Poor Mother Ceres! It is melancholy to think of
her, pursuing her toilsome way all alone, and holding
up that never-dying torch, the flame of which seemed
an emblem of the grief and hope that burned together
in her heart. So much did she suffer, that, though
her aspect had been quite youthful when her troubles
began, she grew to look like an elderly person in a
very brief time. She cared not how she was dressed,
nor had she ever thought of flinging away the wreath
of withered poppies, which she put on the very morning of Proserpina's disappearance. She roamed about
in so wild a way, and with her hair so dishevelled, that
people took her for some distracted creature, and
never dreamed that this was Mother Ceres, who had
the oversight of every seed which the husbandman
planted. Nowadays, however, she gave herself no
trouble about seed-time nor harvest, but left the farmers to take care of their own affairs, and the crops
to fade or flourish, as the case might be. There was
nothing, now, in which Ceres seemed to feel an interest, unless when she saw children at play, or gathering flowers along the wayside. Then, indeed, she
would stand and gaze at them with tears in her eyes.
The children, too, appeared to have a sympathy with
her grief, and would cluster themselves in a little
group about her knees, and look up wistfully in her
face; and Ceres, after giving them a kiss all round,
would lead them to their homes, and advise their
mothers never to let them stray out of sight.

"For if they do," said she, "it may happen to you,
as it has to me, that the iron-hearted King Pluto will

take a liking to your darlings, and snatch them up in his chariot, and carry them away."

One day, during her pilgrimage in quest of the entrance to Pluto's kingdom, she came to the palace of King Celeus, who reigned at Eleusis. Ascending a lofty flight of steps, she entered the portal, and found the royal household in very great alarm about the queen's baby. The infant, it seems, was sickly (being troubled with its teeth, I suppose), and would take no food, and was all the time moaning with pain. The queen — her name was Metanira — was desirous of finding a nurse ; and when she beheld a woman of matronly aspect coming up the palace steps, she thought, in her own mind, that here was the very person whom she needed. So Queen Metanira ran to the door, with the poor wailing baby in her arms, and besought Ceres to take charge of it, or, at least, to tell her what would do it good.

" Will you trust the child entirely to me ? " asked Ceres.

" Yes, and gladly too," answered the queen, " if you will devote all your time to him. For I can see that you have been a mother."

" You are right," said Ceres. " I once had a child of my own. Well; I will be the nurse of this poor, sickly boy. But beware, I warn you, that you do not interfere with any kind of treatment which I may judge proper for him. If you do so, the poor infant must suffer for his mother's folly."

Then she kissed the child, and it seemed to do him good ; for he smiled and nestled closely into her bosom.

So Mother Ceres set her torch in a corner (where it kept burning all the while), and took up her abode

in the palace of King Celeus, as nurse to the little
Prince Demophoön. She treated him as if he were
her own child, and allowed neither the king nor the
queen to say whether he should be bathed in warm or
cold water, or what he should eat, or how often he
should take the air, or when he should be put to bed.
You would hardly believe me, if I were to tell how
quickly the baby prince got rid of his ailments, and
grew fat, and rosy, and strong, and how he had two
rows of ivory teeth in less time than any other little
fellow, before or since. Instead of the palest, and
wretchedest, and puniest imp in the world (as his own
mother confessed him to be when Ceres first took him
in charge), he was now a strapping baby, crowing,
laughing, kicking up his heels, and rolling from one
end of the room to the other. All the good women of
the neighborhood crowded to the palace, and held up
their hands, in unutterable amazement, at the beauty
and wholesomeness of this darling little prince.
Their wonder was the greater, because he was never
seen to taste any food ; not even so much as a cup
of milk.

"Pray, nurse," the queen kept saying, "how is it
that you make the child thrive so ? "

"I was a mother once," Ceres always replied ; "and
having nursed my own child, I know what other children need."

But Queen Metanira, as was very natural, had a
great curiosity to know precisely what the nurse did
to her child. One night, therefore, she hid herself in
the chamber where Ceres and the little prince were
accustomed to sleep. There was a fire in the chimney,
and it had now crumbled into great coals and embers,
which lay glowing on the hearth, with a blaze flicker-

ing up now and then, and flinging a warm and ruddy light upon the walls. Ceres sat before the hearth with the child in her lap, and the firelight making her shadow dance upon the ceiling overhead. She undressed the little prince, and bathed him all over with some fragrant liquid out of a vase. The next thing she did was to rake back the red embers, and make a hollow place among them, just where the backlog had been. At last, while the baby was crowing, and clapping its fat little hands, and laughing in the nurse's face (just as you may have seen your little brother or sister do before going into its warm bath), Ceres suddenly laid him, all naked as he was, in the hollow among the red-hot embers. She then raked the ashes over him, and turned quietly away.

You may imagine, if you can, how Queen Metanira shrieked, thinking nothing less than that her dear child would be burned to a cinder. She burst forth from her hiding-place, and running to the hearth, raked open the fire, and snatched up poor little Prince Demophoön out of his bed of live coals, one of which he was griping in each of his fists. He immediately set up a grievous cry, as babies are apt to do when rudely startled out of a sound sleep. To the queen's astonishment and joy, she could perceive no token of the child's being injured by the hot fire in which he had lain. She now turned to Mother Ceres, and asked her to explain the mystery.

"Foolish woman," answered Ceres, "did you not promise to intrust this poor infant entirely to me? You little know the mischief you have done him. Had you left him to my care, he would have grown up like a child of celestial birth, endowed with superhuman strength and intelligence, and would have lived forever.　Do you imagine that earthly children are to become immortal without being tempered to it in the fiercest heat of the fire?　But you have ruined your own son.　For though he will be a strong man and a hero in his day, yet, on account of your folly, he will grow old, and finally die, like the sons of other women. The weak tenderness of his mother has cost the poor boy an immortality.　Farewell."

Saying these words, she kissed the little prince Demophoön, and sighed to think what he had lost, and took her departure without heeding Queen Metanira, who entreated her to remain, and cover up the child among the hot embers as often as she pleased.　Poor baby!　He never slept so warmly again.

While she dwelt in the king's palace, Mother Ceres had been so continually occupied with taking care of the young prince, that her heart was a little lightened of its grief for Proserpina.　But now, having nothing else to busy herself about, she became just as wretched as before.　At length, in her despair, she came to the dreadful resolution that not a stalk of grain, nor a blade of grass, not a potato, nor a turnip, nor any other vegetable that was good for man or beast to eat, should be suffered to grow until her daughter were restored.　She even forbade the flowers to bloom, lest somebody's heart should be cheered by their beauty.

Now, as not so much as a head of asparagus ever presumed to poke itself out of the ground, without the especial permission of Ceres, you may conceive what a terrible calamity had here fallen upon the earth. The husbandmen ploughed and planted as usual; but there lay the rich black furrows, all as barren as a desert of sand.　The pastures looked as brown in the sweet month of June as ever they did in chill November. The rich man's broad acres and the cottager's small garden-patch were equally blighted. Every little girl's flower-bed showed nothing but dry stalks. The old people shook their white heads, and said that the earth had grown aged like themselves, and was no longer capable of wearing the warm smile of summer on its face. It was really piteous to see the poor, starving cattle and sheep, how they followed behind Ceres, lowing and bleating, as if their instinct taught them to expect help from her; and everybody that was acquainted with her power besought her to have mercy on the human race, and, at all events, to let the grass grow. But Mother Ceres, though naturally of an affectionate disposition, was now inexorable.

"Never," said she. "If the earth is ever again to see any verdure, it must first grow along the path which my daughter will tread in coming back to me."

Finally, as there seemed to be no other remedy, our old friend Quicksilver was sent post haste to King Pluto, in hopes that he might be persuaded to undo the mischief he had done, and to set everything right again, by giving up Proserpina. Quicksilver accordingly made the best of his way to the great gate, took a flying leap right over the three-headed mastiff, and stood at the door of the palace in an inconceivably short time. The servants knew him both by his face and garb; for his short cloak, and his winged cap and shoes, and his snaky staff had often been seen thereabouts in times gone by. He requested to be shown immediately into the king's presence; and Pluto, who heard his voice from the top of the stairs, and who loved to recreate himself with Quicksilver's merry talk, called out to him to come up. And while they settle their business together, we must inquire what Proserpina has been doing ever since we saw her last.

The child had declared, as you may remember, that she would not taste a mouthful of food as long as she should be compelled to remain in King Pluto's palace. How she contrived to maintain her resolution, and at the same time to keep herself tolerably plump and rosy, is more than I can explain; but some young ladies, I am given to understand, possess the faculty of living on air, and Proserpina seems to have possessed it too. At any rate, it was now six months since she left the outside of the earth ; and not a morsel, so far as the attendants were able to testify, had yet passed between her teeth. This was the more creditable to Proserpina, inasmuch as King Pluto had caused her to be tempted day after day, with all manner of sweet-meats, and richly preserved fruits, and delicacies of every sort, such as young people are generally most fond of. But her good mother had often told her of the hurtfulness of these things ; and for that reason alone, if there had been no other, she would have resolutely refused to taste them.

All this time, being of a cheerful and active disposition, the little damsel was not quite so unhappy as you may have supposed. The immense palace had a thousand rooms, and was full of beautiful and wonderful objects. There was a never-ceasing gloom, it is true, which half hid itself among the innumerable pillars, gliding before the child as she wandered among them, and treading stealthily behind her in the echo of her footsteps. Neither was all the dazzle of the precious stones, which flamed with their own light, worth one gleam of natural sunshine ; nor could the most brilliant of the many-colored gems, which Proserpina had for playthings, vie with the simple beauty of the flowers she used to gather. But still, wherever the girl went, among those gilded halls and chambers, it seemed as if she carried nature and sunshine along with her, and as if she scattered dewy blossoms on her right hand and on her left. After Proserpina came, the palace was no longer the same abode of stately artifice and dismal magnificence that it had before been. The inhabitants all felt this, and King Pluto more than any of them.

"My own little Proserpina," he used to say, "I wish you could like me a little better. We gloomy and cloudy-natured persons have often as warm hearts at bottom, as those of a more cheerful character. If you would only stay with me of your own accord, it would make me happier than the possession of a hundred such palaces as this."

"Ah," said Proserpina, "you should have tried to make me like you before carrying me off. And the best thing you can do now is, to let me go again. Then I might remember you sometimes, and think that you were as kind as you knew how to be. Perhaps, too, one day or other, I might come back, and pay you a visit."

"No, no," answered Pluto, with his gloomy smile, "I will not trust you for that. You are too fond of living in the broad daylight, and gathering flowers. What an idle and childish taste that is! Are not these gems, which I have ordered to be dug for you, and which are richer than any in my crown, — are they not prettier than a violet?"

"Not half so pretty," said Proserpina, snatching the gems from Pluto's hand, and flinging them to the other end of the hall. "Oh my sweet violets, shall I never see you again?"

And then she burst into tears. But young people's tears have very little saltness or acidity in them, and do not inflame the eyes so much as those of grown persons; so that it is not to be wondered at if, a few moments afterwards, Proserpina was sporting through the hall almost as merrily as she and the four sea-nymphs had sported along the edge of the surf wave. King Pluto gazed after her, and wished that he, too, was a child. And little Proserpina, when she turned about, and beheld this great king standing in his splendid hall, and looking so grand, and so melancholy, and so lonesome, was smitten with a kind of pity. She ran back to him, and, for the first time in all her life, put her small soft hand in his.

"I love you a little," whispered she, looking up in his face.

" Do you, indeed, my dear child?" cried Pluto, bending his dark face down to kiss her; but Proserpina shrank away from the kiss, for though his features were noble, they were very dusky and grim. " Well, I have not deserved it of you, after keeping you a prisoner for so many months, and starving you, besides. Are you not terribly hungry? Is there nothing which I can get you to eat?"

In asking this question, the king of the mines had a very cunning purpose; for, you will recollect, if Proserpina tasted a morsel of food in his dominions, she would never afterwards be at liberty to quit them.

"No, indeed," said Proserpina. "Your head cook is always baking, and stewing, and roasting, and rolling out paste, and contriving one dish or another, which he imagines may be to my liking. But he might just as well save himself the trouble, poor, fat little man that he is. I have no appetite for anything in the world, unless it were a slice of bread of my mother's own baking, or a little fruit out of her garden."

When Pluto heard this, he began to see that he had mistaken the best method of tempting Proserpina to eat. The cook's made dishes and artificial dainties were not half so delicious, in the good child's opinion, as the simple fare to which Mother Ceres had accustomed her. Wondering that he had never thought of it before, the king now sent one of his trusty attendants, with a large basket, to get some of the finest and juiciest pears, peaches, and plums which could anywhere be found in the upper world. Unfortunately, however, this was during the time when Ceres had forbidden any fruits or vegetables to grow; and, after seeking all over the earth, King Pluto's servant found only a single pomegranate, and that so dried up as to be not worth eating. Nevertheless, since there was no better to be had, he brought this dry, old, withered pomegranate home to the palace, put it on a magnificent golden salver, and carried it up to Proserpina. Now it happened, curiously enough, that, just as the servant was bringing the pomegranate into the back door of the palace, our friend Quicksilver had gone up the front steps, on his errand to get Proserpina away from King Pluto.

As soon as Proserpina saw the pomegranate on the golden salver, she told the servant he had better take it away again.

"I shall not touch it, I assure you," said she. "If I were ever so hungry, I should never think of eating such a miserable, dry pomegranate as that."

"It is the only one in the world," said the servant.

He set down the golden salver, with the wizened

pomegranate upon it, and left the room. When he was gone, Proserpina could not help coming close to the table, and looking at this poor specimen of dried fruit with a great deal of eagerness; for, to say the truth, on seeing something that suited her taste, she felt all the six months' appetite taking possession of her at once. To be sure, it was a very wretched-looking pomegranate, and seemed to have no more juice in it than an oyster-shell. But there was no choice of such things in King Pluto's palace. This was the first fruit she had seen there, and the last she was ever likely to see; and unless she ate it up immediately, it would grow drier than it already was, and be wholly unfit to eat.

"At least, I may smell it," thought Proserpina.

So she took up the pomegranate, and applied it to her nose; and, somehow or other, being in such close neighborhood to her mouth, the fruit found its way into that little red cave. Dear me! what an everlasting pity! Before Proserpina knew what she was about, her teeth had actually bitten it, of their own accord. Just as this fatal deed was done, the door of the apartment opened, and in came King Pluto, followed by Quicksilver, who had been urging him to let his little prisoner go. At the first noise of their entrance, Proserpina withdrew the pomegranate from her mouth. But Quicksilver (whose eyes were very keen, and his wits the sharpest that ever anybody had) perceived that the child was a little confused; and seeing the empty salver, he suspected that she had been taking a sly nibble of something or other. As for honest Pluto, he never guessed at the secret.

"My little Proserpina," said the king, sitting down, and affectionately drawing her between his knees,

" here is Quicksilver, who tells me that a great many misfortunes have befallen innocent people on account of my detaining you in my dominions. To confess the truth, I myself had already reflected that it was an unjustifiable act to take you away from your good mother. But, then, you must consider, my dear child, that this vast palace is apt to be gloomy (although the precious stones certainly shine very bright), and that I am not of the most cheerful disposition, and that therefore it was a natural thing enough to seek for the society of some merrier creature than myself. I hoped you would take my crown for a plaything, and me — ah, you laugh, naughty Proserpina — me, grim as I am, for a playmate. It was a silly expectation."

"Not so extremely silly," whispered Proserpina. "You have really amused me very much, sometimes."

"Thank you," said King Pluto, rather dryly. "But I can see, plainly enough, that you think my palace a dusky prison, and me the iron-hearted keeper of it. And an iron heart I should surely have, if I could detain you here any longer, my poor child, when it is now six months since you tasted food. I give you your liberty. Go with Quicksilver. Hasten home to your dear mother."

Now, although you may not have supposed it, Proserpina found it impossible to take leave of poor King Pluto without some regrets, and a good deal of compunction for not telling him about the pomegranate. She even shed a tear or two, thinking how lonely and cheerless the great palace would seem to him, with all its ugly glare of artificial light, after she herself, — his one little ray of natural sunshine, whom he had stolen, to be sure, but only because he valued her so much, — after she should have departed. I know not how

many kind things she might have said to the disconsolate king of the mines, had not Quicksilver hurried
her away.

"Come along quickly," whispered he in her ear, "or
his Majesty may change his royal mind. And take
care, above all things, that you say nothing of what
was brought you on the golden salver."

In a very short time, they had passed the great
gate-way (leaving the three-headed Cerberus, barking,
and yelping, and growling, with threefold din, behind
them), and emerged upon the surface of the earth.
It was delightful to behold, as Proserpina hastened
along, how the path grew verdant behind and on
either side of her. Wherever she set her blessed foot,
there was at once a dewy flower. The violets gushed
up along the wayside. The grass and the grain began
to sprout with tenfold vigor and luxuriance, to make
up for the dreary months that had been wasted in bar-
renness. The starved cattle immediately set to work
grazing, after their long fast, and ate enormously all
day, and got up at midnight to eat more. But I can
assure you it was a busy time of year with the farmers,
when they found the summer coming upon them with
such a rush. Nor must I forget to say that all the
birds in the whole world hopped about upon the newly
blossoming trees, and sang together in a prodigious
ecstasy of joy.

Mother Ceres had returned to her deserted home,
and was sitting disconsolately on the doorstep, with
her torch burning in her hand. She had been idly
watching the flame for some moments past, when, all
at once, it flickered and went out.

"What does this mean?" thought she. "It was
an enchanted torch, and should have kept burning till
my child came back."

Lifting her eyes, she was surprised to see a sudden verdure flashing over the brown and barren fields, exactly as you may have observed a golden hue gleaming far and wide across the landscape, from the just risen sun.

"Does the earth disobey me?" exclaimed Mother Ceres, indignantly. "Does it presume to be green, when I have bidden it be barren, until my daughter shall be restored to my arms?"

"Then open your arms, dear mother," cried a well-known voice, "and take your little daughter into them."

And Proserpina came running, and flung herself upon her mother's bosom. Their mutual transport is not to be described. The grief of their separation had caused both of them to shed a great many tears; and now they shed a great many more, because their joy could not so well express itself in any other way.

When their hearts had grown a little more quiet, Mother Ceres looked anxiously at Proserpina.

"My child," said she, "did you taste any food while you were in King Pluto's palace?"

"Dearest mother," answered Proserpina, "I will tell you the whole truth. Until this very morning, not a morsel of food had passed my lips. But to-day, they brought me a pomegranate (a very dry one it was, and all shrivelled up, till there was little left of it but seeds and skin), and having seen no fruit for so long a time, and being faint with hunger, I was tempted just to bite it. The instant I tasted it, King Pluto and Quicksilver came into the room. I had not swallowed a morsel; but — dear mother, I hope it was no harm — but six of the pomegranate seeds, I am afraid, remained in my mouth."

"Ah, unfortunate child, and miserable me!" exclaimed Ceres. "For each of those six pomegranate seeds you must spend one month of every year in King Pluto's palace. You are but half restored to your mother. Only six months with me, and six with that good-for-nothing King of Darkness!"

"Do not speak so harshly of poor King Pluto," said Proserpina, kissing her mother. "He has some very good qualities; and I really think I can bear to spend six months in his palace, if he will only let me spend the other six with you. He certainly did very wrong to carry me off; but then, as he says, it was but a dismal sort of life for him, to live in that great gloomy place, all alone; and it has made a wonderful change in his spirits to have a little girl to run up stairs and down. There is some comfort in making him so happy; and so, upon the whole, dearest mother, let us be thankful that he is not to keep me the whole year round."

THE GOLDEN FLEECE.

WHEN Jason, the son of the dethroned King of Iolchos, was a little boy, he was sent away from his parents, and placed under the queerest schoolmaster that ever you heard of. This learned person was one of the people, or quadrupeds, called Centaurs. He lived in a cavern, and had the body and legs of a white horse, with the head and shoulders of a man. His name was Chiron ; and, in spite of his odd appearance, he was a very excellent teacher, and had several scholars, who afterwards did him credit by making a great figure in the world. The famous Hercules was one, and so was Achilles, and Philoctetes, likewise, and Æsculapius, who acquired immense repute as a doctor. The good Chiron taught his pupils how to play upon the harp, and how to cure diseases, and how to use the sword and shield, together with various other branches of education, in which the lads of those days used to be instructed, instead of writing and arithmetic.

I have sometimes suspected that Master Chiron was not really very different from other people, but that, being a kind-hearted and merry old fellow, he was in the habit of making believe that he was a horse, and scrambling about the school-room on all fours, and letting the little boys ride upon his back. And so, when his scholars had grown up, and grown old, and were trotting their grandchildren on their knees, they told them about the sports of their school-days ; and these young folks took the idea that their grandfathers had been taught their letters by a Centaur, half man and half horse. Little children, not quite understanding what is said to them, often get such absurd notions into their heads, you know.

Be that as it may, it has always been told for a fact (and always will be told, as long as the world lasts), that Chiron, with the head of a schoolmaster, had the body and legs of a horse. Just imagine the grave old gentleman clattering and stamping into the school-room on his four hoofs, perhaps treading on some lit-tle fellow's toes, flourishing his switch tail instead of a rod, and, now and then, trotting out of doors to eat a mouthful of grass! I wonder what the blacksmith charged him for a set of iron shoes.

So Jason dwelt in the cave, with this four-footed Chiron, from the time that he was an infant, only a few months old, until he had grown to the full height of a man. He became a very good harper, I suppose, and skilful in the use of weapons, and tolerably ac-quainted with herbs and other doctor's stuff, and, above all, an admirable horseman; for, in teaching young people to ride, the good Chiron must have been without a rival among schoolmasters. At length, being now a tall and athletic youth, Jason resolved to seek his fortune in the world, without asking Chiron's advice, or telling him anything about the matter. This was very unwise, to be sure; and I hope none of you, my little hearers, will ever follow Jason's example. But, you are to understand, he had heard how that he him-self was a prince royal, and how his father, King Æson, had been deprived of the kingdom of Iolchos by a certain Pelias, who would also have killed Jason, had he not been hidden in the Centaur's cave. And,

being come to the strength of a man, Jason determined to set all this business to rights, and to punish
the wicked Pelias for wronging his dear father, and
to cast him down from the throne, and seat himself
there instead.

With this intention, he took a spear in each hand,
and threw a leopard's skin over his shoulders, to keep
off the rain, and set forth on his travels, with his long
yellow ringlets waving in the wind. The part of his
dress on which he most prided himself was a pair of
sandals, that had been his father's. They were hand-
somely embroidered, and were tied upon his feet with
strings of gold. But his whole attire was such as people did not very often see; and as he passed along,
the women and children ran to the doors and windows,
wondering whither this beautiful youth was journeying, with his leopard's skin and his golden-tied sandals, and what heroic deeds he meant to perform, with
a spear in his right hand and another in his left.

I know not how far Jason had travelled, when he
came to a turbulent river, which rushed right across
his pathway, with specks of white foam among its
black eddies, hurrying tumultuously onward, and roaring angrily as it went. Though not a very broad river
in the dry seasons of the year, it was now swollen by
heavy rains and by the melting of the snow on the
sides of Mount Olympus; and it thundered so loudly,
and looked so wild and dangerous, that Jason, bold as
he was, thought it prudent to pause upon the brink.
The bed of the stream seemed to be strewn with sharp
and rugged rocks, some of which thrust themselves
above the water. By and by, an uprooted tree, with
shattered branches, came drifting along the current,
and got entangled among the rocks. Now and then,

a drowned sheep, and once the carcass of a cow, floated past.

In short, the swollen river had already done a great deal of mischief. It was evidently too deep for Jason to wade, and too boisterous for him to swim ; he could see no bridge ; and as for a boat, had there been any, the rocks would have broken it to pieces in an instant.

"See the poor lad," said a cracked voice close to his side. "He must have had but a poor education, since he does not know how to cross a little stream like this. Or is he afraid of wetting his fine golden-stringed sandals ? It is a pity his four-footed school-master is not here to carry him safely across on his back ! "

Jason looked round greatly surprised, for he did not know that anybody was near. But beside him stood an old woman, with a ragged mantle over her head, leaning on a staff, the top of which was carved into the shape of a cuckoo. She looked very aged, and wrinkled, and infirm ; and yet her eyes, which were as brown as those of an ox, were so extremely large and beautiful, that, when they were fixed on Jason's eyes, he could see nothing else but them. The old woman had a pomegranate in her hand, although the fruit was then quite out of season.

"Whither are you going, Jason ? " she now asked.

She seemed to know his name, you will observe ; and, indeed, those great brown eyes looked as if they had a knowledge of everything, whether past or to come. While Jason was gazing at her, a peacock strutted forward and took his stand at the old woman's side.

"I am going to Iolchos," answered the young man, "to bid the wicked King Pelias come down from my father's throne, and let me reign in his stead."

" Ah, well, then," said the old woman, still with the same cracked voice, " if that is all your business, you need not be in a very great hurry. Just take me on your back, there's a good youth, and carry me across the river. I and my peacock have something to do on the other side, as well as yourself."

" Good mother," replied Jason, " your business can hardly be so important as the pulling down a king from his throne. Besides, as you may see for yourself, the river is very boisterous; and if I should chance to stumble, it would sweep both of us away more easily than it has carried off yonder uprooted tree. I would gladly help you if I could; but I doubt whether I am strong enough to carry you across."

" Then," said she, very scornfully, " neither are you strong enough to pull King Pelias off his throne. And, Jason, unless you will help an old woman at her need, you ought not to be a king. What are kings made for, save to succor the feeble and distressed? But do as you please. Either take me on your back, or with my poor old limbs I shall try my best to struggle across the stream."

Saying this, the old woman poked with her staff in the river, as if to find the safest place in its rocky bed where she might make the first step. But Jason, by this time, had grown ashamed of his reluctance to help her. He felt that he could never forgive himself, if this poor feeble creature should come to any harm in attempting to wrestle against the headlong current. The good Chiron, whether half horse or no, had taught him that the noblest use of his strength was to assist the weak; and also that he must treat every young woman as if she were his sister, and every old one like a mother. Remembering these maxims, the

vigorous and beautiful young man knelt down, and requested the good dame to mount upon his back.

"The passage seems to me not very safe," he remarked. "But as your business is so urgent, I will
try to carry you across. If the river sweeps you
away, it shall take me too."

"That, no doubt, will be a great comfort to both of
us," quoth the old woman. "But never fear. We
shall get safely across."

So she threw her arms around Jason's neck; and
lifting her from the ground, he stepped boldly into the
raging and foamy current, and began to stagger away
from the shore. As for the peacock, it alighted on
the old dame's shoulder. Jason's two spears, one in
each hand, kept him from stumbling, and enabled him
to feel his way among the hidden rocks; although,
every instant, he expected that his companion and
himself would go down the stream, together with the
drift-wood of shattered trees, and the carcasses of the
sheep and cow. Down came the cold, snowy torrent
from the steep side of Olympus, raging and thundering as if it had a real spite against Jason, or, at all
events, were determined to snatch off his living burden from his shoulders. When he was half-way
across, the uprooted tree (which I have already told
you about) broke loose from among the rocks, and
bore down upon him, with all its splintered branches
sticking out like the hundred arms of the giant Bria-
reus. It rushed past, however, without touching him.
But the next moment, his foot was caught in a crevice
between two rocks, and stuck there so fast, that, in
the effort to get free, he lost one of his golden-stringed
sandals.

At this accident Jason could not help uttering a
cry of vexation.

"What is the matter, Jason?" asked the old woman.

"Matter enough," said the young man. "I have lost a sandal here among the rocks. And what sort of a figure shall I cut at the court of King Pelias, with a golden-stringed sandal on one foot, and the other foot bare!"

"Do not take it to heart," answered his companion, cheerily. "You never met with better fortune than in losing that sandal. It satisfies me that you are the very person whom the Speaking Oak has been talking about."

There was no time, just then, to inquire what the Speaking Oak had said. But the briskness of her tone encouraged the young man; and besides, he had never in his life felt so vigorous and mighty as since taking this old woman on his back. Instead of being exhausted, he gathered strength as he went on; and, struggling up against the torrent, he at last gained the opposite shore, clambered up the bank, and set down the old dame and her peacock safely on the grass. As soon as this was done, however, he could not help looking rather despondently at his bare foot, with only a remnant of the golden string of the sandal clinging round his ankle.

"You will get a handsomer pair of sandals by and by," said the old woman, with a kindly look out of her beautiful brown eyes. "Only let King Pelias get a glimpse of that bare foot, and you shall see him turn as pale as ashes, I promise you. There is your path. Go along, my good Jason, and my blessing go with you. And when you sit on your throne, remember the old woman whom you helped over the river."

With these words, she hobbled away, giving him a smile over her shoulder as she departed. Whether the light of her beautiful brown eyes threw a glory round about her, or whatever the cause might be, Jason fancied that there was something very noble and majestic in her figure, after all, and that, though her gait seemed to be a rheumatic hobble, yet she moved with as much grace and dignity as any queen on earth. Her peacock, which had now fluttered down from her shoulder, strutted behind her in prodigious pomp, and spread out its magnificent tail on purpose for Jason to admire it.

When the old dame and her peacock were out of sight, Jason set forward on his journey. After travelling a pretty long distance, he came to a town situated at the foot of a mountain, and not a great way from the shore of the sea. On the outside of the town there was an immense crowd of people, not only men and women, but children, too, all in their best clothes, and evidently enjoying a holiday. The crowd was thickest towards the sea-shore; and in that direction, over the people's heads, Jason saw a wreath of smoke curling upward to the blue sky. He inquired of one of the multitude what town it was, near by, and why so many persons were here assembled together.

" This is the kingdom of Iolchos," answered the man, " and we are the subjects of King Pelias. Our monarch has summoned us together, that we may see him sacrifice a black bull to Neptune, who, they say, is his Majesty's father. Yonder is the king, where you see the smoke going up from the altar."

While the man spoke he eyed Jason with great curiosity; for his garb was quite unlike that of the Iolchians, and it looked very odd to see a youth with a leopard's skin over his shoulders, and each hand grasping a spear. Jason perceived, too, that the man

stared particularly at his feet, one of which, you remember, was bare, while the other was decorated with
his father's golden-stringed sandal.

"Look at him! only look at him!" said the man
to his next neighbor. "Do you see? He wears but
one sandal!"

Upon this, first one person, and then another, began
to stare at Jason, and everybody seemed to be greatly
struck with something in his aspect; though they
turned their eyes much oftener towards his feet than
to any other part of his figure. Besides, he could hear
them whispering to one another.

"One sandal! One sandal!" they kept saying.
"The man with one sandal! Here he is at last!
Whence has he come? What does he mean to do?
What will the king say to the one-sandalled man?"

Poor Jason was greatly abashed, and made up his
mind that the people of Iolchos were exceedingly ill
bred, to take such public notice of an accidental deficiency in his dress. Meanwhile, whether it were that
they hustled him forward, or that Jason, of his own
accord, thrust a passage through the crowd, it so happened that he soon found himself close to the smoking
altar, where King Pelias was sacrificing the black bull.
The murmur and hum of the multitude, in their surprise at the spectacle of Jason with his one bare foot,
grew so loud that it disturbed the ceremonies; and the
king, holding the great knife with which he was just
going to cut the bull's throat, turned angrily about,
and fixed his eyes on Jason. The people had now
withdrawn from around him, so that the youth stood
in an open space near the smoking altar, front to front
with the angry King Pelias.

"Who are you?" cried the king, with a terrible

frown. " And how dare you make this disturbance, while I am sacrificing a black bull to my father Neptune ? "

" It is no fault of mine," answered Jason. " Your Majesty must blame the rudeness of your subjects, who have raised all this tumult because one of my feet happens to be bare."

When Jason said this, the king gave a quick, startled glance down at his feet.

" Ha ! " muttered he, " here is the one-sandalled fellow, sure enough ! What can I do with him ? "

And he clutched more closely the great knife in his hand, as if he were half a mind to slay Jason instead of the black bull. The people round about caught up the king's words indistinctly as they were uttered ; and first there was a murmur among them, and then a loud shout.

" The one-sandalled man has come ! The prophecy must be fulfilled ! "

For you are to know that, many years before, King Pelias had been told by the Speaking Oak of Dodona, that a man with one sandal should cast him down from his throne. On this account, he had given strict orders that nobody should ever come into his presence, unless both sandals were securely tied upon his feet ; and he kept an officer in his palace, whose sole business it was to examine people's sandals, and to supply them with a new pair, at the expense of the royal treasury, as soon as the old ones began to wear out. In the whole course of the king's reign, he had never been thrown into such a fright and agitation as by the spectacle of poor Jason's bare foot. But, as he was naturally a bold and hard-hearted man, he soon took courage, and began to consider in what way he might rid himself of this terrible one-sandalled stranger.

"My good young man," said King Pelias, taking the softest tone imaginable, in order to throw Jason off his guard, "you are excessively welcome to my kingdom. Judging by your dress, you must have travelled a long distance; for it is not the fashion to wear leopard-skins in this part of the world. Pray what may I call your name? and where did you receive your education?"

"My name is Jason," answered the young stranger. "Ever since my infancy, I have dwelt in the cave of Chiron the Centaur. He was my instructor, and taught me music, and horsemanship, and how to cure wounds, and likewise how to inflict wounds with my weapons!"

"I have heard of Chiron the schoolmaster," replied King Pelias, "and how that there is an immense deal of learning and wisdom in his head, although it happens to be set on a horse's body. It gives me great delight to see one of his scholars at my court. But, to test how much you have profited under so excellent a teacher, will you allow me to ask you a single question?"

"I do not pretend to be very wise," said Jason. "But ask me what you please, and I will answer to the best of my ability."

Now King Pelias meant cunningly to entrap the young man, and to make him say something that should be the cause of mischief and destruction to himself. So with a crafty and evil smile upon his face, he spoke as follows:—

"What would you do, brave Jason," asked he, "if there were a man in the world, by whom, as you had reason to believe, you were doomed to be ruined and slain,—what would you do, I say, if that man stood before you, and in your power?"

When Jason saw the malice and wickedness which King Pelias could not prevent from gleaming out of his eyes, he probably guessed that the king had discovered what he came for, and that he intended to turn his own words against himself. Still he scorned to tell a falsehood. Like an upright and honorable prince, as he was, he determined to speak out the real truth. Since the king had chosen to ask him the question, and since Jason had promised him an answer, there was no right way, save to tell him precisely what would be the most prudent thing to do, if he had his worst enemy in his power.

Therefore, after a moment's consideration, he spoke up, with a firm and manly voice.

" I would send such a man," said he, " in quest of the Golden Fleece ! "

This enterprise, you will understand, was, of all others, the most difficult and dangerous in the world. In the first place, it would be necessary to make a long voyage through unknown seas. There was hardly a hope, or a possibility, that any young man who should undertake this voyage would either succeed in obtaining the Golden Fleece, or would survive to return home, and tell of the perils he had run. The eyes of King Pelias sparkled with joy, therefore, when he heard Jason's reply.

" Well said, wise man with the one sandal ! " cried he. " Go, then, and, at the peril of your life, bring me back the Golden Fleece."

" I go," answered Jason, composedly. " If I fail, you need not fear that I will ever come back to trouble you again. But if I return to Iolchos with the prize, then, King Pelias, you must hasten down from your lofty throne, and give me your crown and sceptre."

"That I will," said the king, with a sneer. "Meantime, I will keep them very safely for you."

The first thing that Jason thought of doing, after he left the king's presence, was to go to Dodona, and inquire of the Talking Oak what course it was best to pursue. This wonderful tree stood in the centre of an ancient wood. Its stately trunk rose up a hundred feet into the air, and threw a broad and dense shadow over more than an acre of ground. Standing beneath it, Jason looked up among the knotted branches and green leaves, and into the mysterious heart of the old tree, and spoke aloud, as if he were addressing some person who was hidden in the depths of the foliage.

"What shall I do," said he, "in order to win the Golden Fleece?"

At first there was a deep silence, not only within the shadow of the Talking Oak, but all through the solitary wood. In a moment or two, however, the leaves of the oak began to stir and rustle, as if a gentle breeze were wandering amongst them, although the other trees of the wood were perfectly still. The sound grew louder, and became like the roar of a high wind. By and by, Jason imagined that he could distinguish words, but very confusedly, because each separate leaf of the tree seemed to be a tongue, and the whole myriad of tongues were babbling at once. But the noise waxed broader and deeper, until it resembled a tornado sweeping through the oak, and making one great utterance out of the thousand and thousand of little murmurs which each leafy tongue had caused by its rustling. And now, though it still had the tone of mighty wind roaring among the branches, it was also like a deep bass voice, speaking, as distinctly as a tree could be expected to speak, the following words: —

"Go to Argus, the ship-builder, and bid him build a galley with fifty oars."

Then the voice melted again into the indistinct murmur of the rustling leaves, and died gradually away. When it was quite gone, Jason felt inclined to doubt whether he had actually heard the words, or whether his fancy had not shaped them out of the ordinary sound made by a breeze, while passing through the thick foliage of the tree.

But on inquiry among the people of Iolchos, he found that there was really a man in the city, by the name of Argus, who was a very skilful builder of vessels. This showed some intelligence in the oak; else how should it have known that any such person existed? At Jason's request, Argus readily consented to build him a galley so big that it should require fifty strong men to row it; although no vessel of such a size and burden had heretofore been seen in the world. So the head carpenter, and all his journeymen and apprentices, began their work; and for a good while afterwards, there they were, busily employed, hewing out the timbers, and making a great clatter with their hammers; until the new ship, which was called the Argo, seemed to be quite ready for sea. And, as the Talking Oak had already given him such good advice, Jason thought that it would not be amiss to ask for a little more. He visited it again, therefore, and standing beside its huge, rough trunk, inquired what he should do next.

This time, there was no such universal quivering of the leaves, throughout the whole tree, as there had been before. But after a while, Jason observed that the foliage of a great branch which stretched above his head had begun to rustle, as if the wind were

stirring that one bough, while all the other boughs of
the oak were at rest.

"Cut me off!" said the branch, as soon as it could
speak distinctly, — "cut me off! cut me off! and
carve me into a figure-head for your galley."

Accordingly, Jason took the branch at its word, and
lopped it off the tree. A carver in the neighborhood
engaged to make the figure-head. He was a tolerably
good workman, and had already carved several figure-
heads, in what he intended for feminine shapes, and
looking pretty much like those which we see nowadays
stuck up under a vessel's bowsprit, with great staring
eyes, that never wink at the dash of the spray. But
(what was very strange) the carver found that his
hand was guided by some unseen power, and by a skill
beyond his own, and that his tools shaped out an
image which he had never dreamed of. When the
work was finished, it turned out to be the figure of
a beautiful woman with a helmet on her head, from
beneath which the long ringlets fell down upon her
shoulders. On the left arm was a shield, and in its
centre appeared a lifelike representation of the head
of Medusa with the snaky locks. The right arm was
extended, as if pointing onward. The face of this
wonderful statue, though not angry or forbidding, was
so grave and majestic, that perhaps you might call it
severe; and as for the mouth, it seemed just ready
to unclose its lips, and utter words of the deepest
wisdom.

Jason was delighted with the oaken image, and gave
the carver no rest until it was completed, and set up
where a figure-head has always stood, from that time
to this, in the vessel's prow.

"And now," cried he, as he stood gazing at the

calm, majestic face of the statue, "I must go to the Talking Oak, and inquire what next to do."

"There is no need of that, Jason," said a voice which, though it was far lower, reminded him of the mighty tones of the great oak. "When you desire good advice, you can seek it of me."

Jason had been looking straight into the face of the image when these words were spoken. But he could hardly believe either his ears or his eyes. The truth was, however, that the oaken lips had moved, and, to all appearance, the voice had proceeded from the statue's mouth. Recovering a little from his surprise, Jason bethought himself that the image had been carved out of the wood of the Talking Oak, and that, therefore, it was really no great wonder, but on the contrary, the most natural thing in the world, that it should possess the faculty of speech. It would have been very odd, indeed, if it had not. But certainly it was a great piece of good fortune that he should be able to carry so wise a block of wood along with him in his perilous voyage.

"Tell me, wondrous image," exclaimed Jason, — "since you inherit the wisdom of the Speaking Oak of Dodona, whose daughter you are, — tell me, where shall I find fifty bold youths, who will take each of them an oar of my galley? They must have sturdy arms to row, and brave hearts to encounter perils, or we shall never win the Golden Fleece."

"Go," replied the oaken image, — "go, summon all the heroes of Greece."

And, in fact, considering what a great deed was to be done, could any advice be wiser than this which Jason received from the figure-head of his vessel? He lost no time in sending messengers to all the cities,

and making known to the whole people of Greece, that
Prince Jason, the son of King Æson, was going in
quest of the Fleece of Gold, and that he desired the
help of forty-nine of the bravest and strongest young
men alive, to row his vessel and share his dangers.
And Jason himself would be the fiftieth.

At this news, the adventurous youths, all over the
country, began to bestir themselves. Some of them
had already fought with giants, and slain dragons;
and the younger ones, who had not yet met with such
good fortune, thought it a shame to have lived so long
without getting astride of a flying serpent, or sticking their spears into a Chimæra, or, at least, thrusting their right arms down a monstrous lion's throat.
There was a fair prospect that they would meet with
plenty of such adventures before finding the Golden
Fleece. As soon as they could furbish up their helmets and shields, therefore, and gird on their trusty
swords, they came thronging to Iolchos, and clambered
on board the new galley. Shaking hands with Jason,
they assured him that they did not care a pin for their
lives, but would help row the vessel to the remotest
edge of the world, and as much farther as he might
think it best to go.

Many of these brave fellows had been educated by
Chiron, the four-footed pedagogue, and were therefore
old schoolmates of Jason, and knew him to be a lad
of spirit. The mighty Hercules, whose shoulders afterwards held up the sky, was one of them. And
there were Castor and Pollux, the twin brothers, who
were never accused of being chicken-hearted, although
they had been hatched out of an egg; and Theseus,
who was so renowned for killing the Minotaur; and
Lynceus, with his wonderfully sharp eyes, which could

see through a millstone, or look right down into the depths of the earth, and discover the treasures that were there; and Orpheus, the very best of harpers, who sang and played upon his lyre so sweetly, that the brute beasts stood upon their hind legs, and capered merrily to the music. Yes, and at some of his more moving tunes, the rocks bestirred their moss-grown bulk out of the ground, and a grove of forest trees uprooted themselves, and, nodding their tops to one another, performed a country dance.

One of the rowers was a beautiful young woman, named Atalanta, who had been nursed among the mountains by a bear. So light of foot was this fair damsel that she could step from one foamy crest of a wave to the foamy crest of another, without wetting more than the sole of her sandal. She had grown up in a very wild way, and talked much about the rights of women, and loved hunting and war far better than her needle. But, in my opinion, the most remarkable of this famous company were two sons of the North Wind (airy youngsters, and of rather a blustering disposition), who had wings on their shoulders, and, in case of a calm, could puff out their cheeks, and blow almost as fresh a breeze as their father. I ought not to forget the prophets and conjurers, of whom there were several in the crew, and who could foretell what would happen to-morrow, or the next day, or a hundred years hence, but were generally quite unconscious of what was passing at the moment.

Jason appointed Tiphys to be helmsman, because he was a star-gazer, and knew the points of the compass. Lynceus, on account of his sharp sight, was stationed as a lookout in the prow, where he saw a whole day's sail ahead, but was rather apt to overlook things that lay directly under his nose. If the sea only happened to be deep enough, however, Lynceus could tell you exactly what kind of rocks or sands were at the bottom of it; and he often cried out to his companions, that they were sailing over heaps of sunken treasure, which yet he was none the richer for beholding. To confess the truth, few people believed him when he said it.

Well! But when the Argonauts, as these fifty brave adventurers were called, had prepared everything for the voyage, an unforeseen difficulty threatened to end it before it was begun. The vessel, you must understand, was so long, and broad, and ponderous, that the united force of all the fifty was insufficient to shove her into the water. Hercules, I suppose, had not grown to his full strength, else he might have set her afloat as easily as a little boy launches his boat upon a puddle. But here were these fifty heroes pushing, and straining, and growing red in the face, without making the Argo start an inch. At last, quite wearied out, they sat themselves down on the shore, exceedingly disconsolate, and thinking that the vessel must be left to rot and fall in pieces, and that they must either swim across the sea or lose the Golden Fleece.

All at once, Jason bethought himself of the galley's miraculous figure-head.

"O daughter of the Talking Oak," cried he, "how shall we set to work to get our vessel into the water?"

"Seat yourselves," answered the image (for it had known what ought to be done from the very first, and was only waiting for the question to be put),—"seat yourselves, and handle your oars, and let Orpheus play upon his harp."

Immediately the fifty heroes got on board, and seizing their oars, held them perpendicularly in the air,
while Orpheus (who liked such a task far better than
rowing) swept his fingers across the harp. At the
first ringing note of the music, they felt the vessel stir.
Orpheus thrummed away briskly, and the galley slid
at once into the sea, dipping her prow so deeply that
the figure-head drank the wave with its marvellous
lips, and rose again as buoyant as a swan. The rowers plied their fifty oars; the white foam boiled up
before the prow; the water gurgled and bubbled in
their wake; while Orpheus continued to play so lively
a strain of music, that the vessel seemed to dance over
the billows by way of keeping time to it. Thus triumphantly did the Argo sail out of the harbor, amidst
the huzzas and good wishes of everybody except the
wicked old Pelias, who stood on a promontory, scowling at her, and wishing that he could blow out of his
lungs the tempest of wrath that was in his heart, and
so sink the galley with all on board. When they had
sailed above fifty miles over the sea, Lynceus happened
to cast his sharp eyes behind, and said that there was
this bad-hearted king, still perched upon the promontory, and scowling so gloomily that it looked like a
black thunder-cloud in that quarter of the horizon.

In order to make the time pass away more pleas-
antly during the voyage, the heroes talked about the
Golden Fleece. It originally belonged, it appears, to
a Bœotian ram, who had taken on his back two children, when in danger of their lives, and fled with them
over land and sea, as far as Colchis. One of the children, whose name was Helle, fell into the sea and was
drowned. But the other (a little boy, named Phrixus)
was brought safe ashore by the faithful ram, who, how-

ever, was so exhausted that he immediately lay down and died. In memory of this good deed, and as a token of his true heart, the fleece of the poor dead ram was miraculously changed to gold, and became one of the most beautiful objects ever seen on earth. It was hung upon a tree in a sacred grove, where it had now been kept I know not how many years, and was the envy of mighty kings, who had nothing so magnificent in any of their palaces.

If I were to tell you all the adventures of the Argonauts, it would take me till nightfall, and perhaps a great deal longer. There was no lack of wonderful events, as you may judge from what you may have already heard. At a certain island they were hospitably received by King Cyzicus, its sovereign, who made a feast for them, and treated them like brothers. But the Argonauts saw that this good king looked downcast and very much troubled, and they therefore inquired of him what was the matter. King Cyzicus hereupon informed them that he and his subjects were greatly abused and incommoded by the inhabitants of a neighboring mountain, who made war upon them, and killed many people, and ravaged the country. And while they were talking about it, Cyzicus pointed to the mountain, and asked Jason and his companions what they saw there.

" I see some very tall objects," answered Jason ; " but they are at such a distance that I cannot distinctly make out what they are. To tell your Majesty the truth, they look so very strangely that I am in-clined to think them clouds, which have chanced to take something like human shapes."

" I see them very plainly," remarked Lynceus, whose eyes, you know, were as far-sighted as a telescope.

" They are a band of enormous giants, all of whom
have six arms apiece, and a club, a sword, or some
other weapon in each of their hands."

" You have excellent eyes," said King Cyzicus.
"Yes ; they are six-armed giants, as you say, and these
are the enemies whom I and my subjects have to contend with."

The next day, when the Argonauts were about setting sail, down came these terrible giants, stepping a
hundred yards at a stride, brandishing their six arms
apiece, and looking very formidable, so far aloft in
the air.   Each of these monsters was able to carry on
a whole war by himself, for with one of his arms he
could fling immense stones, and wield a club with another, and a sword with a third, while the fourth was
poking a long spear at the enemy, and the fifth and
sixth were shooting him with a bow and arrow.   But,
luckily, though the giants were so huge, and had so
many arms, they had each but one heart, and that no
bigger nor braver than the heart of an ordinary man.
Besides, if they had been like the hundred-armed Bri-
areus, the brave Argonauts would have given them
their hands full of fight.   Jason and his friends went
boldly to meet them, slew a great many, and made
the rest take to their heels, so that, if the giants had
had six legs apiece instead of six arms, it would have
served them better to run away with.

Another strange adventure happened when the voyagers came to Thrace, where they found a poor blind
king, named Phineus, deserted by his subjects, and
living in a very sorrowful way, all by himself.   On
Jason's inquiring whether they could do him any
service, the king answered that he was terribly tormented by three great winged creatures, called Har-

pies, which had the faces of women, and the wings, bodies, and claws of vultures. These ugly wretches were in the habit of snatching away his dinner, and allowed him no peace of his life. Upon hearing this, the Argonauts spread a plentiful feast on the sea-shore, well knowing, from what the blind king said of their greediness, that the Harpies would snuff up the scent of the victuals, and quickly come to steal them away. And so it turned out; for, hardly was the ta-ble set, before the three hideous vulture women came flapping their wings, seized the food in their talons, and flew off as fast as they could. But the two sons of the North Wind drew their swords, spread their pinions, and set off through the air in pursuit of the thieves, whom they at last overtook among some isl-ands, after a chase of hundreds of miles. The two winged youths blustered terribly at the Harpies (for they had the rough temper of their father), and so frightened them with their drawn swords, that they solemnly promised never to trouble King Phineus again.

Then the Argonauts sailed onward, and met with many other marvellous incidents any one of which would make a story by itself. At one time, they landed on an island, and were reposing on the grass, when they suddenly found themselves assailed by what seemed a shower of steel-headed arrows. Some of them stuck in the ground, while others hit against their shields, and several penetrated their flesh. The fifty heroes started up, and looked about them for the hidden enemy, but could find none, nor see any spot, on the whole island, where even a single archer could lie concealed. Still, however, the steel-headed arrows came whizzing among them; and, at last, happening to look upward, they beheld a large flock of birds, hovering and wheeling aloft, and shooting their feathers down upon the Argonauts. These feathers were the steel-headed arrows that had so tormented them. There was no possibility of making any resistance; and the fifty heroic Argonauts might all have been killed or wounded by a flock of troublesome birds, without ever setting eyes on the Golden Fleece, if Jason had not thought of asking the advice of the oaken image.

So he ran to the galley as fast as his legs would carry him.

"O daughter of the Speaking Oak," cried he, all out of breath, "we need your wisdom more than ever before! We are in great peril from a flock of birds, who are shooting us with their steel-pointed feathers. What can we do to drive them away?"

"Make a clatter on your shields," said the image.

On receiving this excellent counsel, Jason hurried back to his companions (who were far more dismayed than when they fought with the six-armed giants), and bade them strike with their swords upon their brazen shields. Forthwith the fifty heroes set heartily to work, banging with might and main, and raised such a terrible clatter that the birds made what haste they could to get away; and though they had shot half the feathers out of their wings, they were soon seen skimming among the clouds, a long distance off, and looking like a flock of wild geese. Orpheus celebrated this victory by playing a triumphant anthem on his harp, and sang so melodiously that Jason begged him to desist, lest, as the steel-feathered birds had been driven away by an ugly sound, they might be enticed back again by a sweet one.

While the Argonauts remained on this island, they saw a small vessel approaching the shore, in which were two young men of princely demeanor, and exceedingly handsome, as young princes generally were in those days. Now, who do you imagine these two voyagers turned out to be? Why, if you will believe me, they were the sons of that very Phrixus, who, in his childhood, had been carried to Colchis on the back of the golden-fleeced ram. Since that time, Phrixus had married the king's daughter; and the two young princes had been born and brought up at Colchis, and had spent their play-days in the outskirts of the grove, in the centre of which the Golden Fleece was hanging upon a tree. They were now on their way to Greece, in hopes of getting back a kingdom that had been wrongfully taken from their father.

When the princes understood whither the Argonauts were going, they offered to turn back and guide them to Colchis. At the same time, however, they spoke as if it were very doubtful whether Jason would succeed in getting the Golden Fleece. According to their account, the tree on which it hung was guarded by a terrible dragon, who never failed to devour, at one mouthful, every person who might venture within his reach.

"There are other difficulties in the way," continued the young princes. "But is not this enough? Ah, brave Jason, turn back before it is too late. It would grieve us to the heart, if you and your nine-and-forty brave companions should be eaten up, at fifty mouthfuls, by this execrable dragon."

"My young friends," quietly replied Jason, "I do not wonder that you think the dragon very terrible. You have grown up from infancy in the fear of this monster, and therefore still regard him with the awe

that children feel for the bugbears and hobgoblins
which their nurses have talked to them about. But,
in my view of the matter, the dragon is merely a
pretty large serpent, who is not half so likely to snap
me up at one mouthful as I am to cut off his ugly
head, and strip the skin from his body. At all events,
turn back who may, I will never see Greece again unless I carry with me the Golden Fleece."

" We will none of us turn back! " cried his nine-
and-forty brave comrades. " Let us get on board the
galley this instant; and if the dragon is to make a
breakfast of us, much good may it do him."

And Orpheus (whose custom it was to set everything to music) began to harp and sing most gloriously, and made every mother's son of them feel as
if nothing in this world were so delectable as to fight
dragons, and nothing so truly honorable as to be eaten
up at one mouthful, in case of the worst.

After this (being now under the guidance of the
two princes, who were well acquainted with the way),
they quickly sailed to Colchis. When the king of the
country, whose name was Æetes, heard of their arrival, he instantly summoned Jason to court. The king
was a stern and cruel-looking potentate; and though
he put on as polite and hospitable an expression as he
could, Jason did not like his face a whit better than
that of the wicked King Pelias, who dethroned his
father.

" You are welcome, brave Jason," said King Æetes.
" Pray, are you on a pleasure voyage? — or do you
meditate the discovery of unknown islands? — or what
other cause has procured me the happiness of seeing
you at my court?"

" Great sir," replied Jason, with an obeisance, —

for Chiron had taught him how to behave with propriety, whether to kings or beggars, — "I have come
hither with a purpose which I now beg your Majesty's
permission to execute. King Pelias, who sits on my
father's throne (to which he has no more right than
to the one on which your excellent Majesty is now
seated), has engaged to come down from it, and to
give me his crown and sceptre, provided I bring him
the Golden Fleece. This, as your Majesty is aware, is
now hanging on a tree here at Colchis; and I humbly
solicit your gracious leave to take it away."

In spite of himself, the king's face twisted itself
into an angry frown; for, above all things else in the
world, he prized the Golden Fleece, and was even suspected of having done a very wicked act, in order to
get it into his own possession. It put him into the
worst possible humor, therefore, to hear that the gallant Prince Jason, and forty-nine of the bravest young
warriors of Greece, had come to Colchis with the sole
purpose of taking away his chief treasure.

"Do you know," asked King Æetes, eying Jason
very sternly, "what are the conditions which you must
fulfil before getting possession of the Golden Fleece?"

"I have heard," rejoined the youth, "that a dragon
lies beneath the tree on which the prize hangs, and
that whoever approaches him runs the risk of being
devoured at a mouthful."

"True," said the king, with a smile that did not
look particularly good-natured. "Very true, young
man. But there are other things as hard, or perhaps
a little harder, to be done, before you can even have
the privilege of being devoured by the dragon. For
example, you must first tame my two brazen-footed
and brazen-lunged bulls, which Vulcan, the wonderful

blacksmith, made for me. There is a furnace in each of their stomachs; and they breathe such hot fire out of their mouths and nostrils, that nobody has hitherto gone nigh them without being instantly burned to a small, black cinder. What do you think of this, my brave Jason?"

"I must encounter the peril," answered Jason, composedly, "since it stands in the way of my purpose."

"After taming the fiery bulls," continued King Æetes, who was determined to scare Jason if possible, "you must yoke them to a plough, and must plough the sacred earth in the grove of Mars, and sow some of the same dragon's teeth from which Cadmus raised a crop of armed men. They are an unruly set of reprobates, those sons of the dragon's teeth; and unless you treat them suitably, they will fall upon you sword in hand. You and your nine-and-forty Argonauts, my bold Jason, are hardly numerous or strong enough to fight with such a host as will spring up."

"My master Chiron," replied Jason, "taught me, long ago, the story of Cadmus. Perhaps I can manage the quarrelsome sons of the dragon's teeth as well as Cadmus did."

"I wish the dragon had him," muttered King Æetes to himself, "and the four-footed pedant, his schoolmaster, into the bargain. Why, what a foolhardy, self-conceited coxcomb he is! We'll see what my fire-breathing bulls will do for him. Well, Prince Jason," he continued, aloud, and as complaisantly as he could, "make yourself comfortable for to-day, and to-morrow morning, since you insist upon it, you shall try your skill at the plough."

While the king talked with Jason, a beautiful young woman was standing behind the throne. She fixed her eyes earnestly upon the youthful stranger, and listened attentively to every word that was spoken; and when Jason withdrew from the king's presence, this young woman followed him out of the room.

"I am the king's daughter," she said to him, "and my name is Medea. I know a great deal of which other young princesses are ignorant, and can do many things which they would be afraid so much as to dream of. If you will trust to me, I can instruct you how to tame the fiery bulls, and sow the dragon's teeth, and get the Golden Fleece."

"Indeed, beautiful princess," answered Jason, "if you will do me this service, I promise to be grateful to you my whole life long."

Gazing at Medea, he beheld a wonderful intelligence in her face. She was one of those persons whose eyes are full of mystery; so that, while looking into them, you seem to see a very great way, as into a deep well, yet can never be certain whether you see into the farthest depths, or whether there be not something else hidden at the bottom. If Jason had been capable of fearing anything, he would have been afraid of making this young princess his enemy; for, beautiful as she now looked, she might, the very next instant, become as terrible as the dragon that kept watch over the Golden Fleece.

"Princess," he exclaimed, "you seem indeed very wise and very powerful. But how can you help me to do the things of which you speak? Are you an enchantress?"

"Yes, Prince Jason," answered Medea, with a smile, "you have hit upon the truth. I am an enchantress. Circe, my father's sister, taught me to be one, and I could tell you, if I pleased, who was the old

woman with the peacock, the pomegranate, and the
cuckoo staff, whom you carried over the river; and,
likewise, who it is that speaks through the lips of the
oaken image, that stands in the prow of your galley.
I am acquainted with some of your secrets, you perceive. It is well for you that I am favorably inclined; for, otherwise, you would hardly escape being
snapped up by the dragon."

"I should not so much care for the dragon," replied
Jason, "if I only knew how to manage the brazen-
footed and fiery-lunged bulls."

"If you are as brave as I think you, and as you
have need to be," said Medea, "your own bold heart
will teach you that there is but one way of dealing
with a mad bull. What it is I leave you to find out
in the moment of peril. As for the fiery breath of
these animals, I have a charmed ointment here, which
will prevent you from being burned up, and cure you
if you chance to be a little scorched."

So she put a golden box into his hand, and directed
him how to apply the perfumed unguent which it contained, and where to meet her at midnight.

"Only be brave," added she, "and before daybreak
the brazen bulls shall be tamed."

The young man assured her that his heart would
not fail him. He then rejoined his comrades, and
told them what had passed between the princess and
himself, and warned them to be in readiness in case
there might be need of their help.

At the appointed hour he met the beautiful Medea
on the marble steps of the king's palace. She gave
him a basket, in which were the dragon's teeth, just
as they had been pulled out of the monster's jaws by
Cadmus, long ago. Medea then led Jason down the

palace steps, and through the silent streets of the city,
and into the royal pasture-ground, where the two brazen-footed bulls were kept. It was a starry night,
with a bright gleam along the eastern edge of the sky,
where the moon was soon going to show herself. After
entering the pasture, the princess paused and looked
around.

" There they are," said she, " reposing themselves
and chewing their fiery cuds in that farthest corner of
the field. It will be excellent sport, I assure you,
when they catch a glimpse of your figure. My father
and all his court delight in nothing so much as to see
a stranger trying to yoke them, in order to come at
the Golden Fleece. It makes a holiday in Colchis
whenever such a thing happens. For my part, I enjoy it immensely. You cannot imagine in what a mere
twinkling of an eye their hot breath shrivels a young
man into a black cinder."

" Are you sure, beautiful Medea," asked Jason,
" quite sure, that the unguent in the gold box will
prove a remedy against those terrible burns ? "

" If you doubt, if you are in the least afraid," said
the princess, looking him in the face by the dim starlight, " you had better never have been born than go
a step nigher to the bulls."

But Jason had set his heart steadfastly on getting
the Golden Fleece ; and I positively doubt whether he
would have gone back without it, even had he been
certain of finding himself turned into a red-hot cinder,
or a handful of white ashes, the instant he made a
step farther. He therefore let go Medea's hand, and
walked boldly forward in the direction whither she
had pointed. At some distance before him he perceived four streams of fiery vapor, regularly appear-

ing, and again vanishing, after dimly lighting up the surrounding obscurity. These, you will understand, were caused by the breath of the brazen bulls, which was quietly stealing out of their four nostrils, as they lay chewing their cuds.

At the first two or three steps which Jason made, the four fiery streams appeared to gush out some-what more plentifully; for the two brazen bulls had heard his foot-tramp, and were lifting up their hot noses to snuff the air. He went a little farther, and by the way in which the red vapor now spouted forth, he judged that the creatures had got upon their feet. Now he could see glowing sparks, and vivid jets of flame. At the next step, each of the bulls made the pasture echo with a terrible roar, while the burning breath, which they thus belched forth, lit up the whole field with a momentary flash. One other stride did bold Jason make; and, suddenly, as a streak of light-ning, on came these fiery animals, roaring like thun-der, and sending out sheets of white flame, which so kindled up the scene that the young man could discern every object more distinctly than by daylight. Most distinctly of all he saw the two horrible creatures gal-loping right down upon him, their brazen hoofs rat-tling and ringing over the ground, and their tails sticking up stiffly into the air, as has always been the fashion with angry bulls. Their breath scorched the herbage before them. So intensely hot it was, indeed, that it caught a dry tree, under which Jason was now standing, and set it all in a light blaze. But as for Jason himself (thanks to Medea's enchanted oint-ment), the white flame curled around his body, with-out injuring him a jot more than if he had been made of asbestos.

Greatly encouraged at finding himself not yet turned into a cinder, the young man awaited the attack of the bulls. Just as the brazen brutes fancied themselves sure of tossing him into the air, he caught one of them by the horn, and the other by his screwed-up tail, and held them in a gripe like that of an iron vice, one with his right hand, the other with his left. Well, he must have been wonderfully strong in his arms, to be sure. But the secret of the matter was, that the brazen bulls were enchanted creatures, and that Jason had broken the spell of their fiery fierceness by his bold way of handling them. And, ever since that time, it has been the favorite method of brave men, when danger assails them, to do what they call "taking the bull by the horns"; and to gripe him by the tail is pretty much the same thing, — that is, to throw aside fear, and overcome the peril by despising it.

It was now easy to yoke the bulls, and to harness them to the plough, which had lain rusting on the ground for a great many years gone by; so long was it before anybody could be found capable of ploughing that piece of land. Jason, I suppose, had been taught how to draw a furrow by the good old Chiron, who, perhaps, used to allow himself to be harnessed to the plough. At any rate, our hero succeeded perfectly well in breaking up the greensward; and, by the time that the moon was a quarter of her journey up the sky, the ploughed field lay before him, a large tract of black earth, ready to be sown with the dragon's teeth. So Jason scattered them broadcast, and harrowed them into the soil with a brush-harrow, and took his stand on the edge of the field, anxious to see what would happen next.

"Must we wait long for harvest-time?" he inquired of Medea, who was now standing by his side.

" Whether sooner or later, it will be sure to come," answered the princess. " A crop of armed men never fails to spring up, when the dragon's teeth have been sown."

The moon was now high aloft in the heavens, and threw its bright beams over the ploughed field, where as yet there was nothing to be seen. Any farmer, on viewing it, would have said that Jason must wait weeks before the green blades would peep from among the clods, and whole months before the yellow grain would be ripened for the sickle. But by and by, all over the field, there was something that glistened in the moon-beams, like sparkling drops of dew. These bright objects sprouted higher, and proved to be the steel heads of spears. Then there was a dazzling gleam from a vast number of polished brass helmets, beneath which, as they grew farther out of the soil, appeared the dark and bearded visages of warriors, struggling to free themselves from the imprisoning earth. The first look that they gave at the upper world was a glare of wrath and defiance. Next were seen their bright breastplates ; in every right hand there was a sword or a spear, and on each left arm a shield; and when this strange crop of warriors had but half grown out of the earth, they struggled, — such was their impatience of restraint, — and, as it were, tore themselves up by the roots. Wherever a dragon's tooth had fallen, there stood a man armed for battle. They made a clangor with their swords against their shields, and eyed one another fiercely ; for they had come into this beautiful world, and into the peaceful moonlight, full of rage and stormy passions, and ready to take the life of every human brother, in recompense of the boon of their own existence.

There have been many other armies in the world that seemed to possess the same fierce nature with the one which had now sprouted from the dragon's teeth; but these, in the moonlit field, were the more excusable, because they never had women for their mothers. And how it would have rejoiced any great captain, who was bent on conquering the world, like Alexander or Napoleon, to raise a crop of armed soldiers as easily as Jason did!

For a while, the warriors stood flourishing their weapons, clashing their swords against their shields, and boiling over with the red-hot thirst for battle. Then they began to shout, " Show us the enemy! Lead us to the charge! Death or victory! Come on, brave comrades! Conquer or die!" and a hundred other outcries, such as men always bellow forth on a battle-field, and which these dragon people seemed to have at their tongues' ends. At last, the front rank caught sight of Jason, who, beholding the flash of so many weapons in the moonlight, had thought it best to draw his sword. In a moment all the sons of the dragon's teeth appeared to take Jason for an enemy; and crying with one voice, "Guard the Golden Fleece!" they ran at him with uplifted swords and protruded spears. Jason knew that it would be impossible to withstand this bloodthirsty battalion with his single arm, but determined, since there was nothing better to be done, to die as valiantly as if he himself had sprung from a dragon's tooth.

Medea, however, bade him snatch up a stone from the ground.

"Throw it among them quickly!" cried she. "It is the only way to save yourself."

The armed men were now so nigh that Jason could

discern the fire flashing out of their enraged eyes, when he let fly the stone, and saw it strike the helmet of a tall warrior, who was rushing upon him with his blade aloft. The stone glanced from this man's helmet to the shield of his nearest comrade, and thence flew right into the angry face of another, hitting him smartly between the eyes. Each of the three who had been struck by the stone took it for granted that his next neighbor had given him a blow; and instead of running any farther towards Jason, they began a fight among themselves. The confusion spread through the host, so that it seemed scarcely a moment before they were all hacking, hewing, and stabbing at one another, lopping off arms, heads, and legs, and doing such memorable deeds that Jason was filled with immense admiration; although, at the same time, he could not help laughing to behold these mighty men punishing each other for an offence which he himself had committed. In an incredibly short space of time (almost as short, indeed, as it had taken them to grow up), all but one of the heroes of the dragon's teeth were stretched lifeless on the field. The last survivor, the bravest and strongest of the whole, had just force enough to wave his crimson sword over his head, and give a shout of exultation, crying, " Victory ! Victory ! Immortal fame ! " when he himself fell down, and lay quietly among his slain brethren.

And there was the end of the army that had sprouted from the dragon's teeth. That fierce and feverish fight was the only enjoyment which they had tasted on this beautiful earth.

" Let them sleep in the bed of honor," said the Princess Medea, with a sly smile at Jason. " The world will always have simpletons enough, just like them,

fighting and dying for they know not what, and fancying that posterity will take the trouble to put laurel
wreaths on their rusty and battered helmets. Could
you help smiling, Prince Jason, to see the self-conceit
of that last fellow, just as he tumbled down?"

"It made me very sad," answered Jason, gravely.
"And, to tell you the truth, princess, the Golden
Fleece does not appear so well worth the winning,
after what I have here beheld."

"You will think differently in the morning," said
Medea. "True, the Golden Fleece may not be so valuable as you have thought it; but then there is nothing better in the world; and one must needs have an
object, you know. Come! Your night's work has
been well performed; and to-morrow you can inform
King Æetes that the first part of your alloted task is
fulfilled."

Agreeably to Medea's advice, Jason went betimes in
the morning to the palace of King Æetes. Entering
the presence - chamber, he stood at the foot of the
throne, and made a low obeisance.

"Your eyes look heavy, Prince Jason," observed
the king; "you appear to have spent a sleepless night.
I hope you have been considering the matter a little
more wisely, and have concluded not to get yourself
scorched to a cinder, in attempting to tame my brazen-
lunged bulls."

"That is already accomplished, may it please your
Majesty," replied Jason. "The bulls have been tamed
and yoked; the field has been ploughed; the dragon's
teeth have been sown broadcast, and harrowed into
the soil; the crop of armed warriors has sprung up,
and they have slain one another, to the last man. And
now I solicit your Majesty's permission to encounter

the dragon, that I may take down the Golden Fleece from the tree, and depart, with my nine-and-forty comrades."

King Æetes scowled, and looked very angry and excessively disturbed ; for he knew that, in accordance with his kingly promise, he ought now to permit Jason to win the fleece, if his courage and skill should enable him to do so. But, since the young man had met with such good luck in the matter of the brazen bulls and the dragon's teeth, the king feared that he would be equally successful in slaying the dragon. And therefore, though he would gladly have seen Jason snapped up at a mouthful, he was resolved (and it was a very wrong thing of this wicked potentate) not to run any further risk of losing his beloved fleece.

" You never would have succeeded in this business, young man," said he, " if my undutiful daughter Medea had not helped you with her enchantments. Had you acted fairly, you would have been, at this instant, a black cinder, or a handful of white ashes. I forbid you, on pain of death, to make any more attempts to get the Golden Fleece. To speak my mind plainly, you shall never set eyes on so much as one of its glistening locks."

Jason left the king's presence in great sorrow and anger. He could think of nothing better to be done than to summon together his forty-nine brave Argonauts, march at once to the grove of Mars, slay the dragon, take possession of the Golden Fleece, get on board the Argo, and spread all sail for Iolchos. The success of the scheme depended, it is true, on the doubtful point whether all the fifty heroes might not be snapped up, at so many mouthfuls, by the dragon. But, as Jason was hastening down the palace steps, the Princess Medea called after him, and beckoned him to return. Her black eyes shone upon him with such a keen intelligence, that he felt as if there were a serpent peeping out of them; and although she had done him so much service only the night before, he was by no means very certain that she would not do him an equally great mischief before sunset. These enchantresses, you must know, are never to be depended upon.

"What says King Æetes, my royal and upright father?" inquired Medea, slightly smiling. "Will he give you the Golden Fleece, without any further risk or trouble?"

"On the contrary," answered Jason, "he is very angry with me for taming the brazen bulls and sowing the dragon's teeth. And he forbids me to make any more attempts, and positively refuses to give up the Golden Fleece, whether I slay the dragon or no."

"Yes, Jason," said the princess, "and I can tell you more. Unless you set sail from Colchis before to-morrow's sunrise, the king means to burn your fifty-oared galley, and put yourself and your forty-nine brave comrades to the sword. But be of good courage. The Golden Fleece you shall have, if it lies within the power of my enchantments to get it for you. Wait for me here an hour before midnight."

At the appointed hour, you might again have seen Prince Jason and the Princess Medea, side by side, stealing through the streets of Colchis, on their way to the sacred grove, in the centre of which the Golden Fleece was suspended to a tree. While they were crossing the pasture-ground, the brazen bulls came towards Jason, lowing, nodding their heads, and thrusting forth their snouts, which, as other cattle do, they loved to have rubbed and caressed by a friendly hand. Their fierce nature was thoroughly tamed; and, with their fierceness, the two furnaces in their stomachs had likewise been extinguished, insomuch that they probably enjoyed far more comfort in grazing and chewing their cuds than ever before. Indeed, it had heretofore been a great inconvenience to these poor animals, that, whenever they wished to eat a mouthful of grass, the fire out of their nostrils had shrivelled it up, before they could manage to crop it. How they contrived to keep themselves alive is more than I can imagine. But now, instead of emitting jets of flame and streams of sulphurous vapor, they breathed the very sweetest of cow breath.

After kindly patting the bulls, Jason followed Medea's guidance into the grove of Mars, where the great oak-trees, that had been growing for centuries, threw so thick a shade that the moonbeams struggled vainly to find their way through it. Only here and there a glimmer fell upon the leaf-strewn earth, or now and then a breeze stirred the boughs aside, and gave Jason a glimpse of the sky, lest, in that deep obscurity, he might forget that there was one, overhead. At length, when they had gone farther and farther into the heart of the duskiness, Medea squeezed Jason's hand.

"Look yonder," she whispered. "Do you see it?"

Gleaming among the venerable oaks, there was a radiance, not like the moonbeams, but rather resembling the golden glory of the setting sun. It proceeded from an object, which appeared to be suspended at about a man's height from the ground, a little farther within the wood.

"What is it?" asked Jason.

" Have you come so far to seek it," exclaimed Medea, "and do you not recognize the meed of all your toils and perils, when it glitters before your eyes? It is the Golden Fleece."

Jason went onward a few steps farther, and then stopped to gaze. Oh, how beautiful it looked, shining with a marvellous light of its own, that inestimable prize, which so many heroes had longed to behold, but had perished in the quest of it, either by the perils of their voyage, or by the fiery breath of the brazen-lunged bulls.

" How gloriously it shines ! " cried Jason, in a rapture. " It has surely been dipped in the richest gold of sunset. Let me hasten onward, and take it to my bosom."

" Stay," said Medea, holding him back. " Have you forgotten what guards it ? "

To say the truth, in the joy of beholding the object of his desires, the terrible dragon had quite slipped out of Jason's memory. Soon, however, something came to pass that reminded him what perils were still to be encountered. An antelope, that probably mistook the yellow radiance for sunrise, came bounding fleetly through the grove. He was rushing straight towards the Golden Fleece, when suddenly there was a frightful hiss, and the immense head and half the scaly body of the dragon was thrust forth (for he was twisted round the trunk of the tree on which the fleece hung), and seizing the poor antelope, swallowed him with one snap of his jaws.

After this feat, the dragon seemed sensible that some other living creature was within reach on which he felt inclined to finish his meal. In various directions he kept poking his ugly snout among the trees, stretching out his neck a terrible long way, now here, now there, and now close to the spot where Jason and the princess were hiding behind an oak. Upon my word, as the head came waving and undulating through the air, and reaching almost within arm's-length of Prince Jason, it was a very hideous and uncomfortable sight. The gape of his enormous jaws was nearly as wide as the gateway of the king's palace.

" Well, Jason," whispered Medea (for she was ill-natured, as all enchantresses are, and wanted to make the bold youth tremble), " what do you think now of your prospect of winning the Golden Fleece ? "

Jason answered only by drawing his sword and making a step forward.

" Stay, foolish youth," said Medea, grasping his arm. " Do not you see you are lost, without me as your good angel ? In this gold box I have a magic potion, which will do the dragon's business far more effectually than your sword."

The dragon had probably heard the voices ; for, swift as lightning, his black head and forked tongue came hissing among the trees again, darting full forty feet at a stretch. As it approached, Medea tossed the contents of the gold box right down the monster's wide open throat. Immediately, with an outrageous hiss and a tremendous wriggle, — flinging his tail up to the tip-top of the tallest tree, and shattering all its branches as it crashed heavily down again, — the dragon fell at full length upon the ground, and lay quite motionless.

" It is only a sleeping potion," said the enchantress to Prince Jason. " One always finds a use for these mischievous creatures, sooner or later ; so I did not wish to kill him outright. Quick ! Snatch the prize, and let us begone. You have won the Golden Fleece."

Jason caught the fleece from the tree, and hurried through the grove, the deep shadows of which were illuminated as he passed by the golden glory of the precious object that he bore along. A little way before him, he beheld the old woman whom he had helped over the stream, with her peacock beside her. She clapped her hands for joy, and beckoning him to make haste, disappeared among the duskiness of the trees. Espying the two winged sons of the North Wind (who were disporting themselves in the moonlight, a few hundred feet aloft), Jason bade them tell the rest of the Argonauts to embark as speedily as possible. But Lynceus, with his sharp eyes, had already caught a glimpse of him, bringing the Golden Fleece, although several stone-walls, a hill, and the black shadows of the grove of Mars intervened between. By his advice, the heroes had seated themselves on the benches of the galley, with their oars held perpendicularly, ready to let fall into the water.

As Jason drew near, he heard the Talking Image calling to him with more than ordinary eagerness, in its grave, sweet voice : —

" Make haste, Prince Jason ! For your life, make haste ! "

With one bound he leaped aboard. At sight of the glorious radiance of the Golden Fleece, the nine-and-forty heroes gave a mighty shout, and Orpheus, striking his harp, sang a song of triumph, to the cadence of which the galley flew over the water, homeward bound, as if careering along with wings !

THE WHOLE HISTORY

OF

GRANDFATHER'S CHAIR.

COMPLETE IN THREE PARTS

INTRODUCTORY NOTE.

———◆———

GRANDFATHER'S CHAIR.

IN a letter which Hawthorne addressed to Longfellow at the time of publishing the "Twice-Told
Tales," he said, speaking of his life up to that time
and his future prospects : —

"I have now, or shall soon have, a sharper spur to
exertion, which I lacked at an earlier period ; for I
see little prospect but that I shall have to scribble for
a living. But this troubles me much less than you
would suppose. I can turn my pen to all sorts of
drudgery, such as children's books, etc."

Precisely what the "sharper spur" was can be con-
jectured only ; but it is not unlikely that thoughts of
marriage had already entered his mind, for certainly
within the term of two years following he had made
that matrimonial engagement which was destined to
be carried out in a life-long union of great happiness.
He had already, in writing "Peter Parley's History"
for Goodrich, demonstrated his fitness for supplying
youthful minds with simple and entertaining literature. It should seem that, having learned something
from his experience with Goodrich, corroborative of
Virgil's *Sic vos non vobis*, he determined to exercise

for his own benefit the faculty of writing for children, which he had thus developed, and had shown himself conscious of in the Longfellow letter just quoted. Accordingly, between the time of issuing his collected stories and the date of his Brook Farm episode, he produced a number of brief narratives, the subjects of which were drawn from those old New England annals which some of his tales and other detached papers — to say nothing of the local coloring in "The Scarlet Letter" — show him to have conned over so thoroughly.

These little stories, connected by dialogue, and by a pleasant fiction concerning an old chair supposed to have figured in the various historical scenes depicted, were first published in diminutive volumes, each one of the three parts appearing separately.

In the prefatory note to the "Twice-Told Tales" the editor has related how Mrs. Hawthorne, before her marriage, drew an illustration for "The Gentle Boy," which was engraved and printed with a special edition of that story. Extracts from his letters to her, written at Salem, during an absence from Brook Farm in September, 1841,[1] indicate that a series of illustrations for the "Grandfather's Chair" stories was contemplated; and presumably she was to furnish the sketches. Hawthorne there offers a number of suggestions for the drawings, that indirectly disclose the vividness and completeness with which he had imagined the scenes described. He proposes as themes for the artist's pencil, Master Cheever's old-fashioned school, the Acadians, the Earl of Loudon's military council at Boston, and Liberty Tree. The reader will find it interesting to refer to these pas-

[1] See *American Note-Books,* September 14–16, 1841.

sages ; but the pictorial project was, apparently, abandoned.

To the literary student " Grandfather's Chair " presents two points deserving notice : one, the fact that the incident of Endicott's cutting the red cross from the banner of England, which furnished the motive for a Twice-Told Tale, is here treated in a manner quite different ; the other, that the exile of the Acadians is chosen by Hawthorne as one of the occurrences likely to appeal to his youthful audience. It will be remembered by every one acquainted with recent American literary history, that Hawthorne surrendered to Longfellow the story which formed the groundwork of " Evangeline." This story was told to Hawthorne in October, 1839,[1] just at the period when he was writing " Grandfather's Chair." Perhaps the editor may be pardoned if he here remarks that he has often been skeptical as to the indifference, which it has sometimes been alleged that Hawthorne displayed towards the pathetic tradition which prompted " Evangeline ; " and that the romancer should, at the very time of hearing the story, have been engaged in treating the exile of the Acadians with a sympathy so unmistakable, as is shown even in his brief child's story, tends to confirm this skepticism. Longfellow had done Hawthorne a great kindness by noticing favorably in the " North American Review " his friend's " Twice-Told Tales." It seems probable enough that Hawthorne, on seeing how much the Evangeline anecdote struck his friend the poet, resolved to yield it up at once, without betraying any intention he may have had of utilizing it himself.

No further comment is required on the contents of

[1] See *American Note-Books,* October 24, of that year.

this collection ; unless it be that the " The Pine-Tree Shillings," by the universal currency which they have enjoyed in school-readers and elsewhere, ought effectually to dispel the frequently expressed opinion that Hawthorne failed to attain general popularity.

G. P. L.

PREFACE.

—◆—

IN writing this ponderous tome, the author's desire
has been to describe the eminent characters and remarkable events of our annals in such a form and
style that the YOUNG may make acquaintance with
them of their own accord. For this purpose, while
ostensibly relating the adventures of a chair, he has
endeavored to keep a distinct and unbroken thread of
authentic history. The chair is made to pass from one
to another of those personages of whom he thought it
most desirable for the young reader to have vivid and
familiar ideas, and whose lives and actions would best
enable him to give picturesque sketches of the times.
On its sturdy oaken legs it trudges diligently from one
scene to another, and seems always to thrust itself in
the way, with most benign complacency, whenever an
historical personage happens to be looking round for
a seat.

There is certainly no method by which the shadowy
outlines of departed men and women can be made to
assume the hues of life more effectually than by con-
necting their images with the substantial and homely
reality of a fireside chair. It causes us to feel at once
that these characters of history had a private and familiar existence, and were not wholly contained within
that cold array of outward action which we are compelled to receive as the adequate representation of

their lives. If this impression can be given, much is accomplished.

Setting aside Grandfather and his auditors, and excepting the adventures of the chair, which form the machinery of the work, nothing in the ensuing pages can be termed fictitious. The author, it is true, has sometimes assumed the license of filling up the outline of history with details for which he has none but imaginative authority, but which, he hopes, do not violate nor give a false coloring to the truth. He believes that, in this respect, his narrative will not be found to convey ideas and impressions of which the reader may hereafter find it necessary to purge his mind.

The author's great doubt is, whether he has succeeded in writing a book which will be readable by the class for whom he intends it. To make a lively and entertaining narrative for children, with such unmalleable material as is presented by the sombre, stern, and rigid characteristics of the Puritans and their descendants, is quite as difficult an attempt as to manufacture delicate playthings out of the granite rocks on which New England is founded.

GRANDFATHER'S CHAIR.

PART I.

CHAPTER I.

GRANDFATHER had been sitting in his old arm-chair all that pleasant afternoon, while the children were pursuing their various sports far off or near at hand. Sometimes you would have said, "Grandfather is asleep"; but still, even when his eyes were closed, his thoughts were with the young people, playing among the flowers and shrubbery of the garden.

He heard the voice of Laurence, who had taken possession of a heap of decayed branches which the gardener had lopped from the fruit-trees, and was building a little hut for his cousin Clara and himself. He heard Clara's gladsome voice, too, as she weeded and watered the flower-bed which had been given her for her own. He could have counted every footstep that Charley took, as he trundled his wheelbarrow along the gravel-walk. And though Grandfather was old and gray-haired, yet his heart leaped with joy whenever little Alice came fluttering, like a butterfly, into the room. She had made each of the children her playmate in turn, and now made Grandfather her playmate too, and thought him the merriest of them all.

At last the children grew weary of their sports;

because a summer afternoon is like a long lifetime to
the young. So they came into the room together, and
clustered round Grandfather's great chair. Little
Alice, who was hardly five years old, took the privilege of the youngest, and climbed his knee. It was
a pleasant thing to behold that fair and golden-haired
child in the lap of the old man, and to think that, different as they were, the hearts of both could be gladdened with the same joys.

"Grandfather," said little Alice, laying her head
back upon his arm, "I am very tired now. You must
tell me a story to make me go to sleep."

"That is not what story-tellers like," answered
Grandfather, smiling. "They are better satisfied
when they can keep their auditors awake."

"But here are Laurence, and Charley, and I,"
cried cousin Clara, who was twice as old as little
Alice. "We will all three keep wide awake. And
pray, Grandfather, tell us a story about this strange-
looking old chair."

Now, the chair in which Grandfather sat was made
of oak, which had grown dark with age, but had been
rubbed and polished till it shone as bright as mahogany. It was very large and heavy, and had a back
that rose high above Grandfather's white head. This
back was curiously carved in open work, so as to represent flowers, and foliage, and other devices, which
the children had often gazed at, but could never understand what they meant. On the very tip-top of the
chair, over the head of Grandfather himself, was a
likeness of a lion's head, which had such a savage grin
that you would almost expect to hear it growl and
snarl.

The children had seen Grandfather sitting in this

chair ever since they could remember anything. Perhaps the younger of them supposed that he and the chair had come into the world together, and that both had always been as old as they were now. At this time, however, it happened to be the fashion for ladies to adorn their drawing-rooms with the oldest and oddest chairs that could be found. It seemed to cousin Clara that, if these ladies could have seen Grandfather's old chair, they would have thought it worth all the rest together. She wondered if it were not even older than Grandfather himself, and longed to know all about its history.

" Do, Grandfather, talk to us about this chair," she repeated.

" Well, child," said Grandfather, patting Clara's cheek, " I can tell you a great many stories of my chair. Perhaps your cousin Laurence would like to hear them too. They would teach him something about the history and distinguished people of his country which he has never read in any of his schoolbooks."

Cousin Laurence was a boy of twelve, a bright scholar, in whom an early thoughtfulness and sensibility began to show themselves. His young fancy kindled at the idea of knowing all the adventures of this venerable chair. He looked eagerly in Grandfather's face; and even Charley, a bold, brisk, restless little fellow of nine, sat himself down on the carpet, and resolved to be quiet for at least ten minutes, should the story last so long.

Meantime, little Alice was already asleep; so Grandfather, being much pleased with such an attentive audience, began to talk about matters that happened long ago.

CHAPTER II.

But before relating the adventures of the chair, Grandfather found it necessary to speak of circumstances that caused the first settlement of New England. For it will soon be perceived that the story of this remarkable chair cannot be told without telling a great deal of the history of the country.

So Grandfather talked about the Puritans, as those persons were called who thought it sinful to practise the religious forms and ceremonies which the Church of England had borrowed from the Roman Catholics. These Puritans suffered so much persecution in England, that, in 1607, many of them went over to Holland, and lived ten or twelve years at Amsterdam and Leyden. But they feared that, if they continued there much longer, they should cease to be English, and should adopt all the manners, and ideas, and feelings of the Dutch. For this and other reasons, in the year 1620 they embarked on board of the ship Mayflower, and crossed the ocean, to the shores of Cape Cod. There they made a settlement, and called it Plymouth, which, though now a part of Massachusetts, was for a long time a colony by itself. And thus was formed the earliest settlement of the Puritans in America.

Meantime, those of the Puritans who remained in England continued to suffer grievous persecution on account of their religious opinions. They began to look around them for some spot where they might worship God, not as the king and bishops thought fit, but

according to the dictates of their own consciences.
When their brethren had gone from Holland to America, they bethought themselves that they likewise might
find refuge from persecution there. Several gentlemen
among them purchased a tract of country on the coast
of Massachusetts Bay, and obtained a charter from
King Charles, which authorized them to make laws for
the settlers. In the year 1628 they sent over a few
people, with John Endicott at their head, to commence
a plantation at Salem. Peter Palfrey, Roger Conant,
and one or two more had built houses there in 1626,
and may be considered as the first settlers of that
ancient town. Many other Puritans prepared to follow Endicott.

"And now we come to the chair, my dear children,"
said Grandfather. "This chair is supposed to have
been made of an oak-tree which grew in the park of
the English Earl of Lincoln between two and three
centuries ago. In its younger days it used, probably,
to stand in the hall of the earl's castle. Do not you
see the coat of arms of the family of Lincoln carved
in the open work of the back? But when his daughter, the Lady Arbella, was married to a certain Mr.
Johnson, the earl gave her this valuable chair."

"Who was Mr. Johnson?" inquired Clara.

"He was a gentleman of great wealth, who agreed
with the Puritans in their religious opinions," answered Grandfather. "And as his belief was the
same as theirs, he resolved that he would live and die
with them. Accordingly, in the month of April, 1630,
he left his pleasant abode and all his comforts in England, and embarked, with Lady Arbella, on board of
a ship bound for America."

As Grandfather was frequently impeded by the

questions and observations of his young auditors, we*
deem it advisable to omit all such prattle as is not
essential to the story. We have taken some pains to
find out exactly what Grandfather said, and here offer
to our readers, as nearly as possible in his own words,
the story of

THE LADY ARBELLA.

The ship in which Mr. Johnson and his lady embarked, taking Grandfather's chair along with them,
was called the Arbella, in honor of the lady herself.
A fleet of ten or twelve vessels, with many hundred
passengers, left England about the same time ; for a
multitude of people, who were discontented with the
king's government and oppressed by the bishops, were
flocking over to the New World. One of the vessels
in the fleet was that same Mayflower which had carried
the Puritan Pilgrims to Plymouth. And now, my
children, I would have you fancy yourselves in the
cabin of the good ship Arbella; because, if you could
behold the passengers aboard that vessel, you would
feel what a blessing and honor it was for New England to have such settlers. They were the best men
and women of their day.

Among the passengers was John Winthrop, who had
sold the estate of his forefathers, and was going to
prepare a new home for his wife and children in the
wilderness. He had the king's charter in his keeping,
and was appointed the first governor of Massachusetts.
Imagine him a person of grave and benevolent aspect,
dressed in a black velvet suit, with a broad ruff around
his neck, and a peaked beard upon his chin. There
was likewise a minister of the gospel whom the English bishops had forbidden to preach, but who knew

that he should have liberty both to preach and pray in the forests of America. He wore a black cloak, called a Geneva cloak, and had a black velvet cap, fitting close to his head, as was the fashion of almost all the Puritan clergymen. In their company came Sir Richard Saltonstall, who had been one of the five first projectors of the new colony. He soon returned to his native country. But his descendants still remain in New England ; and the good old family name is as much respected in our days as it was in those of Sir Richard.

Not only these, but several other men of wealth and pious ministers were in the cabin of the Arbella. One had banished himself forever from the old hall where his ancestors had lived for hundreds of years. Another had left his quiet parsonage, in a country town of England. Others had come from the Universities of Oxford or Cambridge, where they had gained great fame for their learning. And here they all were, tossing upon the uncertain and dangerous sea, and bound for a home that was more dangerous than even the sea itself. In the cabin, likewise, sat the Lady Arbella in her chair, with a gentle and sweet expression on her face, but looking too pale and feeble to endure the hardships of the wilderness.

Every morning and evening the Lady Arbella gave up her great chair to one of the ministers, who took his place in it and read passages from the Bible to his companions. And thus, with prayers, and pious conversation, and frequent singing of hymns, which the breezes caught from their lips and scattered far over the desolate waves, they prosecuted their voyage, and sailed into the harbor of Salem in the month of June.

At that period there were but six or eight dwellings

in the town ; and these were miserable hovels, with
roofs of straw and wooden chimneys. The passengers
in the fleet either built huts with bark and branches
of trees, or erected tents of cloth till they could provide themselves with better shelter. Many of them
went to form a settlement at Charlestown. It was
thought fit that the Lady Arbella should tarry in
Salem for a time : she was probably received as a
guest into the family of John Endicott. He was the
chief person in the plantation, and had the only comfortable house which the new-comers had beheld since
they left England. So now, children, you must imagine Grandfather's chair in the midst of a new scene.

Suppose it a hot summer's day, and the lattice-win-
dows of a chamber in Mr. Endicott's house thrown
wide open. The Lady Arbella, looking paler than she
did on shipboard, is sitting in her chair and thinking
mournfully of far-off England. She rises and goes to
the window. There, amid patches of garden ground
and cornfield, she sees the few wretched hovels of the
settlers, with the still ruder wigwams and cloth tents
of the passengers who had arrived in the same fleet
with herself. Far and near stretches the dismal forest
of pine-trees, which throw their black shadows over
the whole land, and likewise over the heart of this
poor lady.

All the inhabitants of the little village are busy.
One is clearing a spot on the verge of the forest for
his homestead ; another is hewing the trunk of a fallen
pine-tree, in order to build himself a dwelling ; a third
is hoeing in his field of Indian corn. Here comes a
huntsman out of the woods, dragging a bear which he
has shot, and shouting to the neighbors to lend him a
hand. There goes a man to the sea-shore, with

spade and a bucket, to dig a mess of clams, which were a principal article of food with the first settlers. Scattered here and there are two or three dusky figures, clad in mantles of fur, with ornaments of bone hanging from their ears, and the feathers of wild birds in their coal-black hair. They have belts of shell-work slung across their shoulders, and are armed with bows and arrows and flint-headed spears. These are an Indian sagamore and his attendants, who have come to gaze at the labors of the white men. And now rises a cry that a pack of wolves have seized a young calf in the pasture ; and every man snatches up his gun or pike and runs in chase of the marauding beasts.

Poor Lady Arbella watches all these sights, and feels that this New World is fit only for rough and hardy people. None should be here but those who can struggle with wild beasts and wild men, and can toil in the heat or cold, and can keep their hearts firm against all difficulties and dangers. But she is not one of these. Her gentle and timid spirit sinks within her ; and, turning away from the window, she sits down in the great chair and wonders whereabouts in the wilderness her friends will dig her grave.

Mr. Johnson had gone, with Governor Winthrop and most of the other passengers, to Boston, where he intended to build a house for Lady Arbella and himself. Boston was then covered with wild woods, and had fewer inhabitants, even, than Salem. During her husband's absence, poor Lady Arbella felt herself growing ill, and was hardly able to stir from the great chair. Whenever John Endicott noticed her despondency, he doubtless addressed her with words of comfort. " Cheer up, my good lady ! " he would say.

"In a little time, you will love this rude life of the wilderness as I do." But Endicott's heart was as bold and resolute as iron, and he could not understand why a woman's heart should not be of iron too.

Still, however, he spoke kindly to the lady, and then hastened forth to till his cornfield and set out fruit-trees, or to bargain with the Indians for furs, or perchance to oversee the building of a fort. Also, being a magistrate, he had often to punish some idler or evil doer, by ordering him to be set in the stocks or scourged at the whipping-post. Often, too, as was the custom of the times, he and Mr. Higginson, the minister of Salem, held long religious talks together. Thus John Endicott was a man of multifarious business, and had no time to look back regretfully to his native land. He felt himself fit for the New World and for the work that he had to do, and set himself resolutely to accomplish it.

What a contrast, my dear children, between this bold, rough, active man, and the gentle Lady Arbella, who was fading away, like a pale English flower, in the shadow of the forest! And now the great chair was often empty, because Lady Arbella grew too weak to arise from bed.

Meantime, her husband had pitched upon a spot for their new home. He returned from Boston to Salem, travelling through the woods on foot, and leaning on his pilgrim's staff. His heart yearned within him; for he was eager to tell his wife of the new home which he had chosen. But when he beheld her pale and hollow cheek, and found how her strength was wasted, he must have known that her appointed home was in a better land. Happy for him then — happy both for him and her — if they remembered that there was a path to heaven, as well from this heathen wilderness as from the Christian land whence they had come. And so, in one short month from her arrival, the gentle Lady Arbella faded away and died. They dug a grave for her in the new soil, where the roots of the pine-trees impeded their spades; and when her bones had rested there nearly two hundred years, and a city had sprung up around them, a church of stone was built upon the spot.

Charley, almost at the commencement of the foregoing narrative, had galloped away, with a prodigious clatter, upon Grandfather's stick, and was not yet returned. So large a boy should have been ashamed to ride upon a stick. But Laurence and Clara had listened attentively, and were affected by this true story of the gentle lady who had come so far to die so soon. Grandfather had supposed that little Alice was asleep; but towards the close of the story, happening to look down upon her, he saw that her blue eyes were wide open, and fixed earnestly upon his face. The tears had gathered in them, like dew upon a delicate flower; but when Grandfather ceased to speak, the sunshine of her smile broke forth again.

"Oh, the lady must have been so glad to get to heaven!" exclaimed little Alice.

"Grandfather, what became of Mr. Johnson?" asked Clara.

"His heart appears to have been quite broken," answered Grandfather; "for he died at Boston within a month after the death of his wife. He was buried in the very same tract of ground where he had intended to build a dwelling for Lady Arbella and himself. Where their house would have stood, there was his grave."

"I never heard anything so melancholy," said Clara.

"The people loved and respected Mr. Johnson so much," continued Grandfather, "that it was the last request of many of them, when they died, that they might be buried as near as possible to this good man's grave. And so the field became the first burial-ground in Boston. When you pass through Tremont Street, along by King's Chapel, you see a burial-ground, containing many old grave-stones and monuments. That was Mr. Johnson's field."

"How sad is the thought," observed Clara, "that one of the first things which the settlers had to do, when they came to the New World, was to set apart a burial-ground!"

"Perhaps," said Laurence, "if they had found no need of burial-grounds here, they would have been glad, after a few years, to go back to England."

Grandfather looked at Laurence, to discover whether he knew how profound and true a thing he had said.

CHAPTER III.

NOT long after Grandfather had told the story of his great chair, there chanced to be a rainy day. Our friend Charley, after disturbing the household with beat of drum and riotous shouts, races up and down the staircase, overturning of chairs, and much other uproar, began to feel the quiet and confinement within doors intolerable. But as the rain came down in a flood, the little fellow was hopelessly a prisoner, and now stood with sullen aspect at a window, wondering whether the sun itself were not extinguished by so much moisture in the sky.

Charley had already exhausted the less eager activity of the other children; and they had betaken themselves to occupations that did not admit of his companionship. Laurence sat in a recess near the bookcase, reading, not for the first time, the Midsummer Night's Dream. Clara was making a rosary of beads for a little figure of a Sister of Charity, who was to attend the Bunker Hill fair and lend her aid in erecting the Monument. Little Alice sat on Grandfather's footstool, with a picture-book in her hand; and, for every picture, the child was telling Grandfather a story. She did not read from the book (for little Alice had not much skill in reading), but told the story out of her own heart and mind.

Charley was too big a boy, of course, to care anything about little Alice's stories, although Grandfather appeared to listen with a good deal of interest. Often, in a young child's ideas and fancies, there is something which it requires the thought of a lifetime to comprehend. But Charley was of opinion that, if a story must be told, it had better be told by Grandfather than little Alice.

"Grandfather, I want to hear more about your chair," said he.

Now, Grandfather remembered that Charley had galloped away upon a stick in the midst of the narrative of poor Lady Arbella, and I know not whether he would have thought it worth while to tell another story merely to gratify such an inattentive auditor as Charley. But Laurence laid down his book and seconded the request. Clara drew her chair nearer to Grandfather; and little Alice immediately closed her picture-book and looked up into his face. Grandfather had not the heart to disappoint them.

He mentioned several persons who had a share in the settlement of our country, and who would be well worthy of remembrance, if we could find room to tell about them all. Among the rest, Grandfather spoke of the famous Hugh Peters, a minister of the gospel, who did much good to the inhabitants of Salem. Mr. Peters afterwards went back to England, and was chaplain to Oliver Cromwell; but Grandfather did not tell the children what became of this upright and zealous man at last. In fact, his auditors were growing impatient to hear more about the history of the chair.

"After the death of Mr. Johnson," said he, "Grandfather's chair came into the possession of Roger Williams. He was a clergyman, who arrived at Salem, and settled there in 1631. Doubtless the good man has spent many a studious hour in this old chair, either

penning a sermon or reading some abstruse book of
theology, till midnight came upon him unawares. At
that period, as there were few lamps or candles to be
had, people used to read or work by the light of pitch-
pine torches. These supplied the place of the 'midnight oil' to the learned men of New England."

Grandfather went on to talk about Roger Williams,
and told the children several particulars, which we
have not room to repeat. One incident, however,
which was connected with his life, must be related, because it will give the reader an idea of the opinions
and feelings of the first settlers of New England. It
was as follows : —

THE RED CROSS.

While Roger Williams sat in Grandfather's chair
at his humble residence in Salem, John Endicott
would often come to visit him. As the clergy had
great influence in temporal concerns, the minister and
magistrate would talk over the occurrences of the day,
and consult how the people might be governed according to scriptural laws.

One thing especially troubled them both. In the
old national banner of England, under which her soldiers have fought for hundreds of years, there is a red
cross, which has been there ever since the days when
England was in subjection to the pope. The cross,
though a holy symbol, was abhorred by the Puritans,
because they considered it a relic of popish idolatry.
Now, whenever the train-band of Salem was mustered,
the soldiers, with Endicott at their head, had no other
flag to march under than this same old papistical banner of England, with the red cross in the midst of it.
The banner of the red cross, likewise, was flying on

the walls of the fort of Salem; and a similar one was displayed in Boston Harbor, from the fortress on Castle Island.

"I profess, Brother Williams," Captain Endicott would say, after they had been talking of this matter, "it distresses a Christian man's heart to see this idolatrous cross flying over our heads. A stranger, beholding it, would think that we had undergone all our hardships and dangers, by sea and in the wilderness, only to get new dominions for the Pope of Rome."

"Truly, good Mr. Endicott," Roger Williams would answer, "you speak as an honest man and Protestant Christian should. For mine own part, were it my business to draw a sword, I should reckon it sinful to fight under such a banner. Neither can I, in my pulpit, ask the blessing of Heaven upon it."

Such, probably, was the way in which Roger Williams and John Endicott used to talk about the banner of the red cross. Endicott, who was a prompt and resolute man, soon determined that Massachusetts, if she could not have a banner of her own, should at least be delivered from that of the Pope of Rome.

Not long afterwards there was a military muster at Salem. Every able-bodied man in the town and neighborhood was there. All were well armed, with steel caps upon their heads, plates of iron upon their breasts and at their backs, and gorgets of steel around their necks. When the sun shone upon these ranks of iron-clad men, they flashed and blazed with a splendor that bedazzled the wild Indians who had come out of the woods to gaze at them. The soldiers had long pikes, swords, and muskets, which were fired with matches, and were almost as heavy as a small cannon.

These men had mostly a stern and rigid aspect. To

judge by their looks, you might have supposed that there was as much iron in their hearts as there was upon their heads and breasts. They were all devoted Puritans, and of the same temper as those with whom Oliver Cromwell afterwards overthrew the throne of England. They hated all the relics of popish superstition as much as Endicott himself; and yet over their heads was displayed the banner of the red cross.

Endicott was the captain of the company. While the soldiers were expecting his orders to begin their exercise, they saw him take the banner in one hand, holding his drawn sword in the other. Probably he addressed them in a speech, and explained how horrible a thing it was that men, who had fled from popish idolatry into the wilderness, should be compelled to fight under its symbols here. Perhaps he concluded his address somewhat in the following style: —

"And now, fellow-soldiers, you see this old banner of England. Some of you, I doubt not, may think it treason for a man to lay violent hands upon it. But whether or no it be treason to man, I have good assurance in my conscience that it is no treason to God. Wherefore, I have resolved that we will rather be God's soldiers than soldiers of the Pope of Rome; and in that mind I now cut the papal cross out of this banner."

And so he did. And thus, in a province belonging to the crown of England, a captain was found bold enough to deface the king's banner with his sword.

When Winthrop and the other wise men of Massachusetts heard of it they were disquieted, being afraid that Endicott's act would bring great trouble upon himself and them. An account of the matter was carried to King Charles; but he was then so much engrossed by dissensions with his people that he had no leisure to punish the offender. In other times, it might have cost Endicott his life, and Massachusetts her charter.

"I should like to know, Grandfather," said Laurence, when the story was ended, "whether, when Endicott cut the red cross out of the banner, he meant to imply that Massachusetts was independent of England?"

"A sense of the independence of his adopted country must have been in that bold man's heart," answered Grandfather; "but I doubt whether he had given the matter much consideration except in its religious bearing. However, it was a very remarkable affair, and a very strong expression of Puritan character."

Grandfather proceeded to speak further of Roger Williams, and of other persons who sat in the great chair, as will be seen in the following chapter.

CHAPTER IV.

"Roger Williams," said Grandfather, "did not keep possession of the chair a great while. His opinions of civil and religious matters differed, in many respects, from those of the rulers and clergymen of Massachusetts. Now, the wise men of those days believed that the country could not be safe unless all the inhabitants thought and felt alike."

"Does anybody believe so in our days, Grandfather?" asked Laurence.

"Possibly there are some who believe it," said Grandfather; "but they have not so much power to act upon their belief as the magistrates and ministers had in the days of Roger Williams. They had the power to deprive this good man of his home, and to send him out from the midst of them in search of a new place of rest. He was banished in 1634, and went first to Plymouth colony; but as the people there held the same opinions as those of Massachusetts, he was not suffered to remain among them. However, the wilderness was wide enough; so Roger Williams took his staff and travelled into the forest and made treaties with the Indians, and began a plantation which he called Providence."

"I have been to Providence on the railroad," said Charley. "It is but a two-hours' ride."

"Yes, Charley," replied Grandfather; "but when Roger Williams travelled thither, over hills and valleys, and through the tangled woods, and across

swamps and streams, it was a journey of several days.
Well, his little plantation is now grown to be a populous city ; and the inhabitants have a great venera-
tion for Roger Williams. His name is familiar in the
mouths of all, because they see it on their bank-bills.
How it would have perplexed this good clergyman if
he had been told that he should give his name to the
ROGER WILLIAMS BANK ! "

" When he was driven from Massachusetts," said
Laurence, " and began his journey into the woods, he
must have felt as if he were burying himself forever
from the sight and knowledge of men. Yet the whole
country has now heard of him, and will remember him
forever."

" Yes," answered Grandfather ; " it often happens
that the outcasts of one generation are those who are
reverenced as the wisest and best of men by the next.
The securest fame is that which comes after a man's
death. But let us return to our story. When Roger
Williams was banished, he appears to have given the
chair to Mrs. Anne Hutchinson. At all events, it was
in her possession in 1637. She was a very sharp-wit-
ted and well-instructed lady, and was so conscious of
her own wisdom and abilities that she thought it a
pity that the world should not have the benefit of
them. She therefore used to hold lectures in Boston
once or twice a week, at which most of the women attended. Mrs. Hutchinson presided at these meetings,
sitting with great state and dignity in Grandfather's
chair."

" Grandfather, was it positively this very chair ? "
demanded Clara, laying her hand upon its carved elbow.

" Why not, my dear Clara ? " said Grandfather.

" Well, Mrs. Hutchinson's lectures soon caused a
great disturbance ; for the ministers of Boston did not
think it safe and proper that a woman should publicly
instruct the people in religious doctrines.   Moreover,
she made the matter worse by declaring that the Rev.
Mr. Cotton was the only sincerely pious and holy clergyman in New England.   Now, the clergy of those
days had quite as much share in the government of
the country, though indirectly, as the magistrates themselves ; so you may imagine what a host of powerful
enemies were raised up against Mrs. Hutchinson.   A
synod was convened ; that is to say, an assemblage of
all the ministers in Massachusetts.   They declared
that there were eighty-two erroneous opinions on religious subjects diffused among the people, and that
Mrs. Hutchinson's opinions were of the number."

" If they had eighty-two wrong opinions," observed
Charley, " I don't see how they could have any right
ones."

" Mrs. Hutchinson had many zealous friends and
converts," continued Grandfather.   " She was favored
by young Henry Vane, who had come over from England a year or two before, and had since been chosen
governor of the colony, at the age of twenty-four.   But
Winthrop and most of the other leading men, as well
as the ministers, felt an abhorrence of her doctrines.
Thus two opposite parties were formed ; and so fierce
were the dissensions that it was feared the consequence
would be civil war and bloodshed.   But Winthrop
and the ministers being the most powerful, they dis-
armed and imprisoned Mrs. Hutchinson's adherents.
She, like Roger Williams, was banished."

" Dear Grandfather, did they drive the poor woman
into the woods ? " exclaimed little Alice, who contrived

to feel a human interest even in these discords of polemic divinity.

"They did, my darling," replied Grandfather; "and the end of her life was so sad you must not hear it. At her departure, it appears, from the best authorities, that she gave the great chair to her friend Henry Vane. He was a young man of wonderful talents and great learning, who had imbibed the religious opinions of the Puritans, and left England with the intention of spending his life in Massachusetts. The people chose him governor; but the controversy about Mrs. Hutchinson, and other troubles, caused him to leave the country in 1637. You may read the subsequent events of his life in the History of England."

"Yes, Grandfather," cried Laurence; "and we may read them better in Mr. Upham's biography of Vane. And what a beautiful death he died, long afterwards! beautiful, though it was on a scaffold."

"Many of the most beautiful deaths have been there," said Grandfather. "The enemies of a great and good man can in no other way make him so glorious as by giving him the crown of martyrdom."

In order that the children might fully understand the all-important history of the chair, Grandfather now thought fit to speak of the progress that was made in settling several colonies. The settlement of Plymouth, in 1620, has already been mentioned. In 1635 Mr. Hooker and Mr. Stone, two ministers, went on foot from Massachusetts to Connecticut, through the pathless woods, taking their whole congregation along with them. They founded the town of Hartford. In 1638 Mr. Davenport, a very celebrated minister, went, with other people, and began a plantation at New Haven. In the same year, some persons who had been persecuted in Massachusetts went to the Isle of Rhodes, since called Rhode Island, and settled there. About this time, also, many settlers had gone to Maine, and were living without any regular government. There were likewise settlers near Piscataqua River, in the region which is now called New Hampshire.

Thus, at various points along the coast of New England, there were communities of Englishmen. Though these communities were independent of one another, yet they had a common dependence upon England; and, at so vast a distance from their native home, the inhabitants must all have felt like brethren. They were fitted to become one united people at a future period. Perhaps their feelings of brotherhood were the stronger because different nations had formed settlements to the north and to the south. In Canada and Nova Scotia were colonies of French. On the banks of the Hudson River was a colony of Dutch, who had taken possession of that region many years before, and called it New Netherlands.

Grandfather, for aught I know, might have gone on to speak of Maryland and Virginia; for the good old gentleman really seemed to suppose that the whole surface of the United States was not too broad a foundation to place the four legs of his chair upon. But, happening to glance at Charley, he perceived that this naughty boy was growing impatient and meditating another ride upon a stick. So here, for the present, Grandfather suspended the history of his chair.

CHAPTER V.

THE children had now learned to look upon the chair with an interest which was almost the same as if it were a conscious being, and could remember the many famous people whom it had held within its arms.

Even Charley, lawless as he was, seemed to feel that this venerable chair must not be clambered upon nor overturned, although he had no scruple in taking such liberties with every other chair in the house. Clara treated it with still greater reverence, often taking occasion to smooth its cushion, and to brush the dust from the carved flowers and grotesque figures of its oaken back and arms. Laurence would sometimes sit a whole hour, especially at twilight, gazing at the chair, and, by the spell of his imaginations, summoning up its ancient occupants to appear in it again.

Little Alice evidently employed herself in a similar way; for once when Grandfather had gone abroad, the child was heard talking with the gentle Lady Arbella, as if she were still sitting in the chair. So sweet a child as little Alice may fitly talk with angels, such as the Lady Arbella had long since become.

Grandfather was soon importuned for more stories about the chair. He had no difficulty in relating them; for it really seemed as if every person noted in our early history had, on some occasion or other, found repose within its comfortable arms. If Grandfather took pride in anything, it was in being the possessor of such an honorable and historic elbow-chair.

"I know not precisely who next got possession of the chair after Governor Vane went back to England," said Grandfather. "But there is reason to believe that President Dunster sat in it, when he held the first Commencement at Harvard College. You have often heard, children, how careful our forefathers were to give their young people a good education. They had scarcely cut down trees enough to make room for their own dwellings before they began to think of establishing a college. Their principal object was, to rear up pious and learned ministers; and hence old writers call Harvard College a school of the prophets."

"Is the college a school of the prophets now?" asked Charley.

"It is a long while since I took my degree, Charley. You must ask some of the recent graduates," answered Grandfather. "As I was telling you, President Dunster sat in Grandfather's chair in 1642, when he conferred the degree of bachelor of arts on nine young men. They were the first in America who had received that honor. And now, my dear auditors, I must confess that there are contradictory statements and some uncertainty about the adventures of the chair for a period of almost ten years. Some say that it was occupied by your own ancestor, William Hawthorne, first Speaker of the House of Representatives. I have nearly satisfied myself, however, that, during most of this questionable period, it was literally the chair of state. It gives me much pleasure to imagine that several successive governors of Massachusetts sat in it at the council board."

"But, Grandfather," interposed Charley, who was a matter-of-fact little person, "what reason have you to imagine so?"

"Pray do imagine it, Grandfather," said Laurence.

"With Charley's permission, I will," replied Grandfather, smiling. "Let us consider it settled, therefore, that Winthrop, Bellingham, Dudley, and Endicott, each of them, when chosen governor, took his seat in our great chair on election day. In this chair, likewise, did those excellent governors preside while holding consultations with the chief councillors of the province, who were styled assistants. The governor sat in this chair, too, whenever messages were brought to him from the chamber of representatives."

And here Grandfather took occasion to talk rather tediously about the nature and forms of government that established themselves, almost spontaneously, in Massachusetts and the other New England colonies. Democracies were the natural growth of the New World. As to Massachusetts, it was at first intended that the colony should be governed by a council in London. But in a little while the people had the whole power in their own hands, and chose annually the governor, the councillors, and the representatives. The people of Old England had never enjoyed anything like the liberties and privileges which the settlers of New England now possessed. And they did not adopt these modes of government after long study, but in simplicity, as if there were no other way for people to be ruled.

"But, Laurence," continued Grandfather, "when you want instruction on these points, you must seek it in Mr. Bancroft's History. I am merely telling the history of a chair. To proceed. The period during which the governors sat in our chair was not very full of striking incidents. The province was now established on a secure foundation; but it did not increase so rapidly as at first, because the Puritans were no longer driven from England by persecution. However, there was still a quiet and natural growth. The Legislature incorporated towns, and made new purchases of lands from the Indians. A very memorable event took place in 1643. The colonies of Massachusetts, Plymouth, Connecticut, and New Haven formed a union, for the purpose of assisting each other in difficulties, for mutual defence against their enemies. They called themselves the United Colonies of New England."

"Were they under a government like that of the United States?" inquired Laurence.

"No," replied Grandfather; "the different colonies did not compose one nation together; it was merely a confederacy among the governments. It somewhat resembled the league of the Amphictyons, which you remember in Grecian history. But to return to our chair. In 1644 it was highly honored; for Governor Endicott sat in it when he gave audience to an ambassador from the French governor of Acadia, or Nova Scotia. A treaty of peace between Massachusetts and the French colony was then signed."

"Did England allow Massachusetts to make war and peace with foreign countries?" asked Laurence.

"Massachusetts and the whole of New England was then almost independent of the mother country," said Grandfather. "There was now a civil war in England; and the king, as you may well suppose, had his hands full at home, and could pay but little attention to these remote colonies. When the Parliament got the power into their hands, they likewise had enough to do in keeping down the Cavaliers. Thus New England, like a young and hardy lad whose father and mother neglect it, was left to take care of itself. In 1646 King Charles was beheaded. Oliver Cromwell then became Protector of England; and as he was a Puritan himself, and had risen by the valor of the English Puritans, he showed himself a loving and indulgent father to the Puritan colonies in America."

Grandfather might have continued to talk in this dull manner nobody knows how long; but suspecting that Charley would find the subject rather dry, he looked sidewise at that vivacious little fellow, and saw him give an involuntary yawn. Whereupon Grandfather proceeded with the history of the chair, and related a very entertaining incident, which will be found in the next chapter.

CHAPTER VI.

"ACCORDING to the most authentic records, my dear children," said Grandfather, "the chair, about this time, had the misfortune to break its leg. It was probably on account of this accident that it ceased to be the seat of the governors of Massachusetts; for, assuredly, it would have been ominous of evil to the commonwealth if the chair of state had tottered upon three legs. Being therefore sold at auction, — alas! what a vicissitude for a chair that had figured in such high company! — our venerable friend was knocked down to a certain Captain John Hull. This old gentleman, on carefully examining the maimed chair, discovered that its broken leg might be clamped with iron and made as serviceable as ever."

"Here is the very leg that was broken!" exclaimed Charley, throwing himself down on the floor to look at it. "And here are the iron clamps. How well it was mended!"

When they had all sufficiently examined the broken leg, Grandfather told them a story about Captain John Hull and

THE PINE-TREE SHILLINGS.

The Captain John Hull aforesaid was the mint-master of Massachusetts, and coined all the money that was made there. This was a new line of business; for, in the earlier days of the colony, the current coinage consisted of gold and silver money of England,

Portugal, and Spain. These coins being scarce, the people were often forced to barter their commodities instead of selling them.

For instance, if a man wanted to buy a coat, he perhaps exchanged a bear-skin for it. If he wished for a barrel of molasses, he might purchase it with a pile of pine boards. Musket-bullets were used instead of farthings. The Indians had a sort of money, called wampum, which was made of clam-shells; and this strange sort of specie was likewise taken in payment of debts by the English settlers. Bank-bills had never been heard of. There was not money enough of any kind, in many parts of the country, to pay the salaries of the ministers; so that they sometimes had to take quintals of fish, bushels of corn, or cords of wood, instead of silver or gold.

As the people grew more numerous, and their trade one with another increased, the want of current money was still more sensibly felt. To supply the demand, the General Court passed a law for establishing a coinage of shillings, sixpences, and threepences. Captain John Hull was appointed to manufacture this money, and was to have about one shilling out of every twenty to pay him for the trouble of making them.

Hereupon all the old silver in the colony was handed over to Captain John Hull. The battered silver cans and tankards, I suppose, and silver buckles, and broken spoons, and silver buttons of worn-out coats, and silver hilts of swords that had figured at court, — all such curious old articles were doubtless thrown into the melting-pot together. But by far the greater part of the silver consisted of bullion from the mines of South America, which the English buccaneers — who

were little better than pirates — had taken from the
Spaniards, and brought to Massachusetts.

All this old and new silver being melted down and
coined, the result was an immense amount of splendid
shillings, sixpences, and threepences. Each had the
date, 1652, on the one side, and the figure of a pine-
tree on the other. Hence they were called pine-tree
shillings. And for every twenty shillings that he
coined, you will remember, Captain John Hull was
entitled to put one shilling into his own pocket.

The magistrates soon began to suspect that the mint-
master would have the best of the bargain. They offered him a large sum of money if he would but give
up that twentieth shilling which he was continually
dropping into his own pocket. But Captain Hull declared himself perfectly satisfied with the shilling.
And well he might be; for so diligently did he labor,
that, in a few years, his pockets, his money-bags, and
his strong box were overflowing with pine-tree shillings. This was probably the case when he came into
possession of Grandfather's chair; and, as he had
worked so hard at the mint, it was certainly proper
that he should have a comfortable chair to rest himself in.

When the mint-master had grown very rich, a young
man, Samuel Sewell by name, came a-courting to his
only daughter. His daughter — whose name I do not
know, but we will call her Betsey — was a fine, hearty
damsel, by no means so slender as some young ladies
of our own days. On the contrary, having always fed
heartily on pumpkin-pies, doughnuts, Indian puddings,
and other Puritan dainties, she was as round and
plump as a pudding herself. With this round, rosy
Miss Betsey did Samuel Sewell fall in love. As he

was a young man of good character, industrious in his business, and a member of the church, the mint-master very readily gave his consent.

" Yes, you may take her," said he, in his rough way, " and you 'll find her a heavy burden enough! "

On the wedding day, we may suppose that honest John Hull dressed himself in a plum-colored coat, all the buttons of which were made of pine-tree shillings. The buttons of his waistcoat were sixpences ; and the knees of his small-clothes were buttoned with silver threepences. Thus attired, he sat with great dignity in Grandfather's chair; and, being a portly old gentle-man, he completely filled it from elbow to elbow. On the opposite side of the room, between her bridemaids, sat Miss Betsey. She was blushing with all her might, and looked like a full-blown peony, or a great red apple.

There, too, was the bridegroom, dressed in a fine purple coat and gold-lace waistcoat, with as much other finery as the Puritan laws and customs would allow him to put on. His hair was cropped close to his head, because Governor Endicott had forbidden any man to wear it below the ears. But he was a very personable young man ; and so thought the bridemaids and Miss Betsey herself.

The mint-master also was pleased with his new son-in-law ; especially as he had courted Miss Betsey out of pure love, and had said nothing at all about her portion. So, when the marriage ceremony was over, Captain Hull whispered a word to two of his men-ser-vants, who immediately went out, and soon returned, lugging in a large pair of scales. They were such a pair as wholesale merchants use for weighing bulky commodities ; and quite a bulky commodity was now to be weighed in them.

" Daughter Betsey," said the mint-master, " get into one side of these scales."

Miss Betsey — or Mrs. Sewell, as we must now call her — did as she was bid, like a dutiful child, without any question of the why and wherefore. But what her father could mean, unless to make her husband pay for her by the pound (in which case she would have been a dear bargain), she had not the least idea.

" And now," said honest John Hull to the servants, " bring that box hither."

The box to which the mint-master pointed was a huge, square, iron-bound, oaken chest ; it was big enough, my children, for all four of you to play at hide-and-seek in. The servants tugged with might and main, but could not lift this enormous receptacle, and were finally obliged to drag it across the floor. Captain Hull then took a key from his girdle, unlocked the chest, and lifted its ponderous lid. Behold ! it was full to the brim of bright pine-tree shillings, fresh from the mint ; and Samuel Sewell began to think that his father-in-law had got possession of all the money in the Massachusetts treasury. But it was only the mint-master's honest share of the coinage.

Then the servants, at Captain Hull's command, heaped double handfuls of shillings into one side of the scales, while Betsey remained in the other. Jingle, jingle, went the shillings, as handful after handful was thrown in, till, plump and ponderous as she was, they fairly weighed the young lady from the floor.

" There, son Sewell ! " cried the honest mint-master, resuming his seat in Grandfather's chair, " take these shillings for my daughter's portion. Use her kindly, and thank Heaven for her. It is not every wife that 's worth her weight in silver ! "

The children laughed heartily at this legend, and would hardly be convinced but that Grandfather had made it out of his own head. He assured them faithfully, however, that he had found it in the pages of a grave historian, and had merely tried to tell it in a somewhat funnier style. As for Samuel Sewell, he afterwards became chief justice of Massachusetts.

" Well, Grandfather," remarked Clara, " if wedding portions nowadays were paid as Miss Betsey's was, young ladies would not pride themselves upon an airy figure, as many of them do."

CHAPTER VII.

WHEN his little audience next assembled round the chair, Grandfather gave them a doleful history of the Quaker persecution, which began in 1656, and raged for about three years in Massachusetts.

He told them how, in the first place, twelve of the converts of George Fox, the first Quaker in the world, had come over from England. They seemed to be impelled by an earnest love for the souls of men, and a pure desire to make known what they considered a revelation from Heaven. But the rulers looked upon them as plotting the downfall of all government and religion. They were banished from the colony. In a little while, however, not only the first twelve had returned, but a multitude of other Quakers had come to rebuke the rulers and to preach against the priests and steeple-houses.

Grandfather described the hatred and scorn with which these enthusiasts were received. They were thrown into dungeons ; they were beaten with many stripes, women as well as men ; they were driven forth into the wilderness, and left to the tender mercies of wild beasts and Indians. The children were amazed to hear that the more the Quakers were scourged, and imprisoned, and banished, the more did the sect increase, both by the influx of strangers and by converts from among the Puritans. But Grandfather told them that God had put something into the soul of man, which always turned the cruelties of the persecutor to nought.

He went on to relate that, in 1659, two Quakers, named William Robinson and Marmaduke Stephenson, were hanged at Boston. A woman had been sentenced to die with them, but was reprieved on condition of her leaving the colony. Her name was Mary Dyer. In the year 1660 she returned to Boston, although she knew death awaited her there; and, if Grandfather had been correctly informed, an incident had then taken place which connects her with our story. This Mary Dyer had entered the mint-master's dwelling, clothed in sackcloth and ashes, and seated herself in our great chair with a sort of dignity and state. Then she proceeded to deliver what she called a message from Heaven, but in the midst of it they dragged her to prison.

" And was she executed ? " asked Laurence.

" She was," said Grandfather.

" Grandfather," cried Charley, clinching his fist, " I would have fought for that poor Quaker woman ! "

" Ah, but if a sword had been drawn for her," said Laurence, " it would have taken away all the beauty of her death."

It seemed as if hardly any of the preceding stories had thrown such an interest around Grandfather's chair as did the fact that the poor, persecuted, wandering Quaker woman had rested in it for a moment. The children were so much excited that Grandfather found it necessary to bring his account of the persecution to a close.

" In 1660, the same year in which Mary Dyer was executed," said he, " Charles II. was restored to the throne of his fathers. This king had many vices; but he would not permit blood to be shed, under pretence of religion, in any part of his dominions. The Quakers in England told him what had been done to their brethren in Massachusetts; and he sent orders to Governor Endicott to forbear all such proceedings in future. And so ended the Quaker persecution, — one of the most mournful passages in the history of our forefathers."

Grandfather then told his auditors, that, shortly after the above incident, the great chair had been given by the mint-master to the Rev. Mr. John Eliot. He was the first minister of Roxbury. But besides attending to the pastoral duties there, he learned the language of the red men, and often went into the woods to preach to them. So earnestly did he labor for their conversion that he has always been called the apostle to the Indians. The mention of this holy man suggested to Grandfather the propriety of giving a brief sketch of the history of the Indians, so far as they were connected with the English colonists.

A short period before the arrival of the first Pilgrims at Plymouth there had been a very grievous plague among the red men; and the sages and ministers of that day were inclined to the opinion that Providence had sent this mortality in order to make room for the settlement of the English. But I know not why we should suppose that an Indian's life is less precious, in the eye of Heaven, than that of a white man. Be that as it may, death had certainly been very busy with the savage tribes.

In many places the English found the wigwams deserted and the cornfields growing to waste, with none to harvest the grain. There were heaps of earth also, which, being dug open, proved to be Indian graves,

containing bows and flint-headed spears and arrows ;
for the Indians buried the dead warrior's weapons
along with him.   In some spots there were skulls and
other human bones lying unburied.   In 1633, and the
year afterwards, the small-pox broke out among the
Massachusetts Indians, multitudes of whom died by
this terrible disease of the Old World.   These misfortunes made them far less powerful than they had
formerly been.

For nearly half a century after the arrival of the
English the red men showed themselves generally inclined to peace and amity.   They often made submission when they might have made successful war.   The
Plymouth settlers, led by the famous Captain Miles
Standish, slew some of them, in 1623, without any very
evident necessity for so doing.   In 1636, and the following year, there was the most dreadful war that had
yet occurred between the Indians and the English.
The Connecticut settlers, assisted by a celebrated Indian chief named Uncas, bore the brunt of this war,
with but little aid from Massachusetts.   Many hundreds of the hostile Indians were slain or burned in
their wigwams.   Sassacus, their sachem, fled to another tribe, after his own people were defeated ; but
he was murdered by them, and his head was sent to
his English enemies.

From that period down to the time of King Philip's
War, which will be mentioned hereafter, there was not
much trouble with the Indians.   But the colonists were
always on their guard, and kept their weapons ready
for the conflict.

" I have sometimes doubted," said Grandfather,
when he had told these things to the children, — " I
have sometimes doubted whether there was more than

a single man among our forefathers, who realized that an Indian possesses a mind, and a heart, and an immortal soul. That single man was John Eliot. All the rest of the early settlers seemed to think that the Indians were an inferior race of beings, whom the Creator had merely allowed to keep possession of this beautiful country till the white men should be in want of it."

"Did the pious men of those days never try to make Christians of them?" asked Laurence.

"Sometimes, it is true," answered Grandfather, "the magistrates and ministers would talk about civilizing and converting the red people. But, at the bottom of their hearts, they would have had almost as much expectation of civilizing the wild bear of the woods and making him fit for paradise. They felt no faith in the success of any such attempts, because they had no love for the poor Indians. Now, Eliot was full of love for them; and therefore so full of faith and hope that he spent the labor of a lifetime in their behalf."

"I would have conquered them first, and then converted them," said Charley.

"Ah, Charley, there spoke the very spirit of our forefathers!" replied Grandfather. "But Mr. Eliot had a better spirit. He looked upon them as his brethren. He persuaded as many of them as he could to leave off their idle and wandering habits, and to build houses and cultivate the earth, as the English did. He established schools among them and taught many of the Indians how to read. He taught them, likewise, how to pray. Hence they were called 'praying Indians.' Finally, having spent the best years of his life for their good, Mr. Eliot resolved to spend the remainder in doing them a yet greater benefit."

" I know what that was ! " cried Laurence.

" He sat down in his study," continued Grandfather, " and began a translation of the Bible into the Indian tongue. It was while he was engaged in this pious work that the mint-master gave him our great chair. His toil needed it and deserved it."

" O Grandfather, tell us all about that Indian Bible ! " exclaimed Laurence. " I have seen it in the library of the Athenæum ; and the tears came into my eyes to think that there were no Indians left to read it."

CHAPTER VIII.

As Grandfather was a great admirer of the apostle Eliot, he was glad to comply with the earnest request which Laurence had made at the close of the last chapter. So he proceeded to describe how good Mr. Eliot labored, while he was at work upon

THE INDIAN BIBLE.

My dear children, what a task would you think it, even with a long lifetime before you, were you bidden to copy every chapter, and verse, and word in yonder family Bible! Would not this be a heavy toil? But if the task were, not to write off the English Bible, but to learn a language utterly unlike all other tongues, — a language which hitherto had never been learned, except by the Indians themselves, from their mothers' lips, — a language never written, and the strange words of which seemed inexpressible by letters, — if the task were, first to learn this new variety of speech, and then to translate the Bible into it, and to do it so carefully that not one idea throughout the holy book should be changed, — what would induce you to undertake this toil? Yet this was what the apostle Eliot did.

It was a mighty work for a man, now growing old, to take upon himself. And what earthly reward could he expect from it? None; no reward on earth. But he believed that the red men were the descendants of those lost tribes of Israel of whom history has been

able to tell us nothing for thousands of years. He
hoped that God had sent the English across the ocean,
Gentiles as they were, to enlighten this benighted portion of his once chosen race. And when he should be
summoned hence, he trusted to meet blessed spirits
in another world, whose bliss would have been earned
by his patient toil in translating the word of God.
This hope and trust were far dearer to him than anything that earth could offer.

Sometimes, while thus at work, he was visited by
learned men, who desired to know what literary undertaking Mr. Eliot had in hand. They, like himself, had been bred in the studious cloisters of a university, and were supposed to possess all the erudition
which mankind has hoarded up from age to age.
Greek and Latin were as familiar to them as the babble of their childhood. Hebrew was like their mother
tongue. They had grown gray in study; their eyes
were bleared with poring over print and manuscript
by the light of the midnight lamp.

And yet, how much had they left unlearned! Mr.
Eliot would put into their hands some of the pages
which he had been writing; and behold! the gray-
headed men stammered over the long, strange words,
like a little child in his first attempts to read. Then
would the apostle call to him an Indian boy, one of
his scholars, and show him the manuscript which had
so puzzled the learned Englishmen.

"Read this, my child," would he say; "these are
some brethren of mine, who would fain hear the sound
of thy native tongue."

Then would the Indian boy cast his eyes over the
mysterious page, and read it so skilfully that it sounded
like wild music. It seemed as if the forest leaves were

singing in the ears of his auditors, and as if the roar
of distant streams were poured through the young
Indian's voice. Such were the sounds amid which the
language of the red man had been formed; and they
were still heard to echo in it.

The lesson being over, Mr. Eliot would give the Indian boy an apple or a cake, and bid him leap forth
into the open air which his free nature loved. The
apostle was kind to children, and even shared in their
sports sometimes. And when his visitors had bidden
him farewell, the good man turned patiently to his
toil again.

No other Englishman had ever understood the Indian character so well, nor possessed so great an influence over the New England tribes, as the apostle did.
His advice and assistance must often have been valuable to his countrymen in their transactions with the
Indians. Occasionally, perhaps, the governor and
some of the councillors came to visit Mr. Eliot. Perchance they were seeking some method to circumvent
the forest people. They inquired, it may be, how they
could obtain possession of such and such a tract of
their rich land. Or they talked of making the Indians
their servants; as if God had destined them for per-
petual bondage to the more powerful white man.

Perhaps, too, some warlike captain, dressed in his
buff coat, with a corselet beneath it, accompanied the
governor and councillors. Laying his hand upon his
sword hilt, he would declare, that the only method of
dealing with the red men was to meet them with the
sword drawn and the musket presented.

But the apostle resisted both the craft of the politician and the fierceness of the warrior.

"Treat these sons of the forest as men and brethren," he would say; " and let us endeavor to make them Christians. Their forefathers were of that chosen race whom God delivered from Egyptian bondage. Perchance he has destined us to deliver the children from the more cruel bondage of ignorance and idolatry. Chiefly for this end, it may be, we were directed across the ocean."

When these other visitors were gone, Mr. Eliot bent himself again over the half-written page. He dared hardly relax a moment from his toil. He felt that, in the book which he was translating, there was a deep human as well as heavenly wisdom, which would of itself suffice to civilize and refine the savage tribes. Let the Bible be diffused among them, and all earthly good would follow. But how slight a consideration was this, when he reflected that the eternal welfare of a whole race of men depended upon his accomplishment of the task which he had set himself! What if his hands should be palsied? What if his mind should lose its vigor? What if death should come upon him ere the work were done? Then must the red man wander in the dark wilderness of heathenism forever.

Impelled by such thoughts as these, he sat writing in the great chair when the pleasant summer breeze came in through his open casement; and also when the fire of forest logs sent up its blaze and smoke, through the broad stone chimney, into the wintry air. Before the earliest bird sang in the morning the apostle's lamp was kindled; and, at midnight, his weary head was not yet upon its pillow. And at length, leaning back in the great chair, he could say to himself, with a holy triumph, " The work is finished!"

It was finished. Here was a Bible for the Indians.

Those long-lost descendants of the ten tribes of Israel would now learn the history of their forefathers. That grace which the ancient Israelites had forfeited was offered anew to their children.

There is no impiety in believing that, when his long life was over, the apostle of the Indians was welcomed to the celestial abodes by the prophets of ancient days and by those earliest apostles and evangelists who had drawn their inspiration from the immediate presence of the Saviour. They first had preached truth and salvation to the world. And Eliot, separated from them by many centuries, yet full of the same spirit, had borne the like message to the New World of the west. Since the first days of Christianity, there has been no man more worthy to be numbered in the brotherhood of the apostles than Eliot.

" My heart is not satisfied to think," observed Laurence, " that Mr. Eliot's labors have done no good except to a few Indians of his own time. Doubtless he would not have regretted his toil, if it were the means of saving but a single soul. But it is a grievous thing to me that he should have toiled so hard to translate the Bible, and now the language and the people are gone ! The Indian Bible itself is almost the only relic of both."

" Laurence," said his Grandfather, " if ever you should doubt that man is capable of disinterested zeal for his brother's good, then remember how the apostle Eliot toiled. And if you should feel your own self-interest pressing upon your heart too closely, then think of Eliot's Indian Bible. It is good for the world that such a man has lived and left this emblem of his life."

The tears gushed into the eyes of Laurence, and he acknowledged that Eliot had not toiled in vain. Little Alice put up her arms to Grandfather, and drew down his white head beside her own golden locks.

"Grandfather," whispered she, "I want to kiss good Mr. Eliot!"

And, doubtless, good Mr. Eliot would gladly receive the kiss of so sweet a child as little Alice, and would think it a portion of his reward in heaven.

Grandfather now observed that Dr. Francis had written a very beautiful Life of Eliot, which he advised Laurence to peruse. He then spoke of King Philip's War, which began in 1675, and terminated with the death of King Philip, in the following year. Philip was a proud, fierce Indian, whom Mr. Eliot had vainly endeavored to convert to the Christian faith.

"It must have been a great anguish to the apostle," continued Grandfather, "to hear of mutual slaughter and outrage between his own countrymen and those for whom he felt the affection of a father. A few of the praying Indians joined the followers of King Philip. A greater number fought on the side of the English. In the course of the war the little community of red people whom Mr. Eliot had begun to civilize was scattered, and probably never was restored to a flourishing condition. But his zeal did not grow cold; and only about five years before his death he took great pains in preparing a new edition of the Indian Bible."

"I do wish, Grandfather," cried Charley, "you would tell us all about the battles in King Philip's War."

"Oh no!" exclaimed Clara. "Who wants to hear about tomahawks and scalping-knives?"

"No, Charley," replied Grandfather, "I have no time to spare in talking about battles. You must be content with knowing that it was the bloodiest war that the Indians had ever waged against the white men; and that, at its close, the English set King Philip's head upon a pole."

"Who was the captain of the English?" asked Charley.

"Their most noted captain was Benjamin Church, — a very famous warrior," said Grandfather. "But I assure you, Charley, that neither Captain Church, nor any of the officers and soldiers who fought in King Philip's War, did anything a thousandth part so glorious as Mr. Eliot did when he translated the Bible for the Indians."

"Let Laurence be the apostle," said Charley to himself, "and I will be the captain."

CHAPTER IX.

THE children were now accustomed to assemble round Grandfather's chair at all their unoccupied moments; and often it was a striking picture to behold the white-headed old sire, with this flowery wreath of young people around him. When he talked to them, it was the past speaking to the present, or rather to the future, — for the children were of a generation which had not become actual. Their part in life, thus far, was only to be happy and to draw knowledge from a thousand sources. As yet, it was not their time to do.

Sometimes, as Grandfather gazed at their fair, unworldly countenances, a mist of tears bedimmed his spectacles. He almost regretted that it was necessary for them to know anything of the past or to provide aught for the future. He could have wished that they might be always the happy, youthful creatures who had hitherto sported around his chair, without inquiring whether it had a history. It grieved him to think that his little Alice, who was a flower bud fresh from paradise, must open her leaves to the rough breezes of the world, or ever open them in any clime. So sweet a child she was, that it seemed fit her infancy should be immortal.

But such repinings were merely flitting shadows across the old man's heart. He had faith enough to believe, and wisdom enough to know, that the bloom of the flower would be even holier and happier than its bud. Even within himself, though Grandfather was now at that period of life when the veil of mortality is apt to hang heavily over the soul, still, in his inmost being he was conscious of something that he would not have exchanged for the best happiness of childhood. It was a bliss to which every sort of earthly experience — all that he had enjoyed, or suffered, or seen, or heard, or acted, with the broodings of his soul upon the whole — had contributed somewhat. In the same manner must a bliss, of which now they could have no conception, grow up within these children, and form a part of their sustenance for immortality.

So Grandfather, with renewed cheerfulness, continued his history of the chair, trusting that a profounder wisdom than his own would extract, from these flowers and weeds of Time, a fragrance that might last beyond all time.

At this period of the story Grandfather threw a glance backward as far as the year 1660. He spoke of the ill-concealed reluctance with which the Puritans in America had acknowledged the sway of Charles II. on his restoration to his father's throne. When death had stricken Oliver Cromwell, that mighty protector had no sincerer mourners than in New England. The new king had been more than a year upon the throne before his accession was proclaimed in Boston, although the neglect to perform the ceremony might have subjected the rulers to the charge of treason.

During the reign of Charles II., however, the American colonies had but little reason to complain of harsh or tyrannical treatment. But when Charles died, in 1685, and was succeeded by his brother James, the patriarchs of New England began to tremble. King James was a bigoted Roman Catholic, and was known to be of an arbitrary temper. It was feared by all Protestants, and chiefly by the Puritans, that he would assume despotic power and attempt to establish popery throughout his dominions. Our fore-fathers felt that they had no security either for their religion or their liberties.

The result proved that they had reason for their apprehensions. King James caused the charters of all the American colonies to be taken away. The old charter of Massachusetts, which the people regarded as a holy thing and as the foundation of all their liberties, was declared void. The colonists were now no longer freemen; they were entirely dependent on the king's pleasure. At first, in 1685, King James appointed Joseph Dudley, a native of Massachusetts, to be president of New England. But soon afterwards Sir Edmund Andros, an officer of the English army, arrived, with a commission to be governor-general of New England and New York.

The king had given such powers to Sir Edmund Andros that there was now no liberty, nor scarcely any law, in the colonies over which he ruled. The inhabitants were not allowed to choose representatives, and consequently had no voice whatever in the government, nor control over the measures that were adopted. The councillors with whom the governor consulted on matters of state were appointed by himself. This sort of government was no better than an absolute despotism.

"The people suffered much wrong while Sir Edmund Andros ruled over them," continued Grandfather; "and they were apprehensive of much more. He had brought some soldiers with him from England, who took possession of the old fortress on Castle Island and of the fortification on Fort Hill. Sometimes it was rumored that a general massacre of the inhabitants was to be perpetrated by these soldiers. There were reports, too, that all the ministers were to be slain or imprisoned."

" For what? " inquired Charley.

" Because they were the leaders of the people, Charley," said Grandfather. " A minister was a more formidable man than a general in those days. Well, while these things were going on in America, King James had so misgoverned the people of England that they sent over to Holland for the Prince of Orange. He had married the king's daughter, and was therefore considered to have a claim to the crown. On his arrival in England, the Prince of Orange was proclaimed king, by the name of William III. Poor old King James made his escape to France."

Grandfather told how, at the first intelligence of the landing of the Prince of Orange in England, the people of Massachusetts rose in their strength and overthrew the government of Sir Edmund Andros. He, with Joseph Dudley, Edmund Randolph, and his other principal adherents, was thrown into prison. Old Simon Bradstreet, who had been governor when King James took away the charter, was called by the people to govern them again.

" Governor Bradstreet was a venerable old man, nearly ninety years of age," said Grandfather. " He came over with the first settlers, and had been the intimate companion of all those excellent and famous men who laid the foundation of our country. They were all gone before him to the grave, and Bradstreet was the last of the Puritans."

Grandfather paused a moment and smiled, as if he had something very interesting to tell his auditors. He then proceeded : —

" And now, Laurence, — now, Clara, — now, Charley, — now, my dear little Alice, — what chair do you think had been placed in the council chamber, for old Governor Bradstreet to take his seat in? Would you believe that it was this very chair in which Grandfather now sits, and of which he is telling you the history ? "

" I am glad to hear it, with all my heart ! " cried Charley, after a shout of delight. " I thought Grandfather had quite forgotten the chair."

" It was a solemn and affecting sight," said Grandfather, " when this venerable patriarch, with his white beard flowing down upon his breast, took his seat in his chair of state. Within his remembrance, and even since his mature age, the site where now stood the populous town had been a wild and forest-covered peninsula. The province, now so fertile and spotted with thriving villages, had been a desert wilderness. He was surrounded by a shouting multitude, most of whom had been born in the country which he had helped to found. They were of one generation, and he of another. As the old man looked upon them, and beheld new faces everywhere, he must have felt that it was now time for him to go whither his brethren had gone before him."

" Were the former governors all dead and gone? " asked Laurence.

" All of them," replied Grandfather. " Winthrop had been dead forty years. Endicott died, a very old man, in 1665. Sir Henry Vane was beheaded, in London, at the beginning of the reign of Charles II.

And Haynes, Dudley, Bellingham, and Leverett, who had all been governors of Massachusetts, were now likewise in their graves. Old Simon Bradstreet was the sole representative of that departed brotherhood. There was no other public man remaining to connect the ancient system of government and manners with the new system which was about to take its place. The era of the Puritans was now completed."

"I am sorry for it!" observed Laurence; "for though they were so stern, yet it seems to me that there was something warm and real about them. I think, Grandfather, that each of these old governors should have his statue set up in our State House, sculptured out of the hardest of New England granite."

"It would not be amiss, Laurence," said Grandfather; "but perhaps clay, or some other perishable material, might suffice for some of their successors. But let us go back to our chair. It was occupied by Governor Bradstreet from April, 1689, until May, 1692. Sir William Phipps then arrived in Boston with a new charter from King William and a commission to be governor."

CHAPTER X.

"And what became of the chair?" inquired Clara.

"The outward aspect of our chair," replied Grandfather, "was now somewhat the worse for its long and arduous services. It was considered hardly magnificent enough to be allowed to keep its place in the council chamber of Massachusetts. In fact, it was banished as an article of useless lumber. But Sir William Phipps happened to see it, and, being much pleased with its construction, resolved to take the good old chair into his private mansion. Accordingly, with his own gubernatorial hands, he repaired one of its arms, which had been slightly damaged."

"Why, Grandfather, here is the very arm!" interrupted Charley, in great wonderment. "And did Sir William Phipps put in these screws with his own hands? I am sure he did it beautifully! But how came a governor to know how to mend a chair?"

"I will tell you a story about the early life of Sir William Phipps," said Grandfather. "You will then perceive that he well knew how to use his hands."

So Grandfather related the wonderful and true tale of

THE SUNKEN TREASURE.

Picture to yourselves, my dear children, a handsome, old-fashioned room, with a large, open cupboard at one end, in which is displayed a magnificent gold cup, with some other splendid articles of gold and silver plate. In another part of the room, opposite to a tall looking-glass, stands our beloved chair, newly polished, and adorned with a gorgeous cushion of crimson velvet tufted with gold.

In the chair sits a man of strong and sturdy frame, whose face has been roughened by northern tempests and blackened by the burning sun of the West Indies. He wears an immense periwig, flowing down over his shoulders. His coat has a wide embroidery of golden foliage; and his waistcoat, likewise, is all flowered over and bedizened with gold. His red, rough hands, which have done many a good day's work with the hammer and adze, are half covered by the delicate lace ruffles at his wrists. On a table lies his silver-hilted sword; and in a corner of the room stands his gold-headed cane, made of a beautifully polished West India wood.

Somewhat such an aspect as this did Sir William Phipps present when he sat in Grandfather's chair after the king had appointed him governor of Massachusetts. Truly there was need that the old chair should be varnished and decorated with a crimson cushion, in order to make it suitable for such a magnif-icent-looking personage.

But Sir William Phipps had not always worn a gold-embroidered coat, nor always sat so much at his ease as he did in Grandfather's chair. He was a poor man's son, and was born in the province of Maine, where he used to tend sheep upon the hills in his boy-hood and youth. Until he had grown to be a man, he did not even know how to read and write. Tired of tending sheep, he next apprenticed himself to a ship-carpenter, and spent about four years in hewing the crooked limbs of oak-trees into knees for vessels.

In 1673, when he was twenty-two years old, he came to Boston, and soon afterwards was married to a widow lady, who had property enough to set him up in business. It was not long, however, before he lost all the money that he had acquired by his marriage, and became a poor man again. Still he was not discouraged. He often told his wife that, some time or other, he should be very rich, and would build a " fair brick house " in the Green Lane of Boston.

Do not suppose, children, that he had been to a fortune-teller to inquire his destiny. It was his own energy and spirit of enterprise, and his resolution to lead an industrious life, that made him look forward with so much confidence to better days.

Several years passed away, and William Phipps had not yet gained the riches which he promised to himself. During this time he had begun to follow the sea for a living. In the year 1684 he happened to hear of a Spanish ship which had been cast away near the Bahama Islands, and which was supposed to contain a great deal of gold and silver. Phipps went to the place in a small vessel, hoping that he should be able to recover some of the treasure from the wreck. He did not succeed, however, in fishing up gold and silver enough to pay the expenses of his voyage.

But, before he returned, he was told of another Spanish ship, or galleon, which had been cast away near Porto de la Plata. She had now lain as much as fifty years beneath the waves. This old ship had been laden with immense wealth; and, hitherto, nobody had thought of the possibility of recovering any part of it from the deep sea which was rolling and tossing it about. But though it was now an old story, and the most aged people had almost forgotten that such a vessel had been wrecked, William Phipps resolved that the sunken treasure should again be brought to light.

He went to London and obtained admittance to King James, who had not yet been driven from his throne. He told the king of the vast wealth that was lying at the bottom of the sea. King James listened with attention, and thought this a fine opportunity to fill his treasury with Spanish gold. He appointed William Phipps to be captain of a vessel, called the Rose Algier, carrying eighteen guns and ninety-five men. So now he was Captain Phipps of the English navy.

Captain Phipps sailed from England in the Rose Algier, and cruised for nearly two years in the West Indies, endeavoring to find the wreck of the Spanish ship. But the sea is so wide and deep that it is no easy matter to discover the exact spot where a sunken vessel lies. The prospect of success seemed very small; and most people would have thought that Captain Phipps was as far from having money enough to build a " fair brick house " as he was while he tended sheep.

The seamen of the Rose Algier became discouraged, and gave up all hope of making their fortunes by discovering the Spanish wreck. They wanted to compel Captain Phipps to turn pirate. There was a much better prospect, they thought, of growing rich by plundering vessels which still sailed in the sea than by seeking for a ship that had lain beneath the waves full half a century. They broke out in open mutiny; but were finally mastered by Phipps, and compelled to obey his orders. It would have been dangerous, however, to continue much longer at sea with such a crew of mutinous sailors ; and, besides, the Rose Algier was leaky and unseaworthy. So Captain Phipps judged it best to return to England.

Before leaving the West Indies, he met with a Spaniard, an old man, who remembered the wreck of the Spanish ship, and gave him directions how to find the very spot. It was on a reef of rocks, a few leagues from Porto de la Plata.

On his arrival in England, therefore, Captain Phipps solicited the king to let him have another vessel and send him back again to the West Indies. But King James, who had probably expected that the Rose Algier would return laden with gold, refused to have anything more to do with the affair. Phipps might never have been able to renew the search if the Duke of Albemarle and some other noblemen had not lent their assistance. They fitted out a ship, and gave the command to Captain Phipps. He sailed from England, and arrived safely at Porto de la Plata, where he took an adze and assisted his men to build a large boat.

The boat was intended for the purpose of going closer to the reef of rocks than a large vessel could safely venture. When it was finished, the captain sent several men in it to examine the spot where the Spanish ship was said to have been wrecked. They were accompanied by some Indians, who were skilful divers, and could go down a great way into the depths of the sea.

The boat's crew proceeded to the reef of rocks, and rowed round and round it a great many times. They gazed down into the water, which was so transparent that it seemed as if they could have seen the gold and silver at the bottom, had there been any of those precious metals there. Nothing, however, could they see ; nothing more valuable than a curious sea shrub, which was growing beneath the water, in a crevice of the reef of rocks. It flaunted to and fro with the swell and reflux of the waves, and looked as bright and beautiful as if its leaves were gold.

"We won't go back empty-handed," cried an English sailor; and then he spoke to one of the Indian divers. "Dive down and bring me that pretty sea shrub there. That's the only treasure we shall find."

Down plunged the diver, and soon rose dripping from the water, holding the sea shrub in his hand. But he had learned some news at the bottom of the sea.

"There are some ship's guns," said he, the moment he had drawn breath, "some great cannon, among the rocks, near where the shrub was growing."

No sooner had he spoken than the English sailors knew that they had found the very spot where the Spanish galleon had been wrecked, so many years before. The other Indian divers immediately plunged over the boat's side and swam headlong down, groping among the rocks and sunken cannon. In a few moments one of them rose above the water with a heavy lump of silver in his arms. The single lump was worth more than a thousand dollars. The sailors took it into the boat, and then rowed back as speedily as they could, being in haste to inform Captain Phipps of their good luck.

But, confidently as the captain had hoped to find the Spanish wreck, yet, now that it was really found, the news seemed too good to be true. He could not believe it till the sailors showed him the lump of silver.

"Thanks be to God!" then cries Captain Phipps. "We shall every man of us make our fortunes!"

Hereupon the captain and all the crew set to work, with iron rakes and great hooks and lines, fishing for gold and silver at the bottom of the sea. Up came the treasure in abundance. Now they beheld a table of solid silver, once the property of an old Spanish grandee. Now they found a sacramental vessel, which had been destined as a gift to some Catholic church. Now they drew up a golden cup, fit for the King of Spain to drink his wine out of. Perhaps the bony hand of its former owner had been grasping the precious cup, and was drawn up along with it. Now their rakes or fishing-lines were loaded with masses of silver bullion. There were also precious stones among the treasure, glittering and sparkling, so that it is a wonder how their radiance could have been concealed.

There is something sad and terrible in the idea of snatching all this wealth from the devouring ocean, which had possessed it for such a length of years. It seems as if men had no right to make themselves rich with it. It ought to have been left with the skeletons of the ancient Spaniards, who had been drowned when the ship was wrecked, and whose bones were now scattered among the gold and silver.

But Captain Phipps and his crew were troubled with no such thoughts as these. After a day or two they lighted on another part of the wreck, where they found a great many bags of silver dollars. But nobody could have guessed that these were money-bags. By remaining so long in the salt water, they had become covered over with a crust which had the appearance of stone, so that it was necessary to break them in pieces with hammers and axes. When this was done, a stream of silver dollars gushed out upon the deck of the vessel.

The whole value of the recovered treasure, plate, bullion, precious stones, and all, was estimated at more than two millions of dollars. It was dangerous even to look at such a vast amount of wealth. A sea-captain, who had assisted Phipps in the enterprise, utterly lost his reason at the sight of it. He died two years afterwards, still raving about the treasures that lie at the bottom of the sea. It would have been better for this man if he had left the skeletons of the shipwrecked Spaniards in quiet possession of their wealth.

Captain Phipps and his men continued to fish up plate, bullion, and dollars, as plentifully as ever, till their provisions grew short. Then, as they could not feed upon gold and silver any more than old King Midas could, they found it necessary to go in search of better sustenance. Phipps resolved to return to England. He arrived there in 1687, and was received with great joy by the Duke of Albemarle and other English lords who had fitted out the vessel. Well they might rejoice; for they took by far the greater part of the treasure to themselves.

The captain's share, however, was enough to make him comfortable for the rest of his days. It also enabled him to fulfil his promise to his wife, by building a "fair brick house" in the Green Lane of Boston, The Duke of Albemarle sent Mrs. Phipps a magnificent gold cup, worth at least five thousand dollars. Before Captain Phipps left London, King James made him a knight; so that, instead of the obscure ship-carpenter who had formerly dwelt among them, the inhabitants of Boston welcomed him on his return as the rich and famous Sir William Phipps.

CHAPTER XI.

"Sir William Phipps," continued Grandfather, "was too active and adventurous a man to sit still in the quiet enjoyment of his good fortune. In the year 1690 he went on a military expedition against the French colonies in America, conquered the whole province of Acadia, and returned to Boston with a great deal of plunder."

"Why, Grandfather, he was the greatest man that ever sat in the chair!" cried Charley.

"Ask Laurence what he thinks," replied Grandfather, with a smile. "Well, in the same year, Sir William took command of an expedition against Quebec, but did not succeed in capturing the city. In 1692, being then in London, King William III. appointed him governor of Massachusetts. And now, my dear children, having followed Sir William Phipps through all his adventures and hardships till we find him comfortably seated in Grandfather's chair, we will here bid him farewell. May he be as happy in ruling a people as he was while he tended sheep!"

Charley, whose fancy had been greatly taken by the adventurous disposition of Sir William Phipps, was eager to know how he had acted and what happened to him while he held the office of governor. But Grandfather had made up his mind to tell no more stories for the present.

"Possibly, one of these days, I may go on with the adventures of the chair," said he. "But its history becomes very obscure just at this point; and I must search into some old books and manuscripts before proceeding further. Besides, it is now a good time to pause in our narrative; because the new charter, which Sir William Phipps brought over from England, formed a very important epoch in the history of the province."

"Really, Grandfather," observed Laurence, "this seems to be the most remarkable chair in the world. Its history cannot be told without intertwining it with the lives of distinguished men and the great events that have befallen the country."

"True, Laurence," replied Grandfather, smiling; "we must write a book with some such title as this: MEMOIRS OF MY OWN TIMES, BY GRANDFATHER'S CHAIR."

"That would be beautiful!" exclaimed Laurence, clapping his hands.

"But, after all," continued Grandfather, "any other old chair, if it possessed memory and a hand to write its recollections, could record stranger stories than any that I have told you. From generation to generation, a chair sits familiarly in the midst of human interests, and is witness to the most secret and confidential intercourse that mortal man can hold with his fellow. The human heart may best be read in the fireside chair. And as to external events, Grief and Joy keep a continual vicissitude around it and within it. Now we see the glad face and glowing form of Joy, sitting merrily in the old chair, and throwing a warm firelight radiance over all the household. Now, while we thought not of it, the dark-clad mourner, Grief, has stolen into the place of Joy, but not to retain it long. The imagination can hardly grasp so wide a subject as is embraced in the experience of a family chair."

"It makes my breath flutter, my heart thrill, to think of it," said Laurence. "Yes, a family chair must have a deeper history than a chair of state."

"Oh yes!" cried Clara, expressing a woman's feeling on the point in question; "the history of a country is not nearly so interesting as that of a single family would be."

"But the history of a country is more easily told," said Grandfather. "So, if we proceed with our narrative of the chair, I shall still confine myself to its connection with public events."

Good old Grandfather now rose and quitted the room, while the children remained gazing at the chair. Laurence, so vivid was his conception of past times, would hardly have deemed it strange if its former occupants, one after another, had resumed the seat which they had each left vacant such a dim length of years ago.

First, the gentle and lovely Lady Arbella would have been seen in the old chair, almost sinking out of its arms for very weakness; then Roger Williams, in his cloak and band, earnest, energetic, and benevolent; then the figure of Anne Hutchinson, with the like gesture as when she presided at the assemblages of women; then the dark, intellectual face of Vane, "young in years, but in sage counsel old." Next would have appeared the successive governors, Winthrop, Dudley, Bellingham, and Endicott, who sat in the chair while it was a chair of state. Then its ample seat would have been pressed by the comfortable, rotund corporation of the honest mint-master. Then the half-frenzied shape of Mary Dyer, the persecuted Quaker woman, clad in sackcloth and ashes, would have rested in it for a moment. Then the holy, apostolic form of Eliot would have sanctified it. Then would have arisen, like the shade of departed Puritanism, the venerable dignity of the white-bearded Governor Bradstreet. Lastly, on the gorgeous crimson cushion of Grandfather's chair, would have shone the purple and golden magnificence of Sir William Phipps.

But all these, with the other historic personages, in the midst of whom the chair had so often stood, had passed, both in substance and shadow, from the scene of ages. Yet here stood the chair, with the old Lincoln coat of arms, and the oaken flowers and foliage, and the fierce lion's head at the summit, the whole, apparently, in as perfect preservation as when it had first been placed in the Earl of Lincoln's hall. And what vast changes of society and of nations had been wrought by sudden convulsions or by slow degrees since that era!

"This chair had stood firm when the thrones of kings were overturned!" thought Laurence. "Its oaken frame has proved stronger than many frames of government!"

More the thoughtful and imaginative boy might have mused; but now a large yellow cat, a great favorite with all the children, leaped in at the open window. Perceiving that Grandfather's chair was empty, and having often before experienced its comforts, puss laid herself quietly down upon the cushion. Laurence, Clara, Charley, and little Alice all laughed at the idea of such a successor to the worthies of old times.

"Pussy," said little Alice, putting out her hand, into which the cat laid a velvet paw, "you look very wise. Do tell us a story about GRANDFATHER'S CHAIR!"

PART II.

CHAPTER I.

"O GRANDFATHER, dear Grandfather," cried little Alice, "pray tell us some more stories about your chair!"

How long a time had fled since the children had felt any curiosity to hear the sequel of this venerable chair's adventures! Summer was now past and gone, and the better part of autumn likewise. Dreary, chill November was howling out of doors, and vexing the atmosphere with sudden showers of wintry rain, or sometimes with gusts of snow, that rattled like small pebbles against the windows.

When the weather began to grow cool, Grandfather's chair had been removed from the summer parlor into a smaller and snugger room. It now stood by the side of a bright, blazing, wood-fire. Grandfather loved a wood-fire far better than a grate of glowing anthracite, or than the dull heat of an invisible furnace, which seems to think that it has done its duty in merely warming the house. But the wood-fire is a kindly, cheerful, sociable spirit, sympathizing with mankind, and knowing that to create warmth is but one of the good offices which are expected from it. Therefore it dances on the hearth, and laughs broadly throughout the room, and plays a thousand antics, and throws a joyous glow over all the faces that encircle it.

In the twilight of the evening the fire grew brighter and more cheerful. And thus, perhaps, there was something in Grandfather's heart that cheered him most with its warmth and comfort in the gathering twilight of old age. He had been gazing at the red embers as intently as if his past life were all pictured there, or as if it were a prospect of the future world, when little Alice's voice aroused him. "Dear Grandfather," repeated the little girl, more earnestly, "do talk to us again about your chair."

Laurence, and Clara, and Charley, and little Alice had been attracted to other objects for two or three months past. They had sported in the gladsome sunshine of the present, and so had forgotten the shadowy region of the past, in the midst of which stood Grandfather's chair. But now, in the autumnal twilight, illuminated by the flickering blaze of the wood-fire, they looked at the old chair, and thought that it had never before worn such an interesting aspect. There it stood in the venerable majesty of more than two hundred years. The light from the hearth quivered upon the flowers and foliage that were wrought into its oaken back; and the lion's head at the summit seemed almost to move its jaws and shake its mane.

"Does little Alice speak for all of you?" asked Grandfather. "Do you wish me to go on with the adventures of the chair?"

"Oh yes, yes, Grandfather!" cried Clara. "The dear old chair! How strange that we should have forgotten it so long!"

"Oh, pray begin, Grandfather," said Laurence, "for I think, when we talk about old times, it should be in the early evening, before the candles are lighted. The shapes of the famous persons who once sat in the

chair will be more apt to come back, and be seen
among us, in this glimmer and pleasant gloom, than
they would in the vulgar daylight. And, besides, we
can make pictures of all that you tell us among the
glowing embers and white ashes."

Our friend Charley, too, thought the evening the
best time to hear Grandfather's stories, because he
could not then be playing out of doors. So finding
his young auditors unanimous in their petition, the
good old gentleman took up the narrative of the historic chair at the point where he had dropped it.

CHAPTER II.

"You recollect, my dear children," said Grandfather, "that we took leave of the chair in 1692, while it was occupied by Sir William Phipps. This fortunate treasure-seeker, you will remember, had come over from England, with King William's commission, to be governor of Massachusetts. Within the limits of this province were now included the old colony of Plymouth and the territories of Maine and Nova Scotia. Sir William Phipps had likewise brought a new charter from the king, which served instead of a constitution, and set forth the method in which the province was to be governed."

"Did the new charter allow the people all their former liberties?" inquired Laurence.

"No," replied Grandfather. "Under the first charter, the people had been the source of all power. Winthrop, Endicott, Bradstreet, and the rest of them had been governors by the choice of the people, without any interference of the king. But henceforth the governor was to hold his station solely by the king's appointment and during his pleasure; and the same was the case with the lieutenant-governor and some other high officers. The people, however, were still allowed to choose representatives; and the governor's council was chosen by the General Court."

"Would the inhabitants have elected Sir William Phipps," asked Laurence, "if the choice of governor had been left to them?"

"He might probably have been a successful candidate," answered Grandfather; "for his adventures and military enterprises had gained him a sort of renown, which always goes a great way with the people. And he had many popular characteristics, — being a kind, warm-hearted man, not ashamed of his low origin nor haughty in his present elevation. Soon after his arrival, he proved that he did not blush to recognize his former associates."

"How was that?" inquired Charley.

"He made a grand festival at his new brick house," said Grandfather, "and invited all the ship-carpenters of Boston to be his guests. At the head of the table, in our great chair, sat Sir William Phipps himself, treating these hard-handed men as his brethren, cracking jokes with them, and talking familiarly about old times. I know not whether he wore his embroidered dress; but I rather choose to imagine that he had on a suit of rough clothes, such as he used to labor in while he was Phipps the ship-carpenter."

"An aristocrat need not be ashamed of the trade," observed Laurence; "for the Czar Peter the Great once served an apprenticeship to it."

"Did Sir William Phipps make as good a governor as he was a ship-carpenter?" asked Charley.

"History says but little about his merits as a ship-carpenter," answered Grandfather; "but, as a governor, a great deal of fault was found with him. Almost as soon as he assumed the government, he became engaged in a very frightful business, which might have perplexed a wiser and better cultivated head than his. This was the witchcraft delusion."

And here Grandfather gave his auditors such details of this melancholy affair as he thought it fit for them to know. They shuddered to hear that a frenzy, which led to the death of many innocent persons, had originated in the wicked arts of a few children. They belonged to the Rev. Mr. Parris, minister of Salem. These children complained of being pinched and pricked with pins, and otherwise tormented by the shapes of men and women, who were supposed to have power to haunt them invisibly, both in darkness and daylight. Often in the midst of their family and friends the children would pretend to be seized with strange convulsions, and would cry out that the witches were afflicting them.

These stories spread abroad, and caused great tumult and alarm. From the foundation of New England, it had been the custom of the inhabitants, in all matters of doubt and difficulty, to look to their ministers for counsel. So they did now ; but, unfortunately, the ministers and wise men were more deluded than the illiterate people. Cotton Mather, a very learned and eminent clergyman, believed that the whole country was full of witches and wizards, who had given up their hopes of heaven, and signed a covenant with the evil one.

Nobody could be certain that his nearest neighbor or most intimate friend was not guilty of this imaginary crime. The number of those who pretended to be afflicted by witchcraft grew daily more numerous ; and they bore testimony against many of the best and worthiest people. A minister, named George Burroughs, was among the accused. In the months of August and September, 1692, he and nineteen other innocent men and women were put to death. The place of execution was a high hill, on the outskirts of Salem ; so that many of the sufferers, as they stood

beneath the gallows, could discern their own habitations in the town.

The martyrdom of these guiltless persons seemed
only to increase the madness. The afflicted now grew
bolder in their accusations. Many people of rank and
wealth were either thrown into prison or compelled to
flee for their lives. Among these were two sons of old
Simon Bradstreet, the last of the Puritan governors.
Mr. Willard, a pious minister of Boston, was cried out
upon as a wizard in open court. Mrs. Hale, the wife
of the minister of Beverly, was likewise accused.
Philip English, a rich merchant of Salem, found it
necessary to take flight, leaving his property and business in confusion. But a short time afterwards, the
Salem people were glad to invite him back.

"The boldest thing that the accusers did," continued Grandfather, "was to cry out against the govern-
or's own beloved wife. Yes, the lady of Sir William
Phipps was accused of being a witch and of flying
through the air to attend witch-meetings. When the
governor heard this he probably trembled, so that our
great chair shook beneath him."

"Dear Grandfather," cried little Alice, clinging
closer to his knee, "is it true that witches ever come
in the night-time to frighten little children?"

"No, no, dear little Alice," replied Grandfather.
"Even if there were any witches, they would flee away
from the presence of a pure-hearted child. But there
are none; and our forefathers soon became convinced
that they had been led into a terrible delusion. All
the prisoners on account of witchcraft were set free.
But the innocent dead could not be restored to life;
and the hill where they were executed will always remind people of the saddest and most humiliating passage in our history."

Grandfather then said that the next remarkable event, while Sir William Phipps remained in the chair, was the arrival at Boston of an English fleet in 1693. It brought an army which was intended for the conquest of Canada. But a malignant disease, more fatal than the small-pox, broke out among the soldiers and sailors, and destroyed the greater part of them. The infection spread into the town of Boston, and made much havoc there. This dreadful sickness caused the governor and Sir Francis Wheeler, who was commander of the British forces, to give up all thoughts of attacking Canada.

" Soon after this," said Grandfather, " Sir William Phipps quarrelled with the captain of an English frigate, and also with the collector of Boston. Being a man of violent temper, he gave each of them a sound beating with his cane."

" He was a bold fellow," observed Charley, who was himself somewhat addicted to a similar mode of settling disputes.

" More bold than wise," replied Grandfather ; " for complaints were carried to the king, and Sir William Phipps was summoned to England to make the best answer he could. Accordingly he went to London, where, in 1695, he was seized with a malignant fever, of which he died. Had he lived longer, he would probably have gone again in search of sunken treasure. He had heard of a Spanish ship, which was cast away in 1502, during the lifetime of Columbus. Bovadilla, Roldan, and many other Spaniards were lost in her, together with the immense wealth of which they had robbed the South American kings."

" Why, Grandfather ! " exclaimed Laurence, " what magnificent ideas the governor had ! Only think of recovering all that old treasure which had lain almost two centuries under the sea! Methinks Sir William Phipps ought to have been buried in the ocean when he died, so that he might have gone down among the sunken ships and cargoes of treasure which he was always dreaming about in his lifetime."

"He was buried in one of the crowded cemeteries of London," said Grandfather. "As he left no children, his estate was inherited by his nephew, from whom is descended the present Marquis of Normandy. The noble Marquis is not aware, perhaps, that the prosperity of his family originated in the successful enterprise of a New England ship-carpenter."

CHAPTER III.

" AT the death of Sir William Phipps," proceeded Grandfather, " our chair was bequeathed to Mr. Ezekiel Cheever, a famous schoolmaster in Boston. This old gentleman came from London in 1637, and had been teaching school ever since; so that there were now aged men, grandfathers like myself, to whom Master Cheever had taught their alphabet. He was a person of venerable aspect, and wore a long white beard."

" Was the chair placed in his school? " asked Charley.

" Yes, in his school," answered Grandfather; "and we may safely say that it had never before been regarded with such awful reverence, — no, not even when the old governors of Massachusetts sat in it. Even you, Charley, my boy, would have felt some respect for the chair if you had seen it occupied by this famous schoolmaster."

And here grandfather endeavored to give his auditors an idea how matters were managed in schools above a hundred years ago. As this will probably be an interesting subject to our readers, we shall make a separate sketch of it, and call it

THE OLD—FASHIONED SCHOOL.

Now, imagine yourselves, my children, in Master Ezekiel Cheever's school-room. It is a large, dingy room, with a sanded floor, and is lighted by windows

that turn on hinges and have little diamond-shaped
panes of glass.   The scholars sit on long benches, with
desks before them.   At one end of the room is a great
fireplace, so very spacious that there is room enough
for three or four boys to stand in each of the chimney
corners.   This was the good old fashion of fireplaces
when there was wood enough in the forests to keep
people warm without their digging into the bowels of
the earth for coal.

It is a winter's day when we take our peep into the
school-room.   See what great logs of wood have been
rolled into the fireplace, and what a broad, bright
blaze goes leaping up the chimney!   And every few
moments a vast cloud of smoke is puffed into the
room, which sails slowly over the heads of the scholars, until it gradually settles upon the walls and ceiling.   They are blackened with the smoke of many
years already.

Next look at our old historic chair!   It is placed,
you perceive, in the most comfortable part of the room,
where the generous glow of the fire is sufficiently felt
without being too intensely hot.   How stately the old
chair looks, as if it remembered its many famous occupants, but yet were conscious that a greater man is
sitting in it now!   Do you see the venerable schoolmaster, severe in aspect, with a black skullcap on his
head, like an ancient Puritan, and the snow of his
white beard drifting down to his very girdle?   What
boy would dare to play, or whisper, or even glance
aside from his book, while Master Cheever is on the
lookout behind his spectacles?   For such offenders.
if any such there be, a rod of birch is hanging over
the fireplace, and a heavy ferule lies on the master's
desk.

And now school is begun. What a murmur of mul-titudinous tongues, like the whispering leaves of a wind-stirred oak, as the scholars con over their various tasks! Buzz! buzz! buzz! Amid just such a mur-mur has Master Cheever spent above sixty years; and long habit has made it as pleasant to him as the hum of a beehive when the insects are busy in the sunshine.

Now a class in Latin is called to recite. Forth steps a row of queer-looking little fellows, wearing square-skirted coats and small-clothes, with buttons at the knee. They look like so many grandfathers in their second childhood. These lads are to be sent to Cam-bridge and educated for the learned professions. Old Master Cheever has lived so long, and seen so many generations of school-boys grow up to be men, that now he can almost prophesy what sort of a man each boy will be. One urchin shall hereafter be a doctor, and administer pills and potions, and stalk gravely through life, perfumed with assafœtida. Another shall wrangle at the bar, and fight his way to wealth and honors, and, in his declining age, shall be a wor-shipful member of his Majesty's council. A third — and he is the master's favorite — shall be a worthy successor to the old Puritan ministers now in their graves; he shall preach with great unction and effect, and leave volumes of sermons, in print and manuscript, for the benefit of future generations.

But, as they are merely school-boys now, their busi-ness is to construe Virgil. Poor Virgil! whose verses, which he took so much pains to polish, have been misscanned, and misparsed, and misinterpreted by so many generations of idle school-boys. There, sit down, ye Latinists. Two or three of you, I fear, are doomed to feel the master's ferule.

Next comes a class in arithmetic. These boys are
to be the merchants, shopkeepers, and mechanics of
a future period. Hitherto they have traded only in
marbles and apples. Hereafter some will send vessels
to England for broadcloths and all sorts of manufac-
tured wares, and to the West Indies for sugar, and
rum, and coffee. Others will stand behind counters,
and measure tape, and ribbon, and cambric by the
yard. Others will upheave the blacksmith's hammer,
or drive the plane over the carpenter's bench, or take
the lapstone and the awl and learn the trade of shoe-
making. Many will follow the sea, and become bold,
rough sea-captains.

This class of boys, in short, must supply the world
with those active, skilful hands, and clear, sagacious
heads, without which the affairs of life would be
thrown into confusion by the theories of studious and
visionary men. Wherefore, teach them their multi-
plication-table, good Master Cheever, and whip them
well when they deserve it; for much of the country's
welfare depends on these boys.

But, alas! while we have been thinking of other
matters, Master Cheever's watchful eye has caught
two boys at play. Now we shall see awful times. The
two malefactors are summoned before the master's
chair, wherein he sits with the terror of a judge upon
his brow. Our old chair is now a judgment-seat. Ah,
Master Cheever has taken down that terrible birch
rod! Short is the trial, — the sentence quickly passed,
— and now the judge prepares to execute it in person.
Thwack! thwack! thwack! In these good old times,
a schoolmaster's blows were well laid on.

See, the birch rod has lost several of its twigs, and
will hardly serve for another execution. Mercy on

us, what a bellowing the urchins make! My ears are almost deafened, though the clamor comes through the far length of a hundred and fifty years. There, go to your seats, poor boys; and do not cry, sweet little Alice, for they have ceased to feel the pain a long time since.

And thus the forenoon passes away. Now it is twelve o'clock. The master looks at his great silver watch, and then, with tiresome deliberation, puts the ferule into his desk. The little multitude await the word of dismissal with almost irrepressible impatience.

"You are dismissed," says Master Cheever.

The boys retire, treading softly until they have passed the threshold; but, fairly out of the school-room, lo, what a joyous shout! what a scampering and trampling of feet! what a sense of recovered freedom expressed in the merry uproar of all their voices! What care they for the ferule and birch rod now? Were boys created merely to study Latin and arithmetic? No; the better purposes of their being are to sport, to leap, to run, to shout, to slide upon the ice, to snowball.

Happy boys! Enjoy your playtime now, and come again to study and to feel the birch rod and the ferule to-morrow; not till to-morrow; for to-day is Thursday lecture; and, ever since the settlement of Massachusetts, there has been no school on Thursday afternoons. Therefore sport, boys, while you may, for the morrow cometh, with the birch rod and the ferule; and after that another morrow, with troubles of its own.

Now the master has set everything to rights, and is ready to go home to dinner. Yet he goes reluctantly.

The old man has spent so much of his life in the smoky, noisy, buzzing school-room, that, when he has a holiday, he feels as if his place were lost and himself a stranger in the world. But forth he goes; and there stands our old chair, vacant and solitary, till good Master Cheever resumes his seat in it to-morrow morning.

"Grandfather," said Charley, "I wonder whether the boys did not use to upset the old chair when the schoolmaster was out."

"There is a tradition," replied Grandfather, "that one of its arms was dislocated in some such manner. But I cannot believe that any school-boy would behave so naughtily."

As it was now later than little Alice's usual bedtime, Grandfather broke off his narrative, promising to talk more about Master Cheever and his scholars some other evening.

CHAPTER IV.

ACCORDINGLY, the next evening, Grandfather resumed the history of his beloved chair.

"Master Ezekiel Cheever," said he, "died in 1707, after having taught school about seventy years. It would require a pretty good scholar in arithmetic to tell how many stripes he had inflicted, and how many birch rods he had worn out, during all that time, in his fatherly tenderness for his pupils. Almost all the great men of that period, and for many years back, had been whipped into eminence by Master Cheever. Moreover, he had written a Latin Accidence, which was used in schools more than half a century after his death; so that the good old man, even in his grave, was still the cause of trouble and stripes to idle school-boys."

Grandfather proceeded to say, that, when Master Cheever died, he bequeathed the chair to the most learned man that was educated at his school, or that had ever been born in America. This was the renowned Cotton Mather, minister of the Old North Church in Boston.

"And author of the Magnalia, Grandfather, which we sometimes see you reading," said Laurence.

"Yes, Laurence," replied Grandfather. "The Magnalia is a strange, pedantic history, in which true events and real personages move before the reader with the dreamy aspect which they wore in Cotton Mather's singular mind. This huge volume, however,

was written and published before our chair came into
his possession. But, as he was the author of more
books than there are days in the year, we may conclude that he wrote a great deal while sitting in this
chair."

"I am tired of these schoolmasters and learned
men," said Charley. " I wish some stirring man, that
knew how to do something in the world, like Sir
William Phipps, would sit in the chair."

"Such men seldom have leisure to sit quietly in a
chair," said Grandfather. "We must make the best
of such people as we have."

As Cotton Mather was a very distinguished man,
Grandfather took some pains to give the children a
lively conception of his character. Over the door of
his library were painted these words, BE SHORT, — as
a warning to visitors that they must not do the world
so much harm as needlessly to interrupt this great
man's wonderful labors. On entering the room you
would probably behold it crowded, and piled, and
heaped with books. There were huge, ponderous
folios, and quartos, and little duodecimos, in English,
Latin, Greek, Hebrew, Chaldaic, and all other lan-
guages that either originated at the confusion of Babel
or have since come into use.

All these books, no doubt, were tossed about in confusion, thus forming a visible emblem of the manner
in which their contents were crowded into Cotton
Mather's brain. And in the middle of the room stood
a table, on which, besides printed volumes, were
strewn manuscript sermons, historical tracts, and po-
litical pamphlets, all written in such a queer, blind,
crabbed, fantastical hand, that a writing-master would
have gone raving mad at the sight of them. By this

table stood Grandfather's chair, which seemed to have contracted an air of deep erudition, as if its cushion were stuffed with Latin, Greek, and Hebrew, and other hard matters.

In this chair, from one year's end to another, sat that prodigious bookworm, Cotton Mather, sometimes devouring a great book, and sometimes scribbling one as big. In Grandfather's younger days there used to be a wax figure of him in one of the Boston museums, representing a solemn, dark-visaged person, in a minister's black gown, and with a black-letter volume before him.

"It is difficult, my children," observed Grandfather, "to make you understand such a character as Cotton Mather's, in whom there was so much good, and yet so many failings and frailties. Undoubtedly he was a pious man. Often he kept fasts ; and once, for three whole days, he allowed himself not a morsel of food, but spent the time in prayer and religious meditation. Many a live-long night did he watch and pray. These fasts and vigils made him meagre and haggard, and probably caused him to appear as if he hardly belonged to the world."

"Was not the witchcraft delusion partly caused by Cotton Mather ?" inquired Laurence.

"He was the chief agent of the mischief," answered Grandfather ; "but we will not suppose that he acted otherwise than conscientiously. He believed that there were evil spirits all about the world. Doubtless he imagined that they were hidden in the corners and crevices of his library, and that they peeped out from among the leaves of many of his books, as he turned them over, at midnight. He supposed that these unlovely demons were everywhere, in the sunshine as

well as in the darkness, and that they were hidden
in men's hearts, and stole into their most secret
thoughts."

Here Grandfather was interrupted by little Alice,
who hid her face in his lap, and murmured a wish that
he would not talk any more about Cotton Mather and
the evil spirits. Grandfather kissed her, and told her
that angels were the only spirits whom she had anything to do with. He then spoke of the public affairs
of the period.

A new war between France and England had broken
out in 1702, and had been raging ever since. In the
course of it, New England suffered much injury from
the French and Indians, who often came through the
woods from Canada and assaulted the frontier towns.
Villages were sometimes burned, and the inhabitants
slaughtered, within a day's ride of Boston. The people of New England had a bitter hatred against the
French, not only for the mischief which they did with
their own hands, but because they incited the Indians
to hostility.

The New-Englanders knew that they could never
dwell in security until the provinces of France should
be subdued and brought under the English goverr
ment. They frequently, in time of war, undertook
military expeditions against Acadia and Canada, and
sometimes besieged the fortresses by which those territories were defended. But the most earnest wish oi
their hearts was to take Quebec, and so get possession
of the whole province of Canada. Sir William Phipps
had once attempted it, but without success.

Fleets and soldiers were often sent from England t
assist the colonists in their warlike undertakings. I
1710 Port Royal, a fortress of Acadia, was taken by

the English. The next year, in the month of June, a
fleet, commanded by Admiral Sir Hovenden Walker,
arrived in Boston Harbor. On board of this fleet was
the English General Hill, with seven regiments of
soldiers, who had been fighting under the Duke of
Marlborough in Flanders. The government of Massachusetts was called upon to find provisions for the
army and fleet, and to raise more men to assist in
taking Canada.

What with recruiting and drilling of soldiers, there
was now nothing but warlike bustle in the streets of
Boston. The drum and fife, the rattle of arms, and
the shouts of boys were heard from morning till night.
In about a month the fleet set sail, carrying four regiments from New England and New York, besides the
English soldiers. The whole army amounted to at
least seven thousand men. They steered for the
mouth of the river St. Lawrence.

"Cotton Mather prayed most fervently for their
success," continued Grandfather, "both in his pulpit
and when he kneeled down in the solitude of his
library, resting his face on our old chair. But Providence ordered the result otherwise. In a few weeks
tidings were received that eight or nine of the vessels
had been wrecked in the St. Lawrence, and that above
a thousand drowned soldiers had been washed ashore
on the banks of that mighty river. After this misfortune Sir Hovenden Walker set sail for England;
and many pious people began to think it a sin even to
wish for the conquest of Canada."

"I would never give it up so," cried Charley.

"Nor did they, as we shall see," replied Grandfather. "However, no more attempts were made
during this war, which came to a close in 1713. The

people of New England were probably glad of some repose; for their young men had been made soldiers, till many of them were fit for nothing else. And those who remained at home had been heavily taxed to pay for the arms, ammunition, fortifications, and all the other endless expenses of a war. There was great need of the prayers of Cotton Mather and of all pious men, not only on account of the sufferings of the people, but because the old moral and religious character of New England was in danger of being utterly lost."

"How glorious it would have been," remarked Laurence, "if our forefathers could have kept the country unspotted with blood!"

"Yes," said Grandfather; "but there was a stern, warlike spirit in them from the beginning. They seem never to have thought of questioning either the morality or piety of war."

The next event which Grandfather spoke of was one that Cotton Mather, as well as most of the other inhabitants of New England, heartily rejoiced at. This was the accession of the Elector of Hanover to the throne of England, in 1714, on the death of Queen Anne. Hitherto the people had been in continual dread that the male line of the Stuarts, who were descended from the beheaded King Charles and the banished King James, would be restored to the throne. In that case, as the Stuart family were Roman Catholics, it was supposed that they would attempt to establish their own religion throughout the British dominions. But the Elector of Hanover and all his race were Protestants; so that now the descendants of the old Puritans were relieved from many fears and disquietudes.

"The importance of this event," observed Grand

father, " was a thousand times greater than that of a Presidential election in our own days. If the people dislike their President, they may get rid of him in four years ; whereas a dynasty of kings may wear the crown for an unlimited period."

The German elector was proclaimed king from the balcony of the town-house in Boston, by the title of George I. ; while the trumpets sounded, and the people cried amen. That night the town was illuminated ; and Cotton Mather threw aside book and pen, and left Grandfather's chair vacant, while he walked hither and thither to witness the rejoicings.

CHAPTER V.

"Cotton Mather," continued Grandfather, "was a bitter enemy to Governor Dudley; and nobody exulted more than he when that crafty politician was removed from the government, and succeeded by Colonel Shute. This took place in 1716. The new governor had been an officer in the renowned Duke of Marlborough's army, and had fought in some of the great battles in Flanders."

"Now I hope," said Charley, "we shall hear of his doing great things."

"I am afraid you will be disappointed, Charley," answered Grandfather. "It is true that Colonel Shute had probably never led so unquiet a life while fighting the French as he did now, while governing this province of Massachusetts Bay. But his troubles consisted almost entirely of dissensions with the Legislature. The king had ordered him to lay claim to a fixed salary; but the representatives of the people insisted upon paying him only such sums from year to year as they saw fit."

Grandfather here explained some of the circumstances that made the situation of a colonial governor so difficult and irksome. There was not the same feeling towards the chief magistrate now that had existed while he was chosen by the free suffrages of the people. It was felt that as the king appointed the governor, and as he held his office during the king's pleasure, it would be his great object to please the king. But the people thought that a governor ought to have nothing in view but the best interests of those whom he governed.

"The governor," remarked Grandfather, "had two masters to serve, — the king who appointed him; and the people, on whom he depended for his pay. Few men in this position would have ingenuity enough to satisfy either party. Colonel Shute, though a good-natured, well-meaning man, succeeded so ill with the people, that, in 1722, he suddenly went away to England and made complaint to King George. In the mean time Lieutenant-Governor Dummer directed the affairs of the province, and carried on a long and bloody war with the Indians."

"But where was our chair all this time?" asked Clara.

"It still remained in Cotton Mather's library," replied Grandfather; "and I must not omit to tell you an incident which is very much to the honor of this celebrated man. It is the more proper, too, that you should hear it, because it will show you what a terrible calamity the small-pox was to our forefathers. The history of the province (and, of course, the history of our chair) would be incomplete without particular mention of it."

Accordingly Grandfather told the children a story, to which, for want of a better title, we shall give that of

THE REJECTED BLESSING.

One day, in 1721, Doctor Cotton Mather sat in his library reading a book that had been published by the Royal Society of London. But every few moments he laid the book upon the table, and leaned back in Grandfather's chair with an aspect of deep care and

disquietude. There were certain things which troubled him exceedingly, so that he could hardly fix his
thoughts upon what he read.

It was now a gloomy time in Boston. That terrible
disease, the small-pox, had recently made its appearance in the town. Ever since the first settlement of
the country this awful pestilence had come at intervals, and swept away multitudes of the inhabitants.
Whenever it commenced its ravages, nothing seemed
to stay its progress until there were no more victims
for it to seize upon. Oftentimes hundreds of people
at once lay groaning with its agony ; and when it departed, its deep footsteps were always to be traced in
many graves.

The people never felt secure from this calamity.
Sometimes, perhaps, it was brought into the country
by a poor sailor, who had caught the infection in foreign parts, and came hither to die and to be the cause
of many deaths. Sometimes, no doubt, it followed in
the train of the pompous governors when they came
over from England. Sometimes the disease lay hidden in the cargoes of ships, among silks, and brocades,
and other costly merchandise which was imported for
the rich people to wear. And sometimes it started up
seemingly of its own accord, and nobody could tell
whence it came. The physician, being called to attend
the sick person, would look at him, and say, " It is
the small-pox ! Let the patient be carried to the hos-
pital."

And now this dreadful sickness had shown itself
again in Boston. Cotton Mather was greatly afflicted
for the sake of the whole province. He had children,
too, who were exposed to the danger. At that very
moment he heard the voice of his youngest son, for
whom his heart was moved with apprehension.

"Alas! I fear for that poor child," said Cotton Mather to himself. "What shall I do for my son Samuel?"

Again he attempted to drive away these thoughts by taking up the book which he had been reading. And now, all of a sudden, his attention became fixed. The book contained a printed letter that an Italian physician had written upon the very subject about which Cotton Mather was so anxiously meditating. He ran his eye eagerly over the pages; and, behold! a method was disclosed to him by which the small-pox might be robbed of its worst terrors. Such a method was known in Greece. The physicians of Turkey, too, those long-bearded Eastern sages, had been acquainted with it for many years. The negroes of Africa, ignorant as they were, had likewise practised it, and thus had shown themselves wiser than the white men.

"Of a truth," ejaculated Cotton Mather, clasping his hands and looking up to heaven, "it was a merciful Providence that brought this book under mine eye. I will procure a consultation of physicians, and see whether this wondrous inoculation may not stay the progress of the destroyer."

So he arose from Grandfather's chair and went out of the library. Near the door he met his son Samuel, who seemed downcast and out of spirits. The boy had heard, probably, that some of his playmates were taken ill with the small-pox. But, as his father looked cheerfully at him, Samuel took courage, trusting that either the wisdom of so learned a minister would find some remedy for the danger, or else that his prayers would secure protection from on high.

Meanwhile Cotton Mather took his staff and three-cornered hat and walked about the streets, calling at the houses of all the physicians in Boston. They were a very wise fraternity; and their huge wigs, and black dresses, and solemn visages made their wisdom appear even profounder than it was. One after another he acquainted them with the discovery which he had hit upon.

But the grave and sagacious personages would scarcely listen to him. The oldest doctor in town contented himself with remarking that no such thing as inoculation was mentioned by Galen or Hippocrates; and it was impossible that modern physicians should be wiser than those old sages. A second held up his hands in dumb astonishment and horror at the madness of what Cotton Mather proposed to do. A third told him, in pretty plain terms, that he knew not what he was talking about. A fourth requested, in the name of the whole medical fraternity, that Cotton Mather would confine his attention to people's souls, and leave the physicians to take care of their bodies.

In short, there was but a single doctor among them all who would grant the poor minister so much as a patient hearing. This was Doctor Zabdiel Boylston. He looked into the matter like a man of sense, and finding, beyond a doubt, that inoculation had rescued many from death, he resolved to try the experiment in his own family.

And so he did. But when the other physicians heard of it they arose in great fury and began a war of words, written, printed, and spoken, against Cotton Mather and Doctor Boylston. To hear them talk, you would have supposed that these two harmless and benevolent men had plotted the ruin of the country.

The people, also, took the alarm. Many, who thought themselves more pious than their neighbors, contended that, if Providence had ordained them to die of the small-pox, it was sinful to aim at preventing it. The strangest reports were in circulation. Some said that Doctor Boylston had contrived a method for conveying the gout, rheumatism, sick-headache, asthma, and all other diseases from one person to another, and diffusing them through the whole community. Others flatly affirmed that the evil one had got possession of Cotton Mather, and was at the bottom of the whole business.

You must observe, children, that Cotton Mather's fellow-citizens were generally inclined to doubt the wisdom of any measure which he might propose to them. They recollected how he had led them astray in the old witchcraft delusion; and now, if he thought and acted ever so wisely, it was difficult for him to get the credit of it.

The people's wrath grew so hot at his attempt to guard them from the small-pox that he could not walk the streets in peace. Whenever the venerable form of the old minister, meagre and haggard with fasts and vigils, was seen approaching, hisses were heard, and shouts of derision, and scornful and bitter laughter. The women snatched away their children from his path, lest he should do them a mischief. Still, however, bending his head meekly, and perhaps stretching out his hands to bless those who reviled him, he pursued his way. But the tears came into his eyes to think how blindly the people rejected the means of safety that were offered them.

Indeed, there were melancholy sights enough in the streets of Boston to draw forth the tears of a compassionate man. Over the door of almost every dwelling a red flag was fluttering in the air. This was the sig-

nal that the small-pox had entered the house and attacked some member of the family ; or perhaps the
whole family, old and young, were struggling at once
with the pestilence.   Friends and relatives, when they
met one another in the streets, would hurry onward
without a grasp of the hand or scarcely a word of
greeting, lest they should catch or communicate the
contagion ; and often a coffin was borne hastily along.

"Alas ! alas ! " said Cotton Mather to himself,
"what shall be done for this poor, misguided people ?
Oh that Providence would open their eyes, and enable
them to discern good from evil ! "

So furious, however, were the people, that they
threatened vengeance against any person who should
dare to practise inoculation, though it were only in his
own family.   This was a hard case for Cotton Mather,
who saw no other way to rescue his poor child Samuel
from the disease.   But he resolved to save him, even
if his house should be burned over his head.

"I will not be turned aside," said he.   "My townsmen shall see that I have faith in this thing, when I
make the experiment on my beloved son, whose life is
dearer to me than my own.   And when I have saved
Samuel, peradventure they will be persuaded to save
themselves."

Accordingly Samuel was inoculated ; and so was
Mr. Walter, a son-in-law of Cotton Mather.   Doctor
Boylston, likewise, inoculated many persons ; and while
hundreds died who had caught the contagion from
the garments of the sick, almost all were preserved
who followed the wise physician's advice.

But the people were not yet convinced of their mistake.   One night a destructive little instrument, called
a hand-grenade, was thrown into Cotton Mather's win-

dow, and rolled under Grandfather's chair. It was supposed to be filled with gunpowder, the explosion of which would have blown the poor minister to atoms. But the best informed historians are of opinion that the grenade contained only brimstone and assafœtida, and was meant to plague Cotton Mather with a very evil perfume.

This is no strange thing in human experience. Men who attempt to do the world more good than the world is able entirely to comprehend are almost invariably held in bad odor. But yet, if the wise and good man can wait awhile, either the present generation or posterity will do him justice. So it proved in the case which we have been speaking of. In after years, when inoculation was universally practised, and thousands were saved from death by it, the people remembered old Cotton Mather, then sleeping in his grave. They acknowledged that the very thing for which they had so reviled and persecuted him was the best and wisest thing he ever did.

"Grandfather, this is not an agreeable story," observed Clara.

"No, Clara," replied Grandfather. "But it is right that you should know what a dark shadow this disease threw over the times of our forefathers. And now, if you wish to learn more about Cotton Mather, you must read his biography, written by Mr. Peabody, of Springfield. You will find it very entertaining and instructive; but perhaps the writer is somewhat too harsh in his judgment of this singular man. He estimates him fairly, indeed, and understands him well; but he unriddles his character rather by acuteness than by sympathy. Now, his life should have been written by one who, knowing all his faults, would nevertheless love him."

So Grandfather made an end of Cotton Mather, telling his auditors that he died in 1728, at the age of sixty-five, and bequeathed the chair to Elisha Cooke. This gentleman was a famous advocate of the people's rights.

The same year William Burnet, a son of the celebrated Bishop Burnet, arrived in Boston with the commission of governor. He was the first that had been appointed since the departure of Colonel Shute. Governor Burnet took up his residence with Mr. Cooke while the Province House was undergoing repairs. During this period he was always complimented with a seat in Grandfather's chair; and so comfortable did he find it, that, on removing to the Province House, he could not bear to leave it behind him. Mr. Cooke, therefore, requested his acceptance of it.

"I should think," said Laurence, "that the people would have petitioned the king always to appoint a native-born New-Englander to govern them."

"Undoubtedly it was a grievance," answered Grandfather, "to see men placed in this station who perhaps had neither talents nor virtues to fit them for it, and who certainly could have no natural affection for the country. The king generally bestowed the governorships of the American colonies upon needy noblemen, or hangers-on at court, or disbanded officers. The people knew that such persons would be very likely to make the good of the country subservient to the wishes of the king. The Legislature, therefore, endeavored to keep as much power as possible in their own hands, by refusing to settle a fixed salary upon the governors. It was thought better to pay them according to their deserts."

"Did Governor Burnet work well for his money?" asked Charley.

Grandfather could not help smiling at the simplicity of Charley's question. Nevertheless, it put the matter in a very plain point of view.

He then described the character of Governor Burnet, representing him as a good scholar, possessed of much ability, and likewise of unspotted integrity. His story affords a striking example how unfortunate it is for a man, who is placed as ruler over a country, to be compelled to aim at anything but the good of the people. Governor Burnet was so chained down by his instructions from the king that he could not act as he might otherwise have wished. Consequently, his whole term of office was wasted in quarrels with the Legislature.

"I am afraid, children," said Grandfather, "that Governor Burnet found but little rest or comfort in our old chair. Here he used to sit, dressed in a coat which was made of rough, shaggy cloth outside, but of smooth velvet within. It was said that his own character resembled that coat; for his outward manner was rough, but his inward disposition soft and kind. It is a pity that such a man could not have been kept free from trouble. But so harassing were his disputes with the representatives of the people that he fell into a fever, of which he died in 1729. The Legislature had refused him a salary while alive; but they appropriated money enough to give him a splendid and pompous funeral."

And now Grandfather perceived that little Alice had fallen fast asleep, with her head upon his footstool. Indeed, as Clara observed, she had been sleeping from the time of Sir Hovenden Walker's expedition against Quebec until the death of Governor Burnet, — a period of about eighteen years. And yet, after so long a nap, sweet little Alice was a golden-haired child of scarcely five years old.

"It puts me in mind," said Laurence, "of the story of the enchanted princess, who slept many a hundred years, and awoke as young and beautiful as ever."

CHAPTER VI.

A FEW evenings afterwards, cousin Clara happened to inquire of Grandfather whether the old chair had never been present at a ball. At the same time little Alice brought forward a doll, with whom she had been holding a long conversation.

"See, Grandfather!" cried she. "Did such a pretty lady as this ever sit in your great chair?"

These questions led Grandfather to talk about the fashions and manners which now began to be introduced from England into the provinces. The simplicity of the good old Puritan times was fast disappearing. This was partly owing to the increasing number and wealth of the inhabitants, and to the additions which they continually received by the arrival and settlement of people from beyond the sea.

Another cause of a pompous and artificial mode of life, among those who could afford it, was, that the example was set by the royal governors. Under the old charter, the governors were the representatives of the people, and therefore their way of living had probably been marked by a popular simplicity. But now, as they represented the person of the king, they thought it necessary to preserve the dignity of their station by the practice of high and gorgeous ceremonials. And, besides, the profitable offices under the government were filled by men who had lived in London, and had there contracted fashionable and luxurious habits of living which they would not now lay aside. The

wealthy people of the province imitated them; and
thus began a general change in social life.

"So, my dear Clara," said Grandfather, "after our
chair had entered the Province House, it must often
have been present at balls and festivals; though I
cannot give you a description of any particular one.
But I doubt not that they were very magnificent; and
slaves in gorgeous liveries waited on the guests, and
offered them wine in goblets of massive silver."

"Were there slaves in those days!" exclaimed
Clara.

"Yes, black slaves and white," replied Grandfather.
"Our ancestors not only brought negroes from Africa,
but Indians from South America, and white people
from Ireland. These last were sold, not for life, but
for a certain number of years, in order to pay the expenses of their voyage across the Atlantic. Nothing
was more common than to see a lot of likely Irish
girls advertised for sale in the newspapers. As for
the little negro babies, they were offered to be given
away like young kittens."

"Perhaps Alice would have liked one to play with,
instead of her doll," said Charley, laughing.

But little Alice clasped the waxen doll closer to her
bosom.

"Now, as for this pretty doll, my little Alice," said
Grandfather, "I wish you could have seen what splendid dresses the ladies wore in those times. They had
silks, and satins, and damasks, and brocades, and
high head-dresses, and all sorts of fine things. And
they used to wear hooped petticoats of such enormous
size that it was quite a journey to walk round them."

"And how did the gentlemen dress?" asked Charley.

"With full as much magnificence as the ladies," answered Grandfather. "For their holiday suits they had coats of figured velvet, crimson, green, blue, and all other gay colors, embroidered with gold or silver lace. Their waistcoats, which were five times as large as modern ones, were very splendid. Sometimes the whole waistcoat, which came down almost to the knees, was made of gold brocade."

"Why, the wearer must have shone like a golden image!" said Clara.

"And then," continued Grandfather, "they wore various sorts of periwigs, such as the tie, the Spencer, the brigadier, the major, the Albemarle, the Ramillies, the feather-top, and the full bottom. Their three-cornered hats were laced with gold or silver. They had shining buckles at the knees of their small-clothes, and buckles likewise in their shoes. They wore swords with beautiful hilts, either of silver, or sometimes of polished steel, inlaid with gold."

"Oh, I should like to wear a sword!" cried Charley.

"And an embroidered crimson velvet coat," said Clara, laughing, "and a gold brocade waistcoat down to your knees!"

"And knee-buckles and shoe-buckles," said Laurence, laughing also.

"And a periwig," added little Alice, soberly, not knowing what was the article of dress which she recommended to our friend Charley.

Grandfather smiled at the idea of Charley's sturdy little figure in such a grotesque caparison. He then went on with the history of the chair, and told the children that, in 1730, King George II. appointed Jonathan Belcher to be governor of Massachusetts in

place of the deceased Governor Burnet.   Mr. Belcher
was a native of the province, but had spent much of
his life in Europe.

The new governor found Grandfather's chair in the
Province House.   He was struck with its noble and
stately aspect, but was of opinion that age and hard
services had made it scarcely so fit for courtly company as when it stood in the Earl of Lincoln's hall.
Wherefore, as Governor Belcher was fond of splendor, he employed a skilful artist to beautify the chair.
This was done by polishing and varnishing it, and by
gilding the carved work of the elbows, and likewise
the oaken flowers of the back.   The lion's head now
shone like a veritable lump of gold.   Finally Governor
Belcher gave the chair a cushion of blue damask, with
a rich golden fringe.

"Our good old chair being thus glorified," proceeded Grandfather, "it glittered with a great deal
more splendor than it had exhibited just a century
before, when the Lady Arbella brought it over from
England.   Most people mistook it for a chair of the
latest London fashion.   And this may serve for an
example, that there is almost always an old and time-
worn substance under all the glittering show of new
invention."

"Grandfather, I cannot see any of the gilding," remarked Charley, who had been examining the chair
very minutely.

"You will not wonder that it has been rubbed off,"
replied Grandfather, "when you hear all the adventures that have since befallen the chair.   Gilded it
was; and the handsomest room in the Province House
was adorned by it."

There was not much to interest the children in what

happened during the years that Governor Belcher remained in the chair. At first, like Colonel Shute and
Governor Burnet, he was engaged in disputing with
the Legislature about his salary. But, as he found it
impossible to get a fixed sum, he finally obtained the
king's leave to accept whatever the Legislature chose
to give him. And thus the people triumphed, after
this long contest for the privilege of expending their
own money as they saw fit.

The remainder of Governor Belcher's term of office
was principally taken up in endeavoring to settle the
currency. Honest John Hull's pine-tree shillings had
long ago been worn out, or lost, or melted down
again; and their place was supplied by bills of paper
or parchment, which were nominally valued at threepence and upwards. The value of these bills kept
continually sinking, because the real hard money
could not be obtained for them. They were a great
deal worse than the old Indian currency of clam-shells.
These disorders of the circulating medium were a
source of endless plague and perplexity to the rulers
and legislators, not only in Governor Belcher's days,
but for many years before and afterwards.

Finally the people suspected that Governor Belcher
was secretly endeavoring to establish the Episcopal
mode of worship in the provinces. There was enough
of the old Puritan spirit remaining to cause most of
the true sons of New England to look with horror
upon such an attempt. Great exertions were made to
induce the king to remove the governor. Accordingly,
in 1740, he was compelled to resign his office, and
Grandfather's chair into the bargain, to Mr. Shirley.

CHAPTER VII.

"WILLIAM SHIRLEY," said Grandfather, "had come from England a few years before, and begun to practise law in Boston. You will think, perhaps, that, as he had been a lawyer, the new governor used to sit in our great chair reading heavy law-books from morning till night. On the contrary, he was as stirring and active a governor as Massachusetts ever had. Even Sir William Phipps hardly equalled him. The first year or two of his administration was spent in trying to regulate the currency. But in 1744, after a peace of more than thirty years, war broke out between France and England."

"And I suppose," said Charley, "the governor went to take Canada."

"Not exactly, Charley," said Grandfather; "though you have made a pretty shrewd conjecture. He planned, in 1745, an expedition against Louisburg. This was a fortified city, on the island of Cape Breton, near Nova Scotia. Its walls were of immense height and strength, and were defended by hundreds of heavy cannon. It was the strongest fortress which the French possessed in America; and if the king of France had guessed Governor Shirley's intentions, he would have sent all the ships he could muster to protect it."

As the siege of Louisburg was one of the most remarkable events that ever the inhabitants of New England were engaged in, Grandfather endeavored to give his auditors a lively idea of the spirit with which they set about it. We shall call his description

THE PROVINCIAL MUSTER.

The expedition against Louisburg first began to be thought of in the month of January. From that time the governor's chair was continually surrounded by councillors, representatives, clergymen, captains, pilots, and all manner of people, with whom he consulted about this wonderful project.

First of all, it was necessary to provide men and arms. The Legislature immediately sent out a huge quantity of paper-money, with which, as if by magic spell, the governor hoped to get possession of all the old cannon, powder and balls, rusty swords and muskets, and everything else that would be serviceable in killing Frenchmen. Drums were beaten in all the villages of Massachusetts to enlist soldiers for the service. Messages were sent to the other governors of New England, and to New York and Pennsylvania, entreating them to unite in this crusade against the French. All these provinces agreed to give what assistance they could.

But there was one very important thing to be decided. Who shall be the general of this great army? Peace had continued such an unusual length of time, that there was now less military experience among the colonists than at any former period. The old Puritans had always kept their weapons bright, and were never destitute of warlike captains who were skilful in assault or defence. But the swords of their descendants had grown rusty by disuse. There was nobody in New England that knew anything about sieges or any other regular fighting. The only persons at all acquainted

with warlike business were a few elderly men, who had
hunted Indians through the underbrush of the forest
in old Governor Dummer's war.

In this dilemma Governor Shirley fixed upon a
wealthy merchant, named William Pepperell, who was
pretty well known and liked among the people. As
to military skill, he had no more of it than his neighbors. But, as the governor urged him very press-
ingly, Mr. Pepperell consented to shut up his ledger,
gird on a sword, and assume the title of general.

Meantime, what a hubbub was raised by this scheme!
Rub-a-dub-dub! rub-a-dub-dub! The rattle of drums,
beaten out of all manner of time, was heard above
every other sound.

Nothing now was so valuable as arms, of whatever
style and fashion they might be. The bellows blew,
and the hammer clanged continually upon the anvil,
while the blacksmiths were repairing the broken weapons of other wars. Doubtless some of the soldiers
lugged out those enormous, heavy muskets which used
to be fired, with rests, in the time of the early Puritans. Great horse-pistols, too, were found, which would
go off with a bang like a cannon. Old cannon, with
touchholes almost as big as their muzzles, were looked
upon as inestimable treasures. Pikes which, perhaps,
had been handled by Miles Standish's soldiers, now
made their appearance again. Many a young man
ransacked the garret and brought forth his great-
grandfather's sword, corroded with rust and stained
with the blood of King Philip's War.

Never had there been such an arming as this, when
a people, so long peaceful, rose to the war with the best
weapons that they could lay their hands upon. And
still the drums were heard — rub-a-dub-dub! rub-a-

dub-dub ! — in all the towns and villages ; and louder
and more numerous grew the trampling footsteps of
the recruits that marched behind.

And now the army began to gather into Boston.
Tall, lanky, awkward fellows came in squads, and com-
panies, and regiments, swaggering along, dressed in
their brown homespun clothes and blue yarn stockings. They stooped as if they still had hold of the
plough-handles, and marched without any time or tune.
Hither they came, from the cornfields, from the clearing in the forest, from the blacksmith's forge, from the
carpenter's workshop, and from the shoemaker's seat.
They were an army of rough faces and sturdy frames.
A trained officer of Europe would have laughed at
them till his sides had ached. But there was a spirit
in their bosoms which is more essential to soldiership
than to wear red coats and march in stately ranks to
the sound of regular music.

Still was heard the beat of the drum, — rub-a-dub-
dub ! And now a host of three or four thousand men
had found their way to Boston. Little quiet was there
then ! Forth scampered the school-boys, shouting behind the drums. The whole town, the whole land,
was on fire with war.

After the arrival of the troops, they were probably
reviewed upon the Common. We may imagine Governor Shirley and General Pepperell riding slowly
along the line, while the drummers beat strange old
tunes, like psalm-tunes, and all the officers and soldiers
put on their most warlike looks. It would have been
a terrible sight for the Frenchmen, could they but
have witnessed it !

At length, on the 24th of March, 1745, the army
gave a parting shout, and set sail from Boston in ten

or twelve vessels which had been hired by the governor. A few days afterwards an English fleet, commanded by Commodore Peter Warren, sailed also for Louisburg to assist the provincial army. So now, after all this bustle of preparation, the town and province were left in stillness and repose.

But stillness and repose, at such a time of anxious expectation, are hard to bear. The hearts of the old people and women sunk within them when they reflected what perils they had sent their sons, and husbands, and brothers to encounter. The boys loitered heavily to school, missing the rub-a-dub-dub and the trampling march, in the rear of which they had so lately run and shouted. All the ministers prayed earnestly in their pulpits for a blessing on the army of New England. In every family, when the good man lifted up his heart in domestic worship, the burden of his petition was for the safety of those dear ones who were fighting under the walls of Louisburg.

Governor Shirley all this time was probably in an ecstasy of impatience. He could not sit still a moment. He found no quiet, not even in Grandfather's chair; but hurried to and fro, and up and down the staircase of the Province House. Now he mounted to the cupola and looked seaward, straining his eyes to discover if there were a sail upon the horizon. Now he hastened down the stairs, and stood beneath the portal, on the red free-stone steps, to receive some mud-bespattered courier, from whom he hoped to hear tidings of the army. A few weeks after the departure of the troops, Commodore Warren sent a small vessel to Boston with two French prisoners. One of them was Monsieur Bouladrie, who had been commander of a battery outside of the walls of Louisburg.

The other was the Marquis de la Maison Forte, captain of a French frigate which had been taken by Commodore Warren's fleet. These prisoners assured Governor Shirley that the fortifications of Louisburg were far too strong ever to be stormed by the provincial army.

Day after day and week after week went on. The people grew almost heart-sick with anxiety; for the flower of the country was at peril in this adventurous expedition. It was now daybreak on the morning of the 3d of July.

But hark! what sound is this? The hurried clang of a bell! There is the Old North pealing suddenly out! — there the Old South strikes in! — now the peal comes from the church in Brattle Street! — the bells of nine or ten steeples are all flinging their iron voices at once upon the morning breeze! Is it joy, or alarm? There goes the roar of a cannon too! A royal salute is thundered forth. And now we hear the loud exulting shout of a multitude assembled in the street. Huzza! huzza! Louisburg has surrendered! Huzza!

" O Grandfather, how glad I should have been to live in those times!" cried Charley. "And what reward did the king give to General Pepperell and Governor Shirley?"

"He made Pepperell a baronet; so that he was now to be called Sir William Pepperell," replied Grandfather. "He likewise appointed both Pepperell and Shirley to be colonels in the royal army. These rewards, and higher ones, were well deserved; for this was the greatest triumph that the English met with in the whole course of that war. General Pepperell became a man of great fame. I have seen a full-length portrait of him, representing him in a splendid scarlet uniform, standing before the walls of Louisburg, while several bombs are falling through the air."

"But did the country gain any real good by the conquest of Louisburg?" asked Laurence. "Or was all the benefit reaped by Pepperell and Shirley?"

"The English Parliament," replied Grandfather, "agreed to pay the colonists for all the expenses of the siege. Accordingly, in 1749, two hundred and fifteen chests of Spanish dollars and one hundred casks of copper coin were brought from England to Boston. The whole amount was about a million of dollars. Twenty-seven carts and trucks carried this money from the wharf to the provincial treasury. Was not this a pretty liberal reward?"

"The mothers of the young men who were killed at the siege of Louisburg would not have thought it so," said Laurence.

"No, Laurence," rejoined Grandfather; "and every warlike achievement involves an amount of physical and moral evil, for which all the gold in the Spanish mines would not be the slightest recompense. But we are to consider that this siege was one of the occasions on which the colonists tested their ability for war, and thus were prepared for the great contest of the Revolution. In that point of view, the valor of our forefathers was its own reward."

Grandfather went on to say that the success of the expedition against Louisburg induced Shirley and Pepperell to form a scheme for conquering Canada. This plan, however, was not carried into execution.

In the year 1746 great terror was excited by the arrival of a formidable French fleet upon the coast. It was commanded by the Duke d'Anville, and consisted of forty ships of war, besides vessels with soldiers on board. With this force the French intended to retake Louisburg, and afterwards to ravage the whole of New England. Many people were ready to give up the country for lost.

But the hostile fleet met with so many disasters and losses by storm and shipwreck, that the Duke d'Anville is said to have poisoned himself in despair. The officer next in command threw himself upon his sword and perished. Thus deprived of their commanders, the remainder of the ships returned to France. This was as great a deliverance for New England as that which Old England had experienced in the days of Queen Elizabeth, when the Spanish Armada was wrecked upon her coast.

" In 1747," proceeded Grandfather, "Governor Shirley was driven from the Province House, not by a hostile fleet and army, but by a mob of the Boston people. They were so incensed at the conduct of the British Commodore Knowles, who had impressed some of their fellow-citizens, that several thousands of them surrounded the council chamber and threw stones and brickbats into the windows. The governor attempted to pacify them; but not succeeding, he thought it necessary to leave the town and take refuge within the walls of Castle William. Quiet was not restored until Commodore Knowles had sent back the impressed men. This affair was a flash of spirit that might have warned the English not to venture upon any oppressive measures against their colonial brethren."

Peace being declared between France and England in 1748, the governor had now an opportunity to sit at his ease in Grandfather's chair. Such repose, however, appears not to have suited his disposition; for

in the following year he went to England, and thence
was despatched to France on public business. Meanwhile, as Shirley had not resigned his office, Lieutenant-Governor Phipps acted as chief magistrate in
his stead.

CHAPTER VIII.

In the early twilight of Thanksgiving Eve came Laurence, and Clara, and Charley, and little Alice hand in hand, and stood in a semicircle round Grandfather's chair. They had been joyous throughout that day of festivity, mingling together in all kinds of play, so that the house had echoed with their airy mirth.

Grandfather, too, had been happy though not mirthful. He felt that this was to be set down as one of the good Thanksgivings of his life. In truth, all his former Thanksgivings had borne their part in the present one; for his years of infancy, and youth, and manhood, with their blessings and their griefs, had flitted before him while he sat silently in the great chair. Vanished scenes had been pictured in the air. The forms of departed friends had visited him. Voices to be heard no more on earth had sent an echo from the infinite and the eternal. These shadows, if such they were, seemed almost as real to him as what was actually present, — as the merry shouts and laughter of the children, — as their figures, dancing like sunshine before his eyes.

He felt that the past was not taken from him. The happiness of former days was a possession forever. And there was something in the mingled sorrow of his lifetime that became akin to happiness, after being long treasured in the depths of his heart. There it underwent a change, and grew more precious than pure gold.

And now came the children, somewhat aweary with their wild play, and sought the quiet enjoyment of Grandfather's talk. The good old gentleman rubbed his eyes and smiled round upon them all. He was glad, as most aged people are, to find that he was yet of consequence, and could give pleasure to the world. After being so merry all day long, did these children desire to hear his sober talk? Oh, then, old Grandfather had yet a place to fill among living men, — or at least among boys and girls!

"Begin quick, Grandfather," cried little Alice; "for pussy wants to hear you."

And truly our yellow friend, the cat, lay upon the hearth-rug, basking in the warmth of the fire, pricking up her ears, and turning her head from the children to Grandfather, and from Grandfather to the children, as if she felt herself very sympathetic with them all. A loud purr, like the singing of a tea-kettle or the hum of a spinning-wheel, testified that she was as comfortable and happy as a cat could be. For puss had feasted; and therefore, like Grandfather and the children, had kept a good Thanksgiving.

"Does pussy want to hear me?" said Grandfather, smiling. "Well, we must please pussy, if we can."

And so he took up the history of the chair from the epoch of the peace of 1748. By one of the provisions of the treaty, Louisburg, which the New-Englanders had been at so much pains to take, was restored to the King of France.

The French were afraid that, unless their colonies should be better defended than heretofore, another war might deprive them of the whole. Almost as soon as peace was declared, therefore, they began to build strong fortifications in the interior of North

America. It was strange to behold these warlike castles on the banks of solitary lakes and far in the midst of woods. The Indian, paddling his birch canoe on Lake Champlain, looked up at the high ramparts of Ticonderoga, stone piled on stone, bristling with cannon, and the white flag of France floating above. There were similar fortifications on Lake Ontario, and near the great Falls of Niagara, and at the sources of the Ohio River. And all around these forts and castles lay the eternal forest, and the roll of the drum died away in those deep solitudes.

The truth was, that the French intended to build forts all the way from Canada to Louisiana. They would then have had a wall of military strength at the back of the English settlements so as completely to hem them in. The King of England considered the building of these forts as a sufficient cause of war, which was accordingly commenced in 1754.

"Governor Shirley," said Grandfather, "had returned to Boston in 1753. While in Paris he had married a second wife, a young French girl, and now brought her to the Province House. But when war was breaking out it was impossible for such a bustling man to stay quietly at home, sitting in our old chair, with his wife and children round about him. He therefore obtained a command in the English forces."

"And what did Sir William Pepperell do?" asked Charley.

"He stayed at home," said Grandfather, "and was general of the militia. The veteran regiments of the English army which were now sent across the Atlantic would have scorned to fight under the orders of an old American merchant. And now began what aged people call the old French War. It would be going too far astray from the history of our chair to tell you one half of the battles that were fought. I cannot even allow myself to describe the bloody defeat of General Braddock, near the sources of the Ohio River, in 1755. But I must not omit to mention that, when the English general was mortally wounded and his army routed, the remains of it were preserved by the skill and valor of GEORGE WASHINGTON."

At the mention of this illustrious name the children started as if a sudden sunlight had gleamed upon the history of their country, now that the great deliverer had arisen above the horizon.

Among all the events of the old French War, Grandfather thought that there was none more interesting than the removal of the inhabitants of Acadia. From the first settlement of this ancient province of the French, in 1604, until the present time, its people could scarcely ever know what kingdom held dominion over them. They were a peaceful race, taking no delight in warfare, and caring nothing for military renown. And yet, in every war, their region was infested with iron-hearted soldiers, both French and English, who fought one another for the privilege of ill treating these poor, harmless Acadians. Sometimes the treaty of peace made them subjects of one king, sometimes of another.

At the peace of 1748 Acadia had been ceded to England. But the French still claimed a large portion of it, and built forts for its defence. In 1755 these forts were taken, and the whole of Acadia was conquered by three thousand men from Massachusetts, under the command of General Winslow. The inhabitants were accused of supplying the French with provisions, and of doing other things that violated their neutrality.

"These accusations were probably true," observed Grandfather; "for the Acadians were descended from the French, and had the same friendly feelings towards them that the people of Massachusetts had for the English. But their punishment was severe. The English determined to tear these poor people from their native homes and scatter them abroad."

The Acadians were about seven thousand in number. A considerable part of them were made prisoners, and transported to the English colonies. All their dwellings and churches were burned, their cattle were killed, and the whole country was laid waste, so that none of them might find shelter or food in their old homes after the departure of the English. One thousand of the prisoners were sent to Massachusetts; and Grandfather allowed his fancy to follow them thither, and tried to give his auditors an idea of their situation.

We shall call this passage the story of

THE ACADIAN EXILES.

A sad day it was for the poor Acadians when the armed soldiers drove them, at the point of the bayonet, down to the sea-shore. Very sad were they, likewise, while tossing upon the ocean in the crowded transport vessels. But methinks it must have been sadder still when they were landed on the Long Wharf in Boston, and left to themselves on a foreign strand.

Then, probably, they huddled together and looked into one another's faces for the comfort which was not there. Hitherto they had been confined on board of separate vessels, so that they could not tell whether their relatives and friends were prisoners along with them. But now, at least, they could tell that many had been left behind or transported to other regions.

Now a desolate wife might be heard calling for her husband. He, alas! had gone, she knew not whither; or perhaps had fled into the woods of Acadia, and had now returned to weep over the ashes of their dwelling.

An aged widow was crying out in a querulous, lamentable tone for her son, whose affectionate toil had supported her for many a year. He was not in the crowd of exiles; and what could this aged widow do but sink down and die? Young men and maidens, whose hearts had been torn asunder by separation, had hoped, during the voyage, to meet their beloved ones at its close. Now they began to feel that they were separated forever. And perhaps a lonesome little girl, a golden-haired child of five years old, the very picture of our little Alice, was weeping and wailing for her mother, and found not a soul to give her a kind word.

Oh, how many broken bonds of affection were here! Country lost, — friends lost, — their rural wealth of cottage, field, and herds all lost together! Every tie between these poor exiles and the world seemed to be cut off at once. They must have regretted that they had not died before their exile; for even the English would not have been so pitiless as to deny them graves in their native soil. The dead were happy; for they were not exiles!

While they thus stood upon the wharf, the curiosity and inquisitiveness of the New England people would naturally lead them into the midst of the poor Acadians. Prying busybodies thrust their heads into the circle wherever two or three of the exiles were conversing together. How puzzled did they look at the outlandish sound of the French tongue! There were seen the New England women, too. They had just come out of their warm, safe homes, where everything was regular and comfortable, and where their husbands and children would be with them at nightfall. Surely they could pity the wretched wives and mothers of Acadia! Or did the sign of the cross which the Acadians continually made upon their breasts, and which was abhorred by the descendants of the Puritans, — did that sign exclude all pity?

Among the spectators, too, was the noisy brood of Boston school-boys, who came running, with laughter and shouts, to gaze at this crowd of oddly dressed foreigners. At first they danced and capered around them, full of merriment and mischief. But the despair of the Acadians soon had its effect upon these thoughtless lads, and melted them into tearful sympathy.

At a little distance from the throng might be seen the wealthy and pompous merchants whose warehouses stood on Long Wharf. It was difficult to touch these rich men's hearts; for they had all the comforts of the world at their command; and when they walked abroad their feelings were seldom moved, except by the roughness of the pavement irritating their gouty toes. Leaning upon their gold-headed canes, they watched the scene with an aspect of composure. But let us hope they distributed some of their superfluous coin among these hapless exiles to purchase food and a night's lodging.

After standing a long time at the end of the wharf, gazing seaward, as if to catch a glimpse of their lost Acadia, the strangers began to stray into the town.

They went, we will suppose, in parties and groups, here a hundred, there a score, there ten, there three or four, who possessed some bond of unity among themselves. Here and there, was one, who, utterly desolate, stole away by himself, seeking no companionship.

Whither did they go? I imagine them wandering about the streets, telling the townspeople, in outlandish, unintelligible words, that no earthly affliction ever equalled what had befallen them. Man's brotherhood with man was sufficient to make the New-Englanders understand this language. The strangers wanted food. Some of them sought hospitality at the doors of the stately mansions which then stood in the vicinity of Hanover Street and the North Square. Others were applicants at the humble wooden tenements, where dwelt the petty shopkeepers and mechanics. Pray Heaven that no family in Boston turned one of these poor exiles from their door! It would be a reproach upon New England, — a crime worthy of heavy retribution, — if the aged women and children, or even the strong men, were allowed to feel the pinch of hunger.

Perhaps some of the Acadians, in their aimless wanderings through the town, found themselves near a large brick edifice, which was fenced in from the street by an iron railing, wrought with fantastic figures. They saw a flight of red freestone steps ascending to a portal, above which was a balcony and balustrade. Misery and desolation give men the right of free passage everywhere. Let us suppose, then, that they mounted the flight of steps and passed into the Province House. Making their way into one of the apartments, they beheld a richly-clad gentleman, seated in a stately chair, with gilding upon the carved work of its back, and a gilded lion's head at the summit. This was Governor Shirley, meditating upon matters of war and state, in Grandfather's chair!

If such an incident did happen, Shirley, reflecting what a ruin of peaceful and humble hopes had been wrought by the cold policy of the statesman and the iron hand of the warrior, might have drawn a deep moral from it. It should have taught him that the poor man's hearth is sacred, and that armies and nations have no right to violate it. It should have made him feel that England's triumph and increased dominion could not compensate to mankind nor atone to Heaven for the ashes of a single Acadian cottage. But it is not thus that statesmen and warriors moralize.

" Grandfather," cried Laurence, with emotion trembling in his voice, " did iron-hearted War itself ever do so hard and cruel a thing as this before ? "

" You have read in history, Laurence, of whole regions wantonly laid waste," said Grandfather. " In the removal of the Acadians, the troops were guilty of no cruelty or outrage, except what was inseparable from the measure."

Little Alice, whose eyes had all along been brimming full of tears, now burst forth a-sobbing ; for Grandfather had touched her sympathies more than he intended.

" To think of a whole people homeless in the world ! " said Clara, with moistened eyes. " There never was anything so sad ! "

" It was their own fault ! " cried Charley, energetically. " Why did not they fight for the country where they were born. Then, if the worst had happened to them, they could only have been killed and buried there. They would not have been exiles then."

" Certainly their lot was as hard as death," said Grandfather. " All that could be done for them in

the English provinces was, to send them to the alms-
houses, or bind them out to taskmasters. And this
was the fate of persons who had possessed a comfort-
ble property in their native country. Some of them
found means to embark for France; but though it was
the land of their forefathers, it must have been a foreign land to them. Those who remained behind always cherished a belief that the King of France would
never make peace with England till his poor Acadians
were restored to their country and their homes."

"And did he?" inquired Clara.

"Alas! my dear Clara," said Grandfather, "it is
improbable that the slightest whisper of the woes of
Acadia ever reached the ears of Louis XV. The exiles grew old in the British provinces, and never saw
Acadia again. Their descendants remain among us to
this day. They have forgotten the language of their
ancestors, and probably retain no tradition of their
misfortunes. But, methinks, if I were an American
poet, I would choose Acadia for the subject of my
song."

Since Grandfather first spoke these words, the most
famous of American poets has drawn sweet tears from
all of us by his beautiful poem Evangeline.

And now, having thrown a gentle gloom around the
Thanksgiving fireside by a story that made the chil-
dren feel the blessing of a secure and peaceful hearth,
Grandfather put off the other events of the old French
War till the next evening.

CHAPTER IX.

In the twilight of the succeeding eve, when the red beams of the fire were dancing upon the wall, the children besought Grandfather to tell them what had next happened to the old chair.

"Our chair," said Grandfather, "stood all this time in the Province House. But Governor Shirley had seldom an opportunity to repose within its arms. He was leading his troops through the forest, or sailing in a flat-boat on Lake Ontario, or sleeping in his tent, while the awful cataract of Niagara sent its roar through his dreams. At one period, in the early part of the war, Shirley had the chief command of all the king's forces in America."

"Did his young wife go with him to the war?" asked Clara.

"I rather imagine," replied Grandfather, "that she remained in Boston. This lady, I suppose, had our chair all to herself, and used to sit in it during those brief intervals when a young Frenchwoman can be quiet enough to sit in a chair. The people of Massachusetts were never fond of Governor Shirley's young French wife. They had a suspicion that she betrayed the military plans of the English to the generals of the French armies."

"And was it true?" inquired Clara.

"Probably not," said Grandfather. "But the mere suspicion did Shirley a great deal of harm. Partly, perhaps, for this reason, but much more on account of his inefficiency as a general, he was deprived of his command in 1756, and recalled to England. He never afterwards made any figure in public life."

As Grandfather's chair had no locomotive properties, and did not even run on castors, it cannot be supposed to have marched in person to the old French War. But Grandfather delayed its momentous history while he touched briefly upon some of the bloody battles, sieges, and onslaughts, the tidings of which kept continually coming to the ears of the old inhabitants of Boston. The woods of the North were populous with fighting men. All the Indian tribes uplifted their tomahawks, and took part either with the French or English. The rattle of musketry and roar of cannon disturbed the ancient quiet of the forest, and actually drove the bears and other wild beasts to the more cultivated portion of the country in the vicinity of the seaports. The children felt as if they were transported back to those forgotten times, and that the couriers from the army, with the news of a battle lost or won, might even now be heard galloping through the streets. Grandfather told them about the battle of Lake George in 1755, when the gallant Colonel Williams, a Massachusetts officer, was slain, with many of his countrymen. But General Johnson and General Lyman, with their army, drove back the enemy and mortally wounded the French leader, who was called the Baron Dieskau. A gold watch, pilfered from the poor baron, is still in existence, and still marks each moment of time without complaining of weariness, although its hands have been in motion ever since the hour of battle.

In the first years of the war there were many disasters on the English side. Among these was the loss of Fort Oswego in 1756, and of Fort William Henry in the following year. But the greatest misfortune that befell the English during the whole war was the repulse of General Abercrombie, with his army, from the ramparts of Ticonderoga in 1758. He attempted to storm the walls; but a terrible conflict ensued, in which more than two thousand Englishmen and New-Englanders were killed or wounded. The slain soldiers now lie buried around that ancient fortress. When the plough passes over the soil, it turns up here and there a mouldering bone.

Up to this period, none of the English generals had shown any military talent. Shirley, the Earl of Loudon, and General Abercrombie had each held the chief command at different times; but not one of them had won a single important triumph for the British arms. This ill success was not owing to the want of means; for, in 1758, General Abercrombie had fifty thousand soldiers under his command. But the French general, the famous Marquis de Montcalm, possessed a great genius for war, and had something within him that taught him how battles were to be won.

At length, in 1759, Sir Jeffrey Amherst was appointed commander-in-chief of all the British forces in America. He was a man of ability and a skilful soldier. A plan was now formed for accomplishing that object which had so long been the darling wish of the New-Englanders, and which their fathers had so many times attempted. This was the conquest of Canada.

Three separate armies were to enter Canada from different quarters. One of the three, commanded by General Prideaux, was to embark on Lake Ontario and proceed to Montreal. The second, at the head of which was Sir Jeffrey Amherst himself, was destined to reach the river St. Lawrence, by the way of Lake Champlain, and then go down the river to meet the third army. This last, led by General Wolfe, was to enter the St. Lawrence from the sea and ascend the river to Quebec. It is to Wolfe and his army that England owes one of the most splendid triumphs ever written in her history.

Grandfather described the siege of Quebec, and told how Wolfe led his soldiers up a rugged and lofty precipice, that rose from the shore of the river to the plain on which the city stood. This bold adventure was achieved in the darkness of night. At daybreak tidings were carried to the Marquis de Montcalm that the English army was waiting to give him battle on the Plains of Abraham. This brave French general ordered his drums to strike up, and immediately marched to encounter Wolfe.

He marched to his own death. The battle was the most fierce and terrible that had ever been fought in America. General Wolfe was at the head of his soldiers, and, while encouraging them onward, received a mortal wound. He reclined against a stone in the agonies of death; but it seemed as if his spirit could not pass away while the fight yet raged so doubtfully. Suddenly a shout came pealing across the battle-field. "They flee! they flee!" and, for a moment, Wolfe lifted his languid head. "Who flee?" he inquired. "The French," replied an officer. "Then I die satisfied!" said Wolfe, and expired in the arms of victory.

"If ever a warrior's death were glorious, Wolfe's was so," said Grandfather; and his eye kindled, though he was a man of peaceful thoughts and gentle spirit. "His life-blood streamed to baptize the soil which he had added to the dominion of Britain. His dying breath was mingled with his army's shout of victory."

"Oh, it was a good death to die!" cried Charley, with glistening eyes. "Was it not a good death, Laurence?"

Laurence made no reply; for his heart burned within him, as the picture of Wolfe, dying on the blood-stained field of victory, arose to his imagination; and yet he had a deep inward consciousness that, after all, there was a truer glory than could thus be won.

"There were other battles in Canada after Wolfe's victory," resumed Grandfather; "but we may consider the old French War as having terminated with this great event. The treaty of peace, however, was not signed until 1763. The terms of the treaty were very disadvantageous to the French; for all Canada, and all Acadia, and the Island of Cape Breton, — in short, all the territories that France and England had been fighting about for nearly a hundred years, — were surrendered to the English."

"So now, at last," said Laurence, "New England had gained her wish. Canada was taken."

"And now there was nobody to fight with but the Indians," said Charley.

Grandfather mentioned two other important events. The first was the great fire of Boston in 1760, when the glare from nearly three hundred buildings, all in flames at once, shone through the windows of the Province House, and threw a fierce lustre upon the gilded foliage and lion's head of our old chair. The second event was the proclamation, in the same year, of George III. as King of Great Britain. The blast of the trumpet sounded from the balcony of the Town House, and awoke the echoes far and wide, as if to challenge all mankind to dispute King George's title.

Seven times, as the successive monarchs of Britain ascended the throne, the trumpet peal of proclamation had been heard by those who sat in our venerable chair. But when the next king put on his father's crown, no trumpet peal proclaimed it to New England. Long before that day America had shaken off the royal government.

CHAPTER X.

Now that Grandfather had fought through the old French War, in which our chair made no very distinguished figure, he thought it high time to tell the children some of the more private history of that praiseworthy old piece of furniture.

"In 1757," said Grandfather, "after Shirley had been summoned to England, Thomas Pownall was appointed governor of Massachusetts. He was a gay and fashionable English gentleman, who had spent much of his life in London, but had a considerable acquaintance with America. The new governor appears to have taken no active part in the war that was going on; although, at one period, he talked of marching against the enemy at the head of his company of cadets. But, on the whole, he probably concluded that it was more befitting a governor to remain quietly in our chair, reading the newspapers and official documents."

"Did the people like Pownall?" asked Charley.

"They found no fault with him," replied Grandfather. "It was no time to quarrel with the governor when the utmost harmony was required in order to defend the country against the French. But Pownall did not remain long in Massachusetts. In 1759 he was sent to be governor of South Carolina. In thus exchanging one government for another, I suppose he felt no regret, except at the necessity of leaving Grandfather's chair behind him."

"He might have taken it to South Carolina," observed Clara.

"It appears to me," said Laurence, giving the rein to his fancy, "that the fate of this ancient chair was, somehow or other, mysteriously connected with the fortunes of old Massachusetts. If Governor Pownall had put it aboard the vessel in which he sailed for South Carolina, she would probably have lain wind-bound in Boston Harbor. It was ordained that the chair should not be taken away. Don't you think so, Grandfather ?"

"It was kept here for Grandfather and me to sit in together," said little Alice, "and for Grandfather to tell stories about."

"And Grandfather is very glad of such a companion and such a theme," said the old gentleman, with a smile. "Well, Laurence, if our oaken chair, like the wooden palladium of Troy, was connected with the country's fate, yet there appears to have been no supernatural obstacle to its removal from the Province House. In 1760 Sir Francis Bernard, who had been governor of New Jersey, was appointed to the same office in Massachusetts. He looked at the old chair, and thought it quite too shabby to keep company with a new set of mahogany chairs and an aristocratic sofa which had just arrived from London. He therefore ordered it to be put away in the garret."

The children were loud in their exclamations against this irreverent conduct of Sir Francis Bernard. But Grandfather defended him as well as he could. He observed that it was then thirty years since the chair had been beautified by Governor Belcher. Most of the gilding was worn off by the frequent scourings which it had undergone beneath the hands of a black slave. The damask cushion, once so splendid, was now squeezed out of all shape, and absolutely in tatters, so many were the ponderous gentlemen who had deposited their weight upon it during these thirty years.

Moreover, at a council held by the Earl of Loudon with the governors of New England in 1757, his lordship, in a moment of passion, had kicked over the chair with his military boot. By this unprovoked and unjustifiable act, our venerable friend had suffered a fracture of one of its rungs.

" But," said Grandfather, " our chair, after all, was not destined to spend the remainder of it days in the inglorious obscurity of a garret. Thomas Hutchinson, lieutenant-governor of the province, was told of Sir Francis Bernard's design. This gentleman was more familiar with thé history of New England than any other man alive. He knew all the adventures and vicissitudes through which the old chair had passed, and could have told as accurately as your own Grandfather who were the personages that had occupied it. Often, while visiting at the Province House, he had eyed the chair with admiration, and felt a longing desire to become the possessor of it. He now waited upon Sir Francis Bernard, and easily obtained leave to carry it home."

" And I hope," said Clara, " he had it varnished and gilded anew."

" No," answered Grandfather. " What Mr. Hutchinson desired was, to restore the chair as much as possible to its original aspect, such as it had appeared when it was first made out of the Earl of Lincoln's oak-tree. For this purpose he ordered it to be well scoured with soap and sand and polished with wax, and then provided it with a substantial leather cushion. When all was completed to his mind he sat down in the old chair, and began to write his History of Massachusetts."

"Oh, that was a bright thought in Mr. Hutchinson!" exclaimed Laurence. "And no doubt the dim figures of the former possessors of the chair flitted around him as he wrote, and inspired him with a knowledge of all that they had done and suffered while on earth."

" Why, my dear Laurence," replied Grandfather, smiling, "if Mr. Hutchinson was favored with any such extraordinary inspiration, he made but a poor use of it in his history; for a duller piece of composition never came from any man's pen. However, he was accurate, at least, though far from possessing the brilliancy or philosophy of Mr. Bancroft."

" But if Hutchinson knew the history of the chair," rejoined Laurence, "his heart must have been stirred by it."

"It must, indeed," said Grandfather. "It would be entertaining and instructive, at the present day, to imagine what were Mr. Hutchinson's thoughts as he looked back upon the long vista of events with which this chair was so remarkably connected."

And Grandfather allowed his fancy to shape out an image of Lieutenant-Governor Hutchinson, sitting in an evening reverie by his fireside, and meditating on the changes that had slowly passed around the chair.

A devoted monarchist, Hutchinson would heave no sigh for the subversion of the original republican government, the purest that the world had seen, with which the colony began its existence. While reverencing the grim and stern old Puritans as the founders of his native land, he would not wish to recall them

from their graves, nor to awaken again that king-resisting spirit which he imagined to be laid asleep with
them forever. Winthrop, Dudley, Bellingham, Endicott, Leverett, and Bradstreet, — all these had had
their day. Ages might come and go, but never again
would the people's suffrages place a republican governor in their ancient chair of state.

Coming down to the epoch of the second charter,
Hutchinson thought of the ship-carpenter Phipps,
springing from the lowest of the people and attaining
to the loftiest station in the land. But he smiled to
perceive that this governor's example would awaken
no turbulent ambition in the lower orders; for it was
a king's gracious boon alone that made the ship-carpenter a ruler. Hutchinson rejoiced to mark the grad-
ual growth of an aristocratic class, to whom the common people, as in duty bound, were learning humbly
to resign the honors, emoluments, and authority of
state. He saw — or else deceived himself — that,
throughout this epoch, the people's disposition to self-
government had been growing weaker through long
disuse, and now existed only as a faint traditionary
feeling.

The lieutenant-governor's reverie had now come
down to the period at which he himself was sitting
in the historic chair. He endeavored to throw his
glance forward over the coming years. There, probably, he saw visions of hereditary rank for himself
and other aristocratic colonists. He saw the fertile
fields of New England proportioned out among a few
great landholders, and descending by entail from generation to generation. He saw the people a race of
tenantry, dependent on their lords. He saw stars,
garters, coronets, and castles.

"But," added Grandfather, turning to Laurence, "the lieutenant-governor's castles were built nowhere but among the red embers of the fire before which he was sitting. And, just as he had constructed a baronial residence for himself and his posterity, the fire rolled down upon the hearth and crumbled it to ashes!"

Grandfather now looked at his watch, which hung within a beautiful little ebony temple, supported by four Ionic columns. He then laid his hand on the golden locks of little Alice, whose head had sunk down upon the arm of our illustrious chair.

"To bed, to bed, dear child!" said he. "Grandfather has put you to sleep already by his stories about these FAMOUS OLD PEOPLE."

PART III.

CHAPTER I.

On the evening of New-Year's Day Grandfather was walking to and fro across the carpet, listening to the rain which beat hard against the curtained windows. The riotous blast shook the casement as if a strong man were striving to force his entrance into the comfortable room. With every puff of the wind the fire leaped upward from the hearth, laughing and rejoicing at the shrieks of the wintry storm.

Meanwhile Grandfather's chair stood in its customary place by the fireside. The bright blaze gleamed upon the fantastic figures of its oaken back, and shone through the open work, so that a complete pattern was thrown upon the opposite side of the room. Sometimes, for a moment or two, the shadow remained immovable, as if it were painted on the wall. Then all at once it began to quiver, and leap, and dance with a frisky motion. Anon, seeming to remember that these antics were unworthy of such a dignified and venerable chair, it suddenly stood still. But soon it began to dance anew.

"Only see how Grandfather's chair is dancing!" cried little Alice.

And she ran to the wall and tried to catch hold of the flickering shadow; for, to children of five years old, a shadow seems almost as real as a substance.

"I wish," said Clara, "Grandfather would sit down in the chair and finish its history."

If the children had been looking at Grandfather, they would have noticed that he paused in his walk across the room when Clara made this remark. The kind old gentleman was ready and willing to resume his stories of departed times. But he had resolved to wait till his auditors should request him to proceed, in order that they might find the instructive history of the chair a pleasure, and not a task.

" Grandfather," said Charley, " I am tired to death of this dismal rain and of hearing the wind roar in the chimney. I have had no good time all day. It would be better to hear stories about the chair than to sit doing nothing and thinking of nothing."

To say the truth, our friend Charley was very much out of humor with the storm, because it had kept him all day within doors, and hindered him from making a trial of a splendid sled, which Grandfather had given him for a New-Year's gift. As all sleds, nowadays, must have a name, the one in question had been honored with the title of Grandfather's chair, which was painted in golden letters on each of the sides. Charley greatly admired the construction of the new vehicle, and felt certain that it would outstrip any other sled that ever dashed adown the long slopes of the Common.

As for Laurence, he happened to be thinking, just at this moment, about the history of the chair. Kind old Grandfather had made him a present of a volume of engraved portraits, representing the features of eminent and famous people of all countries. Among them Laurence found several who had formerly occupied our chair or been connected with its adventures. While Grandfather walked to and fro across the room, the imaginative boy was gazing at the his-

toric chair. He endeavored to summon up the portraits which he had seen in his volume, and to place
them, like living figures, in the empty seat.

"The old chair has begun another year of its existence, to-day," said Laurence. "We must make haste,
or it will have a new history to be told before we finish
the old one."

"Yes, my children," replied Grandfather, with a
smile and a sigh, "another year has been added to
those of the two centuries and upward which have
passed since the Lady Arbella brought this chair over
from England. It is three times as old as your Grandfather; but a year makes no impression on its oaken
frame, while it bends the old man nearer and nearer
to the earth; so let me go on with my stories while I
may."

Accordingly Grandfather came to the fireside and
seated himself in the venerable chair. The lion's head
looked down with a grimly good-natured aspect as the
children clustered around the old gentleman's knees.
It almost seemed as if a real lion were peeping over
the back of the chair, and smiling at the group of
auditors with a sort of lion-like complaisance. Little
Alice, whose fancy often inspired her with singular
ideas, exclaimed that the lion's head was nodding at
her, and that it looked as if it were going to open its
wide jaws and tell a story.

But as the lion's head appeared to be in no haste to
speak, and as there was no record or tradition of its
having spoken during the whole existence of the chair,
Grandfather did not consider it worth while to wait.

CHAPTER II.

" CHARLEY, my boy," said Grandfather, " do you remember who was the last occupant of the chair?"

" It was Lieutenant - Governor Hutchinson," answered Charley. " Sir Francis Bernard, the new governor, had given him the chair, instead of putting it away in the garret of the Province House. And when we took leave of Hutchinson he was sitting by his fireside, and thinking of the past adventures of the chair and of what was to come."

" Very well," said Grandfather; " and you recollect that this was in 1763, or thereabouts, at the close of the old French War. Now, that you may fully comprehend the remaining adventures of the chair, I must make some brief remarks on the situation and character of the New England colonies at this period."

So Grandfather spoke of the earnest loyalty of our fathers during the old French War, and after the conquest of Canada had brought that war to a triumphant close.

The people loved and reverenced the King of England even more than if the ocean had not rolled its waves between him and them; for, at the distance of three thousand miles, they could not discover his bad qualities and imperfections. Their love was increased by the dangers which they had encountered in order to heighten his glory and extend his dominion. Throughout the war the American colonists had fought side by side with the soldiers of Old England; and nearly thirty thousand young men had laid down their lives for the honor of King George. And the survivors loved him the better because they had done and suffered so much for his sake.

But there were some circumstances that caused America to feel more independent of England than at an earlier period. Canada and Acadia had now become British provinces; and our fathers were no longer afraid of the bands of French and Indians who used to assault them in old times. For a century and a half this had been the great terror of New England. Now the old French soldier was driven from the North forever. And even had it been otherwise, the English colonies were growing so populous and powerful that they might have felt fully able to protect themselves without any help from England.

There were thoughtful and sagacious men, who began to doubt whether a great country like America would always be content to remain under the government of an island three thousand miles away. This was the more doubtful, because the English Parliament had long ago made laws which were intended to be very beneficial to England at the expense of America. By these laws the colonists were forbidden to manufacture articles for their own use, or to carry on trade with any nation but the English.

"Now," continued Grandfather, "if King George III. and his counsellors had considered these things wisely, they would have taken another course than they did. But when they saw how rich and populous the colonies had grown, their first thought was how they might make more profit out of them than heretofore. England was enormously in debt at the close of the old French War; and it was pretended that this debt had been contracted for the defence of the American colonies, and that, therefore, a part of it ought to be paid by them."

" Why, this was nonsense !" exclaimed Charley. " Did not our fathers spend their lives, and their money too, to get Canada for King George ? "

" True, they did," said Grandfather ; " and they told the English rulers so. But the king and his ministers would not listen to good advice. In 1765 the British Parliament passed a Stamp Act."

" What was that ? " inquired Charley.

" The Stamp Act," replied Grandfather, " was a law by which all deeds, bonds, and other papers of the same kind were ordered to be marked with the king's stamp ; and without this mark they were declared illegal and void. Now, in order to get a blank sheet of paper with the king's stamp upon it, people were obliged to pay threepence more than the actual value of the paper. And this extra sum of threepence was a tax, and was to be paid into the king's treasury."

" I am sure threepence was not worth quarrelling about ! " remarked Clara.

" It was not for threepence, nor for any amount of money, that America quarrelled with England," replied Grandfather ; " it was for a great principle. The colonists were determined not to be taxed except by their own representatives. They said that neither the king and Parliament, nor any other power on earth, had a right to take their money out of their pockets unless they freely gave it. And, rather than pay threepence when it was unjustly demanded, they resolved to sacrifice all the wealth of the country, and their lives along with it. They therefore made a most stubborn resistance to the Stamp Act."

"That was noble!" exclaimed Laurence. "I understand how it was. If they had quietly paid the tax of threepence, they would have ceased to be freemen, and would have become tributaries of England. And so they contended about a great question of right and wrong, and put everything at stake for it."

"You are right, Laurence," said Grandfather, "and it was really amazing and terrible to see what a change came over the aspect of the people the moment the English Parliament had passed this oppressive act. The former history of our chair, my children, has given you some idea of what a harsh, unyielding, stern set of men the old Puritans were. For a good many years back, however, it had seemed as if these characteristics were disappearing. But no sooner did England offer wrong to the colonies than the descendants of the early settlers proved that they had the same kind of temper as their forefathers. The moment before, New England appeared like a humble and loyal subject of the crown; the next instant, she showed the grim, dark features of an old king-resisting Puritan."

Grandfather spoke briefly of the public measures that were taken in opposition to the Stamp Act. As this law affected all the American colonies alike, it naturally led them to think of consulting together in order to procure its repeal. For this purpose the Legislature of Massachusetts proposed that delegates from every colony should meet in Congress. Accordingly nine colonies, both Northern and Southern, sent delegates to the city of New York.

"And did they consult about going to war with England?" asked Charley.

"No, Charley," answered Grandfather; "a great deal of talking was yet to be done before England

and America could come to blows. The Congress
stated the rights and grievances of the colonists. They
sent a humble petition to the king, and a memorial to
the Parliament, beseeching that the Stamp Act might
be repealed. This was all that the delegates had it
in their power to do."

" They might as well have stayed at home, then,"
said Charley.

" By no means," replied Grandfather. "It was a
most important and memorable event, this first coming together of the American people by their representatives from the North and South. If England
had been wise, she would have trembled at the first
word that was spoken in such an assembly."

These remonstrances and petitions, as Grandfather
observed, were the work of grave, thoughtful, and prudent men. Meantime the young and hot-headed people went to work in their own way. It is probable
that the petitions of Congress would have had little or
no effect on the British statesmen if the violent deeds
of the American people had not shown how much excited the people were. LIBERTY TREE was soon heard
of in England.

" What was Liberty Tree ? " inquired Clara.

" It was an old elm-tree," answered Grandfather,
" which stood near the corner of Essex Street, opposite the Boylston Market. Under the spreading
branches of this great tree the people used to assemble
whenever they wished to express their feelings and
opinions. Thus, after a while, it seemed as if the liberty of the country was connected with Liberty Tree."

" It was glorious fruit for a tree to bear," remarked
Laurence.

" It bore strange fruit, sometimes," said Grandfather. " One morning in August, 1765, two figures were found hanging on the sturdy branches of Liberty Tree. They were dressed in square-skirted coats and small-clothes ; and, as their wigs hung down over their faces, they looked like real men. One was intended to represent the Earl of Bute, who was supposed to have advised the king to tax America. The other was meant for the effigy of Andrew Oliver, a gentleman belonging to one of the most respectable families in Massachusetts."

" What harm had he done ? " inquired Charley.

" The king had appointed him to be distributor of the stamps," answered Grandfather. " Mr. Oliver would have made a great deal of money by this busi- ness. But the people frightened him so much by hanging him in effigy, and afterwards by breaking into his house, that he promised to have nothing to do with the stamps. And all the king's friends through- out America were compelled to make the same prom- ise."

CHAPTER III.

"LIEUTENANT-GOVERNOR HUTCHINSON," continued Grandfather, "now began to be unquiet in our old chair. He had formerly been much respected and beloved by the people, and had often proved himself a friend to their interests. But the time was come when he could not be a friend to the people without ceasing to be a friend to the king. It was pretty generally understood that Hutchinson would act according to the king's wishes, right or wrong, like most of the other gentlemen who held offices under the crown. Besides, as he was brother-in-law of Andrew Oliver, the people now felt a particular dislike to him."

"I should think," said Laurence, "as Mr. Hutchinson had written the history of our Puritan forefathers, he would have known what the temper of the people was, and so have taken care not to wrong them."

"He trusted in the might of the King of England," replied Grandfather, "and thought himself safe under the shelter of the throne. If no dispute had arisen between the king and the people, Hutchinson would have had the character of a wise, good, and patriotic magistrate. But, from the time that he took part against the rights of his country, the people's love and respect were turned to scorn and hatred, and he never had another hour of peace."

In order to show what a fierce and dangerous spirit was now aroused among the inhabitants, Grandfather related a passage from history which we shall call

THE HUTCHINSON MOB.

On the evening of the 26th of August, 1765, a bonfire was kindled in King Street. It flamed high upward, and threw a ruddy light over the front of the Town House, on which was displayed a carved representation of the royal arms. The gilded vane of the cupola glittered in the blaze. The kindling of this bonfire was the well-known signal for the populace of Boston to assemble in the street.

Before the tar-barrels, of which the bonfire was made, were half burned out, a great crowd had come together. They were chiefly laborers and seafaring men, together with many young apprentices, and all those idle people about town who are ready for any kind of mischief. Doubtless some school-boys were among them.

While these rough figures stood round the blazing bonfire, you might hear them speaking bitter words against the high officers of the province. Governor Bernard, Hutchinson, Oliver, Storey, Hallowell, and other men whom King George delighted to honor, were reviled as traitors to the country. Now and then, perhaps, an officer of the crown passed along the street, wearing the gold-laced hat, white wig, and embroidered waistcoat which were the fashion of the day. But when the people beheld him they set up a wild and angry howl; and their faces had an evil aspect, which was made more terrible by the flickering blaze of the bonfire.

"I should like to throw the traitor right into that blaze!" perhaps one fierce rioter would say.

"Yes; and all his brethren too!" another might reply; "and the governor and old Tommy Hutchinson into the hottest of it!"

"And the Earl of Bute along with them!" muttered a third; "and burn the whole pack of them under King George's nose! No matter if it singed him!"

Some such expressions as these, either shouted aloud or muttered under the breath, were doubtless heard in King Street. The mob, meanwhile, were growing fiercer and fiercer, and seemed ready even to set the town on fire for the sake of burning the king's friends out of house and home. And yet, angry as they were, they sometimes broke into a loud roar of laughter, as if mischief and destruction were their sport.

But we must now leave the rioters for a time, and take a peep into the lieutenant-governor's splendid mansion. It was a large brick house, decorated with Ionic pilasters, and stood in Garden Court Street, near the North Square.

While the angry mob in King Street were shouting his name, Lieutenant-Governor Hutchinson sat quietly in Grandfather's chair, unsuspicious of the evil that was about to fall upon his head. His beloved family were in the room with him. He had thrown off his embroidered coat and powdered wig, and had on a loose-flowing gown and purple-velvet cap. He had likewise laid aside the cares of state and all the thoughts that had wearied and perplexed him throughout the day.

Perhaps, in the enjoyment of his home, he had forgotten all about the Stamp Act, and scarcely remembered that there was a king, across the ocean, who had resolved to make tributaries of the New-Englanders. Possibly, too, he had forgotten his own ambition, and would not have exchanged his situation, at that moment, to be governor, or even a lord.

The wax candles were now lighted, and showed a handsome room, well provided with rich furniture. On the walls hung the pictures of Hutchinson's ancestors, who had been eminent men in their day, and were honorably remembered in the history of the country. Every object served to mark the residence of a rich, aristocratic gentleman, who held himself high above the common people, and could have nothing to fear from them. In a corner of the room, thrown carelessly upon a chair, were the scarlet robes of the chief justice. This high office, as well as those of lieutenant-governor, councillor, and judge of probate, was filled by Hutchinson.

Who or what could disturb the domestic quiet of such a great and powerful personage as now sat in Grandfather's chair?

The lieutenant-governor's favorite daughter sat by his side. She leaned on the arm of our great chair, and looked up affectionately into her father's face, rejoicing to perceive that a quiet smile was on his lips. But suddenly a shade came across her countenance. She seemed to listen attentively, as if to catch a distant sound.

" What is the matter, my child ? " inquired Hutchinson.

" Father, do not you hear a tumult in the streets ? " said she.

The lieutenant-governor listened. But his ears were duller than those of his daughter ; he could hear nothing more terrible than the sound of a summer breeze, sighing among the tops of the elm-trees.

" No, foolish child ! " he replied, playfully patting her cheek. " There is no tumult. Our Boston mobs

are satisfied with what mischief they have already
done. The king's friends need not tremble."

So Hutchinson resumed his pleasant and peaceful
meditations, and again forgot that there were any
troubles in the world. But his family were alarmed,
and could not help straining their ears to catch the
slightest sound. More and more distinctly they heard
shouts, and then the trampling of many feet. While
they were listening, one of the neighbors rushed
breathless into the room.

"A mob! a terrible mob!" cried he. "They have
broken into Mr. Storey's house, and into Mr. Hallowell's, and have made themselves drunk with the liq-
uors in his cellar; and now they are coming hither, as
wild as so many tigers. Flee, lieutenant-governor, for
your life! for your life!"

"Father, dear father, make haste!" shrieked his
children.

But Hutchinson would not hearken to them. He
was an old lawyer; and he could not realize that the
people would do anything so utterly lawless as to assault him in his peaceful home. He was one of King
George's chief officers; and it would be an insult and
outrage upon the king himself if the lieutenant-governor should suffer any wrong.

"Have no fears on my account," said he. "I am
perfectly safe. The king's name shall be my protection."

Yet he bade his family retire into one of the neighboring houses. His daughter would have remained;
but he forced her away.

The huzzas and riotous uproar of the mob were now
heard, close at hand. The sound was terrible, and
struck Hutchinson with the same sort of dread as if

an enraged wild beast had broken loose and were roaring for its prey. He crept softly to the window. There he beheld an immense concourse of people, filling all the street and rolling onward to his house. It was like a tempestuous flood, that had swelled beyond its bounds and would sweep everything before it. Hutchinson trembled; he felt, at that moment, that the wrath of the people was a thousand-fold more terrible than the wrath of a king.

That was a moment when a loyalist and an aristocrat like Hutchinson might have learned how powerless are kings, nobles, and great men, when the low and humble range themselves against them. King George could do nothing for his servant now. Had King George been there he could have done nothing for himself. If Hutchinson had understood this lesson, and remembered it, he need not, in after years, have been an exile from his native country, nor finally have laid his bones in a distant land.

There was now a rush against the doors of the house. The people sent up a hoarse cry. At this instant the lieutenant-governor's daughter, whom he had supposed to be in a place of safety, ran into the room and threw her arms around him. She had returned by a private entrance.

"Father, are you mad?" cried she. "Will the king's name protect you now? Come with me, or they will have your life."

"True," muttered Hutchinson to himself; "what care these roarers for the name of king? I must flee, or they will trample me down on the floor of my own dwelling."

Hurrying away, he and his daughter made their escape by the private passage at the moment when the rioters broke into the house. The foremost of them rushed up the staircase, and entered the room which Hutchinson had just quitted. There they beheld our good old chair facing them with quiet dignity, while the lion's head seemed to move its jaws in the unsteady light of their torches. Perhaps the stately aspect of our venerable friend, which had stood firm through a century and a half of trouble, arrested them for an instant. But they were thrust forward by those behind, and the chair lay overthrown.

Then began the work of destruction. The carved and polished mahogany tables were shattered with heavy clubs and hewn to splinters with axes. The marble hearths and mantel-pieces were broken. The volumes of Hutchinson's library, so precious to a studious man, were torn out of their covers, and the leaves sent flying out of the windows. Manuscripts, containing secrets of our country's history, which are now lost forever, were scattered to the winds.

The old ancestral portraits, whose fixed countenances looked down on the wild scene, were rent from the walls. The mob triumphed in their downfall and destruction, as if these pictures of Hutchinson's forefathers had committed the same offences as their descendant. A tall looking-glass, which had hitherto presented a reflection of the enraged and drunken multitude, was now smashed into a thousand fragments. We gladly dismiss the scene from the mirror of our fancy.

Before morning dawned the walls of the house were all that remained. The interior was a dismal scene of ruin. A shower pattered in at the broken windows; and when Hutchinson and his family returned, they stood shivering in the same room where the last evening had seen them so peaceful and happy.

"Grandfather," said Laurence, indignantly, "if the people acted in this manner, they were not worthy of even so much liberty as the King of England was willing to allow them."

"It was a most unjustifiable act, like many other popular movements at that time," replied Grandfather. "But we must not decide against the justice of the people's cause merely because an excited mob was guilty of outrageous violence. Besides, all these things were done in the first fury of resentment. Afterwards the people grew more calm, and were more influenced by the counsel of those wise and good men who conducted them safely and gloriously through the Revolution."

Little Alice, with tears in her blue eyes, said that she hoped the neighbors had not let Lieutenant-Governor Hutchinson and his family be homeless in the street, but had taken them into their houses and been kind to them. Cousin Clara, recollecting the perilous situation of our beloved chair, inquired what had become of it.

"Nothing was heard of our chair for some time afterwards," answered Grandfather. "One day in September, the same Andrew Oliver, of whom I before told you, was summoned to appear at high noon under Liberty Tree. This was the strangest summons that had ever been heard of; for it was issued in the name of the whole people, who thus took upon themselves the authority of a sovereign power. Mr. Oliver dared not disobey. Accordingly, at the appointed hour he went, much against his will, to Liberty Tree."

Here Charley interposed a remark that poor Mr. Oliver found but little liberty under Liberty Tree. Grandfather assented.

"It was a stormy day," continued he. "The equi-
noctial gale blew violently, and scattered the yellow
leaves of Liberty Tree all along the street. Mr. Oliver's wig was dripping with water-drops; and he
probably looked haggard, disconsolate, and humbled
to the earth. Beneath the tree, in Grandfather's
chair, — our own venerable chair, — sat Mr. Richard
Dana, a justice of the peace. He administered an
oath to Mr. Oliver that he would never have anything
to do with distributing the stamps. A vast concourse
of people heard the oath, and shouted when it was
taken."

"There is something grand in this," said Laurence.
"I like it, because the people seem to have acted with
thoughtfulness and dignity; and this proud gentleman,
one of his Majesty's high officers, was made to feel
that King George could not protect him in doing
wrong."

"But it was a sad day for poor Mr. Oliver," observed Grandfather. "From his youth upward it had
probably been the great principle of his life to be
faithful and obedient to the king. And now, in his
old age, it must have puzzled and distracted him to
find the sovereign people setting up a claim to his
faith and obedience."

Grandfather closed the evening's conversation by
saying that the discontent of America was so great,
that, in 1766, the British Parliament was compelled
to repeal the Stamp Act. The people made great
rejoicings, but took care to keep Liberty Tree well
pruned and free from caterpillars and canker-worms.
They foresaw that there might yet be occasion for
them to assemble under its far-projecting shadow.

CHAPTER IV.

THE next evening, Clara, who remembered that our chair had been left standing in the rain under Liberty Tree, earnestly besought Grandfather to tell when and where it had next found shelter. Perhaps she was afraid that the venerable chair, by being exposed to the inclemency of a September gale, might get the rheumatism in its aged joints.

"The chair," said Grandfather, "after the ceremony of Mr. Oliver's oath, appears to have been quite forgotten by the multitude. Indeed, being much bruised and rather rickety, owing to the violent treatment it had suffered from the Hutchinson mob, most people would have thought that its days of usefulness were over. Nevertheless, it was conveyed away under cover of the night and committed to the care of a skilful joiner. He doctored our old friend so successfully, that, in the course of a few days, it made its appearance in the public room of the British Coffee House, in King Street."

"But why did not Mr. Hutchinson get possession of it again?" inquired Charley.

"I know not," answered Grandfather, "unless he considered it a dishonor and disgrace to the chair to have stood under Liberty Tree. At all events, he suffered it to remain at the British Coffee House, which was the principal hotel in Boston. It could not possibly have found a situation where it would be more in the midst of business and bustle, or would witness more important events, or be occupied by a greater variety of persons."

Grandfather went on to tell the proceedings of the despotic king and ministry of England after the repeal of the Stamp Act. They could not bear to think that their right to tax America should be disputed by the people. In the year 1767, therefore, they caused Parliament to pass an act for laying a duty on tea and some other articles that were in general use. Nobody could now buy a pound of tea without paying a tax to King George. This scheme was pretty craftily contrived; for the women of America were very fond of tea, and did not like to give up the use of it.

But the people were as much opposed to this new act of Parliament as they had been to the Stamp Act. England, however, was determined that they should submit. In order to compel their obedience, two regiments, consisting of more than seven hundred British soldiers, were sent to Boston. They arrived in September, 1768, and were landed on Long Wharf. Thence they marched to the Common with loaded muskets, fixed bayonets, and great pomp and parade. So now, at last, the free town of Boston was guarded and overawed by redcoats as it had been in the days of old Sir Edmund Andros.

In the month of November more regiments arrived. There were now four thousand troops in Boston. The Common was whitened with their tents. Some of the soldiers were lodged in Faneuil Hall, which the inhabitants looked upon as a consecrated place, because it had been the scene of a great many meetings in favor of liberty. One regiment was placed in the Town House, which we now call the Old State House. The lower floor of this edifice had hitherto been used by the merchants as an exchange. In the upper stories were the chambers of the judges, the representatives, and the governor's council. The venerable councillors could not assemble to consult about the welfare of the province without being challenged by sentinels and passing among the bayonets of the British soldiers.

Sentinels likewise were posted at the lodgings of the officers in many parts of the town. When the inhabitants approached they were greeted by the sharp question, "Who goes there?" while the rattle of the soldier's musket was heard as he presented it against their breasts. There was no quiet even on the sabbath day. The pious descendants of the Puritans were shocked by the uproar of military music; the drum, fife, and bugle drowning the holy organ peal and the voices of the singers. It would appear as if the British took every method to insult the feelings of the people.

"Grandfather," cried Charley, impatiently, "the people did not go to fighting half soon enough! These British redcoats ought to have been driven back to their vessels the very moment they landed on Long Wharf."

"Many a hot-headed young man said the same as you do, Charley," answered Grandfather. "But the elder and wiser people saw that the time was not yet come. Meanwhile, let us take another peep at our old chair."

"Ah, it drooped its head, I know," said Charley, "when it saw how the province was disgraced. Its old Puritan friends never would have borne such doings."

"The chair," proceeded Grandfather, "was now continually occupied by some of the high tories, as the king's friends were called, who frequented the British Coffee House. Officers of the Custom House, too, which stood on the opposite side of King Street, often sat in the chair wagging their tongues against John Hancock."

" Why against him ? " asked Charley.

" Because he was a great merchant and contended against paying duties to the king," said Grandfather.

" Well, frequently, no doubt, the officers of the British regiments, when not on duty, used to fling themselves into the arms of our venerable chair. Fancy one of them, a red-nosed captain in his scarlet uniform, playing with the hilt of his sword, and making a circle of his brother officers merry with ridiculous jokes at the expense of the poor Yankees. And perhaps he would call for a bottle of wine, or a steaming bowl of punch, and drink confusion to all rebels."

" Our grave old chair must have been scandalized at such scenes," observed Laurence ; " the chair that had been the Lady Arbella's, and which the holy apostle Eliot had consecrated."

" It certainly was little less than sacrilege," replied Grandfather ; " but the time was coming when even the churches, where hallowed pastors had long preached the word of God, were to be torn down or desecrated by the British troops. Some years passed, however, before such things were done."

Grandfather now told his auditors that, in 1769, Sir Francis Bernard went to England after having been governor of Massachusetts ten years. He was a gentleman of many good qualities, an excellent scholar, and a friend to learning. But he was naturally of an arbitrary disposition ; and he had been bred at the University of Oxford, where young men were taught that

the divine right of kings was the only thing to be regarded in matters of government. Such ideas were ill
adapted to please the people of Massachusetts. They
rejoiced to get rid of Sir Francis Bernard, but liked
his successor, Lieutenant-Governor Hutchinson, no
better than himself.

About this period the people were much incensed at
an act committed by a person who held an office in
the Custom House. Some lads, or young men, were
snowballing his windows. He fired a musket at them,
and killed a poor German boy, only eleven years old.
This event made a great noise in town and country,
and much increased the resentment that was already
felt against the servants of the crown.

" Now, children," said Grandfather, " I wish to
make you comprehend the position of the British
troops in King Street. This is the same which we
now call State Street. On the south side of the Town
House, or Old State House, was what military men
call a court of guard, defended by two brass cannons,
which pointed directly at one of the doors of the above
edifice. A large party of soldiers were always stationed in the court of guard. The Custom House
stood at a little distance down King Street, nearly
where the Suffolk Bank now stands, and a sentinel
was continually pacing before its front."

" I shall remember this to-morrow," said Charley ;
" and I will go to State Street, so as to see exactly
where the British troops were stationed."

" And before long," observed Grandfather, " I shall
have to relate an event which made King Street sadly
famous on both sides of the Atlantic. The history of
our chair will soon bring us to this melancholy business."

Here Grandfather described the state of things which arose from the ill will that existed between the inhabitants and the redcoats. The old and sober part of the townspeople were very angry at the government for sending soldiers to overawe them. But those gray-headed men were cautious, and kept their thoughts and feelings in their own breasts, without putting themselves in the way of the British bayonets.

The younger people, however, could hardly be kept within such prudent limits. They reddened with wrath at the very sight of a soldier, and would have been willing to come to blows with them at any moment. For it was their opinion that every tap of a British drum within the peninsula of Boston was an insult to the brave old town.

" It was sometimes the case," continued Grandfather, " that affrays happened between such wild young men as these and small parties of the soldiers. No weapons had hitherto been used except fists or cudgels. But when men have loaded muskets in their hands, it is easy to foretell that they will soon be turned against the bosoms of those who provoke their anger."

" Grandfather," said little Alice, looking fearfully into his face, " your voice sounds as though you were going to tell us something awful ! "

CHAPTER V.

LITTLE ALICE, by her last remark, proved herself a good judge of what was expressed by the tones of Grandfather's voice. He had given the above description of the enmity between the townspeople and the soldiers in order to prepare the minds of his auditors for a very terrible event. It was one that did more to heighten the quarrel between England and America than anything that had yet occurred.

Without further preface, Grandfather began the story of

THE BOSTON MASSACRE.

It was now the 3d of March, 1770. The sunset music of the British regiments was heard as usual throughout the town. The shrill fife and rattling drum awoke the echoes in King Street, while the last ray of sunshine was lingering on the cupola of the Town House. And now all the sentinels were posted. One of them marched up and down before the Custom House, treading a short path through the snow, and longing for the time when he would be dismissed to the warm fireside of the guard room. Meanwhile Captain Preston was, perhaps, sitting in our great chair before the hearth of the British Coffee House. In the course of the evening there were two or three slight commotions, which seemed to indicate that trouble was at hand. Small parties of young men stood at the corners of the streets or walked along the narrow pavements. Squads of soldiers who were dismissed from duty passed by them, shoulder to shoulder, with the regular step which they had learned at the drill. Whenever these encounters took place, it appeared to be the object of the young men to treat the soldiers with as much incivility as possible.

"Turn out, you lobsterbacks!" one would say. "Crowd them off the sidewalks!" another would cry. "A redcoat has no right in Boston streets!"

"O, you rebel rascals!" perhaps the soldiers would reply, glaring fiercely at the young men. "Some day or other we 'll make our way through Boston streets at the point of the bayonet!"

Once or twice such disputes as these brought on a scuffle; which passed off, however, without attracting much notice. About eight o'clock, for some unknown cause, an alarm-bell rang loudly and hurriedly.

At the sound many people ran out of their houses, supposing it to be an alarm of fire. But there were no flames to be seen, nor was there any smell of smoke in the clear, frosty air; so that most of the townsmen went back to their own firesides and sat talking with their wives and children about the calamities of the times. Others who were younger and less prudent remained in the streets; for there seems to have been a presentiment that some strange event was on the eve of taking place.

Later in the evening, not far from nine o'clock, several young men passed by the Town House and walked down King Street. The sentinel was still on his post in front of the Custom House, pacing to and fro; while, as he turned, a gleam of light from some neighboring window glittered on the barrel of his musket. At no great distance were the barracks and the guard-house, where his comrades were probably telling stories of battle and bloodshed.

Down towards the Custom House, as I told you, came a party of wild young men. When they drew near the sentinel he halted on his post, and took his musket from his shoulder, ready to present the bayonet at their breasts.

" Who goes there?" he cried, in the gruff, peremptory tones of a soldier's challenge.

The young men, being Boston boys, felt as if they had a right to walk their own streets without being accountable to a British redcoat, even though he challenged them in King George's name. They made some rude answer to the sentinel. There was a dispute, or perhaps a scuffle. Other soldiers heard the noise, and ran hastily from the barracks to assist their comrades. At the same time many of the townspeople rushed into King Street by various avenues, and gathered in a crowd round about the Custom House. It seemed wonderful how such a multitude had started up all of a sudden.

The wrongs and insults which the people had been suffering for many months now kindled them into a rage. They threw snowballs and lumps of ice at the soldiers. As the tumult grew louder it reached the ears of Captain Preston, the officer of the day. He immediately ordered eight soldiers of the main guard to take their muskets and follow him. They marched across the street, forcing their way roughly through the crowd, and pricking the townspeople with their bayonets.

A gentleman (it was Henry Knox, afterwards general of the American artillery) caught Captain Preston's arm.

" For Heaven's sake, sir," exclaimed he, " take heed what you do, or there will be bloodshed."

" Stand aside! " answered Captain Preston, haughtily. " Do not interfere, sir. Leave me to manage the affair."

Arriving at the sentinel's post, Captain Preston drew up his men in a semicircle, with their faces to the crowd and their rear to the Custom House. When the people saw the officer and beheld the threatening attitude with which the soldiers fronted them, their rage became almost uncontrollable.

" Fire, you lobsterbacks! " bellowed some.

" You dare not fire, you cowardly redcoats! " cried others.

" Rush upon them! " shouted many voices. " Drive the rascals to their barracks! Down with them! Down with them! Let them fire if they dare! "

Amid the uproar, the soldiers stood glaring at the people with the fierceness of men whose trade was to shed blood.

Oh, what a crisis had now arrived! Up to this very moment, the angry feelings between England and America might have been pacified. England had but to stretch out the hand of reconciliation, and acknowledge that she had hitherto mistaken her rights, but would do so no more. Then the ancient bonds of brotherhood would again have been knit together as firmly as in old times. The habit of loyalty, which had grown as strong as instinct, was not utterly overcome. The perils shared, the victories won, in the old French War, when the soldiers of the colonies fought side by side with their comrades from beyond the sea, were unforgotten yet. England was still that beloved country which the colonists called their home. King

George, though he had frowned upon America, was still reverenced as a father.

But should the king's soldiers shed one drop of American blood, then it was a quarrel to the death. Never, never would America rest satisfied until she had torn down the royal authority and trampled it in the dust.

"Fire, if you dare, villains!" hoarsely shouted the people, while the muzzles of the muskets were turned upon them. "You dare not fire!"

They appeared ready to rush upon the levelled bayonets. Captain Preston waved his sword, and uttered a command which could not be distinctly heard amid the uproar of shouts that issued from a hundred throats. But his soldiers deemed that he had spoken the fatal mandate, "Fire!" The flash of their muskets lighted up the streets, and the report rang loudly between the edifices. It was said, too, that the figure of a man, with a cloth hanging down over his face, was seen to step into the balcony of the Custom House and discharge a musket at the crowd.

A gush of smoke had overspread the scene. It rose heavily, as if it were loath to reveal the dreadful spectacle beneath it. Eleven of the sons of New England lay stretched upon the street. Some, sorely wounded, were struggling to rise again. Others stirred not nor groaned; for they were past all pain. Blood was streaming upon the snow; and that purple stain in the midst of King Street, though it melted away in the next day's sun, was never forgotten nor forgiven by the people.

Grandfather was interrupted by the violent sobs of little Alice. In his earnestness he had neglected to soften down the narrative so that it might not terrify the heart of this unworldly infant. Since Grandfather began the history of our chair, little Alice had listened to many tales of war. But probably the idea had never really impressed itself upon her mind that men have shed the blood of their fellow-creatures. And now that this idea was forcibly presented to her, it affected the sweet child with bewilderment and horror.

"I ought to have remembered our dear little Alice," said Grandfather reproachfully to himself. "Oh, what a pity! Her heavenly nature has now received its first impression of earthly sin and violence. Well, Clara, take her to bed and comfort her. Heaven grant that she may dream away the recollection of the Boston massacre!"

"Grandfather," said Charley, when Clara and little Alice had retired, "did not the people rush upon the soldiers and take revenge?"

"The town drums beat to arms," replied Grandfather, "the alarm-bells rang, and an immense multitude rushed into King Street. Many of them had weapons in their hands. The British prepared to defend themselves. A whole regiment was drawn up in the street, expecting an attack; for the townsmen appeared ready to throw themselves upon the bayonets."

"And how did it end?" asked Charley.

"Governor Hutchinson hurried to the spot," said Grandfather, "and besought the people to have patience, promising that strict justice should be done. A day or two afterward the British troops were withdrawn from town and stationed at Castle William. Captain Preston and the eight soldiers were tried for murder. But none of them were found guilty. The judges told the jury that the insults and violence which had been offered to the soldiers justified them in firing at the mob."

"The Revolution," observed Laurence, who had said but little during the evening, "was not such a calm, majestic movement as I supposed. I do not love to hear of mobs and broils in the street. These things were unworthy of the people when they had such a great object to accomplish."

"Nevertheless, the world has seen no grander movement than that of our Revolution from first to last," said Grandfather. "The people, to a man, were full of a great and noble sentiment. True, there may be much fault to find with their mode of expressing this sentiment; but they knew no better; the necessity was upon them to act out their feelings in the best manner they could. We must forgive what was wrong in their actions, and look into their hearts and minds for the honorable motives that impelled them."

"And I suppose," said Laurence, "there were men who knew how to act worthily of what they felt."

"There were many such," replied Grandfather; "and we will speak of some of them hereafter."

Grandfather here made a pause. That night Charley had a dream about the Boston massacre, and thought that he himself was in the crowd and struck down Captain Preston with a great club. Laurence dreamed that he was sitting in our great chair, at the window of the British Coffee House, and beheld the whole scene which Grandfather had described. It seemed to him, in his dream, that, if the townspeople and the soldiers would but have heard him speak a single word, all the slaughter might have been averted. But there was such an uproar that it drowned his voice.

The next morning the two boys went together to State Street and stood on the very spot where the first blood of the Revolution had been shed. The Old State House was still there, presenting almost the same aspect that it had worn on that memorable evening, one-and-seventy years ago. It is the sole remaining witness of the Boston massacre.

CHAPTER VI.

THE next evening the astral lamp was lighted earlier than usual, because Laurence was very much engaged in looking over the collection of portraits which had been his New-Year's gift from Grandfather.

Among them he found the features of more than one famous personage who had been connected with the adventures of our old chair. Grandfather bade him draw the table nearer to the fireside; and they looked over the portraits together, while Clara and Charley likewise lent their attention. As for little Alice, she sat in Grandfather's lap, and seemed to see the very men alive whose faces were there represented.

Turning over the volume, Laurence came to the portrait of a stern, grim-looking man, in plain attire, of much more modern fashion than that of the old Puritans. But the face might well have befitted one of those iron-hearted men. Beneath the portrait was the name of Samuel Adams.

"He was a man of great note in all the doings that brought about the Revolution," said Grandfather. "His character was such, that it seemed as if one of the ancient Puritans had been sent back to earth to animate the people's hearts with the same abhorrence of tyranny that had distinguished the earliest settlers. He was as religious as they, as stern and inflexible, and as deeply imbued with democratic principles. He, better than any one else, may be taken as a representative of the people of New England, and of the spirit with which they engaged in the Revolutionary struggle. He was a poor man, and earned his bread by a humble occupation; but with his tongue and pen he made the King of England tremble on his throne. Remember him, my children, as one of the strong men of our country."

"Here is one whose looks show a very different character," observed Laurence, turning to the portrait of John Hancock. "I should think, by his splendid dress and courtly aspect, that he was one of the king's friends."

"There never was a greater contrast than between Samuel Adams and John Hancock," said Grandfather. "Yet they were of the same side in politics, and had an equal agency in the Revolution. Hancock was born to the inheritance of the largest fortune in New England. His tastes and habits were aristocratic. He loved gorgeous attire, a splendid mansion, magnificent furniture, stately festivals, and all that was glittering and pompous in external things. His manners were so polished that there stood not a nobleman at the footstool of King George's throne who was a more skilful courtier than John Hancock might have been. Nevertheless, he in his embroidered clothes, and Samuel Adams in his threadbare coat, wrought together in the cause of liberty. Adams acted from pure and rigid principle. Hancock, though he loved his country, yet thought quite as much of his own popularity as he did of the people's rights. It is remarkable that these two men, so very different as I describe them, were the only two exempted from pardon by the king's proclamation."

On the next leaf of the book was the portrait of General Joseph Warren. Charley recognized the name, and said that here was a greater man than either Hancock or Adams.

"Warren was an eloquent and able patriot," replied Grandfather. "He deserves a lasting memory for his zealous efforts in behalf of liberty. No man's voice was more powerful in Faneuil Hall than Joseph Warren's. If his death had not happened so early in the contest, he would probably have gained a high name as a soldier."

The next portrait was a venerable man, who held his thumb under his chin, and, through his spectacles, appeared to be attentively reading a manuscript.

"Here we see the most illustrious Boston boy that ever lived," said Grandfather. "This is Benjamin Franklin. But I will not try to compress into a few sentences the character of the sage, who, as a Frenchman expressed it, snatched the lightning from the sky and the sceptre from a tyrant. Mr. Sparks must help you to the knowledge of Franklin."

The book likewise contained portraits of James Otis and Josiah Quincy. Both of them, Grandfather observed, were men of wonderful talents and true patriotism. Their voices were like the stirring tones of a trumpet arousing the country to defend its freedom. Heaven seemed to have provided a greater number of eloquent men than had appeared at any other period, in order that the people might be fully instructed as to their wrongs and the method of resistance.

"It is marvellous," said Grandfather, "to see how many powerful writers, orators, and soldiers started up just at the time when they were wanted. There was a man for every kind of work. It is equally wonderful that men of such different characters were all made to unite in the one object of establishing the freedom and independence of America. There was an over-ruling Providence above them."

" Here was another great man," remarked Laurence pointing to the portrait of John Adams.

" Yes; an earnest, warm-tempered, honest, and most able man," said Grandfather. " At the period of which we are now speaking he was a lawyer in Boston. He was destined in after years to be ruler over the whole American people, whom he contributed so much to form into a nation."

Grandfather here remarked that many a New-Englander, who had passed his boyhood and youth in obscurity, afterward attained to a fortune which he never could have foreseen even in his most ambitious dreams. John Adams, the second President of the United States and the equal of crowned kings, was once a schoolmaster and country lawyer. Hancock, the first signer of the Declaration of Independence, served his apprenticeship with a merchant. Samuel Adams, afterwards governor of Massachusetts, was a small tradesman and a tax-gatherer. General Warren was a physician, General Lincoln a farmer, and General Knox a bookbinder. General Nathaniel Greene, the best soldier, except Washington, in the Revolutionary army, was a Quaker and a blacksmith. All these became illustrious men, and can never be forgotten in American history.

" And any boy who is born in America may look forward to the same things," said our ambitious friend Charley.

After these observations, Grandfather drew the book of portraits towards him and showed the children several British peers and members of Parliament who had exerted themselves either for or against the rights

of America. There were the Earl of Bute, Mr. Gren-
ville, and Lord North. These were looked upon as
deadly enemies to our country.

Among the friends of America was Mr. Pitt, afterward Earl of Chatham, who spent so much of his wondrous eloquence in endeavoring to warn England of
the consequences of her injustice. He fell down on
the floor of the House of Lords after uttering almost
his dying words in defence of our privileges as freemen. There was Edmund Burke, one of the wisest
men and greatest orators that ever the world produced.
There was Colonel Barré, who had been among our
fathers, and knew that they had courage enough to die
for their rights. There was Charles James Fox, who
never rested until he had silenced our enemies in the
House of Commons.

"It is very remarkable to observe how many of the
ablest orators in the British Parliament were favorable to America," said Grandfather. "We ought to
remember these great Englishmen with gratitude ; for
their speeches encouraged our fathers almost as much
as those of our own orators in Faneuil Hall and under
Liberty Tree. Opinions which might have been received with doubt, if expressed only by a native American, were set down as true, beyond dispute, when they
came from the lips of Chatham, Burke, Barré, or Fox."

"But, Grandfather," asked Laurence, "were there
no able and eloquent men in this country who took
the part of King George?"

"There were many men of talent who said what
they could in defence of the king's tyrannical proceedings," replied Grandfather. "But they had the
worst side of the argument, and therefore seldom said
anything worth remembering. Moreover, their hearts

were faint and feeble ; for they felt that the people scorned and detested them. They had no friends, no defence, except in the bayonets of the British troops. A blight fell upon all their faculties, because they were contending against the rights of their own native land."

" What were the names of some of them ? " inquired Charley.

" Governor Hutchinson, Chief Justice Oliver, Judge Auchmuty, the Rev. Mather Byles, and several other clergymen, were among the most noted loyalists," answered Grandfather.

" I wish the people had tarred and feathered every man of them ! " cried Charley.

" That wish is very wrong, Charley," said Grandfather. " You must not think that there is no integrity and honor except among those who stood up for the freedom of America. For aught I know, there was quite as much of these qualities on one side as on the other. Do you see nothing admirable in a faithful adherence to an unpopular cause ? Can you not respect that principle of loyalty which made the royalists give up country, friends, fortune, everything, rather than be false to their king ? It was a mistaken principle ; but many of them cherished it honorably, and were martyrs to it."

" Oh, I was wrong ! " said Charley, ingenuously. " And I would risk my life rather than one of those good old royalists should be tarred and feathered."

" The time is now come when we may judge fairly of them," continued Grandfather. " Be the good and true men among them honored ; for they were as much our countrymen as the patriots were. And, thank Heaven, our country need not be ashamed of her sons,

— of most of them at least, — whatever side they took in the Revolutionary contest."

Among the portraits was one of King George III. Little Alice clapped her hands, and seemed pleased with the bluff good-nature of his physiognomy. But Laurence thought it strange that a man with such a face, indicating hardly a common share of intellect, should have had influence enough on human affairs to convulse the world with war. Grandfather observed that this poor king had always appeared to him one of the most unfortunate persons that ever lived. He was so honest and conscientious, that, if he had been only a private man, his life would probably have been blameless and happy. But his was that worst of fortunes, — to be placed in a station far beyond his abilities.

"And so," said Grandfather, "his life, while he retained what intellect Heaven had gifted him with, was one long mortification. At last he grew crazed with care and trouble. For nearly twenty years the monarch of England was confined as a madman. In his old age, too, God took away his eyesight; so that his royal palace was nothing to him but a dark, lonesome prison-house."

CHAPTER VII.

"OUR old chair," resumed Grandfather, "did not now stand in the midst of a gay circle of British officers. The troops, as I told you, had been removed to Castle William immediately after the Boston massacre. Still, however, there were many tories, custom house officers, and Englishmen who used to assemble in the British Coffee House and talk over the affairs of the period. Matters grew worse and worse; and in 1773 the people did a deed which incensed the king and ministry more than any of their former doings."

Grandfather here described the affair, which is known by the name of the Boston Tea Party. The Americans, for some time past, had left off importing tea, on account of the oppressive tax. The East India Company, in London, had a large stock of tea on hand, which they had expected to sell to the Americans, but could find no market for it. But, after a while, the government persuaded this company of merchants to send the tea to America.

"How odd it is," observed Clara, "that the liberties of America should have had anything to do with a cup of tea!"

Grandfather smiled, and proceeded with his narrative. When the people of Boston heard that several cargoes of tea were coming across the Atlantic, they held a great many meetings at Faneuil Hall, in the Old South Church, and under Liberty Tree. In the midst of their debates, three ships arrived in the harbor with the tea on board. The people spent more than a fortnight in consulting what should be done. At last, on the 16th of December, 1773, they demanded of Governor Hutchinson that he should immediately send the ships back to England.

The governor replied that the ships must not leave the harbor until the custom house duties upon the tea should be paid. Now, the payment of these duties was the very thing against which the people had set their faces; because it was a tax unjustly imposed upon America by the English government. Therefore, in the dusk of the evening, as soon as Governor Hutchinson's reply was received, an immense crowd hastened to Griffin's Wharf, where the tea-ships lay. The place is now called Liverpool Wharf.

"When the crowd reached the wharf," said Grandfather, "they saw that a set of wild-looking figures were already on board of the ships. You would have imagined that the Indian warriors of old times had come back again; for they wore the Indian dress, and had their faces covered with red and black paint, like the Indians when they go to war. These grim figures hoisted the tea-chests on the decks of the vessels, broke them open, and threw all the contents into the harbor."

"Grandfather," said little Alice, "I suppose Indians don't love tea; else they would never waste it so."

"They were not real Indians, my child," answered Grandfather. "They were white men in disguise; because a heavy punishment would have been inflicted on them if the king's officers had found who they were. But it was never known. From that day to this, though the matter has been talked of by all the world, nobody can tell the names of those Indian figures. Some people say that there were very famous men among them, who afterwards became governors and generals. Whether this be true I cannot tell."

When tidings of this bold deed were carried to England, King George was greatly enraged. Parliament immediately passed an act, by which all vessels were forbidden to take in or discharge their cargoes at the port of Boston. In this way they expected to ruin all the merchants, and starve the poor people, by depriving them of employment. At the same time another act was passed, taking away many rights and privileges which had been granted in the charter of Massachusetts.

Governor Hutchinson, soon afterward, was summoned to England, in order that he might give his advice about the management of American affairs. General Gage, an officer of the old French War, and since commander-in-chief of the British forces in America, was appointed governor in his stead. One of his first acts was to make Salem, instead of Boston, the metropolis of Massachusetts, by summoning the General Court to meet there.

According to Grandfather's description, this was the most gloomy time that Massachusetts had ever seen. The people groaned under as heavy a tyranny as in the days of Sir Edmund Andros. Boston looked as if it were afflicted with some dreadful pestilence, — so sad were the inhabitants, and so desolate the streets. There was no cheerful hum of business. The merchants shut up their warehouses, and the laboring men stood idle about the wharves. But all America felt interested in the good town of Boston; and contributions were raised, in many places, for the relief of the poor inhabitants.

" Our dear old chair ! " exclaimed Clara. " How dismal it must have been now ! "

" Oh," replied Grandfather, " a gay throng of officers had now come back to the British Coffee House ; so that the old chair had no lack of mirthful company. Soon after General Gage became governor a great many troops had arrived, and were encamped upon the Common. Boston was now a garrisoned and fortified town ; for the general had built a battery across the Neck, on the road to Roxbury, and placed guards for its defence. Everything looked as if a civil war were close at hand."

" Did the people make ready to fight ? " asked Charley.

" A Continental Congress assembled at Philadelphia," said Grandfather, " and proposed such measures as they thought most conducive to the public good. A Provincial Congress was likewise chosen in Massachusetts. They exhorted the people to arm and discipline themselves. A great number of minutemen were enrolled. The Americans called them minute-men, because they engaged to be ready to fight at a minute's warning. The English officers laughed, and said that the name was a very proper one, because the minute-men would run away the minute they saw the enemy. Whether they would fight or run was soon to be proved."

Grandfather told the children that the first open resistance offered to the British troops, in the province of Massachusetts, was at Salem. Colonel Timothy Pickering, with thirty or forty militia-men, prevented the English colonel, Leslie, with four times as many regular soldiers, from taking possession of some military stores. No blood was shed on this occasion ; but soon afterward it began to flow.

General Gage sent eight hundred soldiers to Concord, about eighteen miles from Boston, to destroy some ammunition and provisions which the colonists had collected there. They set out on their march on the evening of the 18th of April, 1775. The next morning, the general sent Lord Percy with nine hundred men to strengthen the troops that had gone before. All that day the inhabitants of Boston heard various rumors. Some said that the British were making great slaughter among our countrymen. Others affirmed that every man had turned out with his musket, and that not a single soldier would ever get back to Boston.

" It was after sunset," continued Grandfather, " when the troops, who had marched forth so proudly, were seen entering Charlestown. They were covered with dust, and so hot and weary that their tongues hung out of their mouths. Many of them were faint with wounds. They had not all returned. Nearly three hundred were strewn, dead or dying, along the road from Concord. The yeomanry had risen upon the invaders and driven them back."

" Was this the battle of Lexington ? " asked Charley.

" Yes," replied Grandfather ; " it was so called, because the British, without provocation, had fired upon a party of minute-men, near Lexington meeting-house, and killed eight of them. That fatal volley, which was fired by order of Major Pitcairn, began the war of the Revolution."

About this time, if Grandfather had been correctly informed, our chair disappeared from the British Coffee House. The manner of its departure cannot be satisfactorily ascertained. Perhaps the keeper of the

Coffee House turned it out of doors on account of its old-fashioned aspect. Perhaps he sold it as a curiosity. Perhaps it was taken, without leave, by some person who regarded it as public property because it had once figured under Liberty Tree. Or perhaps the old chair, being of a peaceable disposition, had made use of its four oaken legs and run away from the seat of war.

"It would have made a terrible clattering over the pavement," said Charley, laughing.

"Meanwhile," continued Grandfather, "during the mysterious non-appearance of our chair, an army of twenty thousand men had started up and come to the siege of Boston. General Gage and his troops were cooped up within the narrow precincts of the peninsula. On the 17th of June, 1775, the famous battle of Bunker Hill was fought. Here General Warren fell. The British got the victory, indeed, but with the loss of more than a thousand officers and men."

"O Grandfather," cried Charley, "you must tell us about that famous battle."

"No, Charley," said Grandfather, "I am not like other historians. Battles shall not hold a prominent place in the history of our quiet and comfortable old chair. But to-morrow evening, Laurence, Clara, and yourself, and dear little Alice too, shall visit the Diorama of Bunker Hill. There you shall see the whole business, the burning of Charlestown and all, with your own eyes, and hear the cannon and musketry with your own ears."

CHAPTER VIII.

THE next evening but one, when the children had
given Grandfather a full account of the Diorama of
Bunker Hill, they entreated him not to keep them
any longer in suspense about the fate of his chair.
The reader will recollect that, at the last accounts, it
had trotted away upon its poor old legs nobody knew
whither. But, before gratifying their curiosity, Grandfather found it necessary to say something about public events.

The Continental Congress, which was assembled at
Philadelphia, was composed of delegates from all the
colonies. They had now appointed George Washington, of Virginia, to be commander-in-chief of all the
American armies. He was, at that time, a member of
Congress; but immediately left Philadelphia, and began his journey to Massachusetts. On the 3d of July,
1775, he arrived at Cambridge, and took command of
the troops which were besieging General Gage.

" O Grandfather," exclaimed Laurence, " it makes
my heart throb to think what is coming now. We
are to see General Washington himself."

The children crowded around Grandfather and
looked earnestly into his face. Even little Alice opened
her sweet blue eyes, with her lips apart, and almost
held her breath to listen; so instinctive is the reverence of childhood for the father of his country. Grandfather paused a moment; for he felt as if it might be
irreverent to introduce the hallowed shade of Washing-

ton into a history where an ancient elbow-chair occupied the most prominent place. However, he determined to proceed with his narrative, and speak of the hero when it was needful, but with an unambitious simplicity.

So Grandfather told his auditors, that, on General Washington's arrival at Cambridge, his first care was to reconnoitre the British troops with his spy-glass, and to examine the condition of his own army. He found that the American troops amounted to about fourteen thousand men. They were extended all round the peninsula of Boston, a space of twelve miles, from the high grounds of Roxbury on the right to Mystic River on the left. Some were living in tents of sail-cloth, some in shanties rudely constructed of boards, some in huts of stone or turf with curious windows and doors of basket-work.

In order to be near the centre and oversee the whole of this wide-stretched army, the commander-in-chief made his headquarters at Cambridge, about half a mile from the colleges. A mansion-house, which perhaps had been the country seat of some tory gentleman, was provided for his residence.

" When General Washington first entered this mansion," said Grandfather, "he was ushered up the staircase and shown into a handsome apartment. He sat down in a large chair, which was the most conspicuous object in the room. The noble figure of Washington would have done honor to a throne. As he sat there, with his hand resting on the hilt of his sheathed sword, which was placed between his knees, his whole aspect well befitted the chosen man on whom his country leaned for the defence of her dearest rights. America seemed safe under his protection. His face was grander than any sculptor had ever wrought in

marble; none could behold him without awe and reverence. Never before had the lion's head at the summit of the chair looked down upon such a face and
form as Washington's."

" Why, Grandfather ! " cried Clara, clasping her
hands in amazement, " was it really so? Did General
Washington sit in our great chair ? "

" I knew how it would be," said Laurence; " I foresaw it the moment Grandfather began to speak."

Grandfather smiled. But, turning from the personal and domestic life of the illustrious leader, he
spoke of the methods which Washington adopted to
win back the metropolis of New England from the
British.

The army, when he took command of it, was without any discipline or order. The privates considered
themselves as good as their officers; and seldom
thought it necessary to obey their commands, unless
they understood the why and wherefore. Moreover,
they were enlisted for so short a period, that, as soon
as they began to be respectable soldiers, it was time to
discharge them. Then came new recruits, who had to
be taught their duty before they could be of any service. Such was the army with which Washington had
to contend against more than twenty veteran British
regiments.

Some of the men had no muskets, and almost all
were without bayonets. Heavy cannon, for battering
the British fortifications, were much wanted. There
was but a small quantity of powder and ball, few tools
to build intrenchments with, and a great deficiency of
provisions and clothes for the soldiers. Yet, in spite
of these perplexing difficulties, the eyes of the whole
people were fixed on General Washington, expecting

him to undertake some great enterprise against the hostile army.

The first thing that he found necessary was to bring his own men into better order and discipline. It is wonderful how soon he transformed this rough mob of country people into the semblance of a regular army. One of Washington's most invaluable characteristics was the faculty of bringing order out of confusion. All business with which he had any concern seemed to regulate itself as if by magic. The influence of his mind was like light gleaming through an unshaped world. It was this faculty, more than any other, that made him so fit to ride upon the storm of the Revolution when everything was unfixed and drifting about in a troubled sea.

"Washington had not been long at the head of the army," proceeded Grandfather, "before his soldiers thought as highly of him as if he had led them to a hundred victories. They knew that he was the very man whom the country needed, and the only one who could bring them safely through the great contest against the might of England. They put entire confidence in his courage, wisdom, and integrity."

"And were they not eager to follow him against the British?" asked Charley.

"Doubtless they would have gone whithersoever his sword pointed the way," answered Grandfather; "and Washington was anxious to make a decisive assault upon the enemy. But as the enterprise was very hazardous, he called a council of all the generals in the army. Accordingly they came from their different posts, and were ushered into the reception-room. The commander-in-chief arose from our great chair to greet them."

" What were their names? " asked Charley.

" There was General Artemas Ward," replied
Grandfather, " a lawyer by profession. He had
commanded the troops before Washington's arrival.
Another was General Charles Lee, who had been a
colonel in the English army, and was thought to possess vast military science. He came to the council,
followed by two or three dogs which were always at
his heels. There was General Putnam, too, who was
known all over New England by the name of Old
Put."

" Was it he who killed the wolf? " inquired Charley.

" The same," said Grandfather; " and he had done
good service in the old French War. His occupation
was that of a farmer; but he left his plough in the
furrow at the news of Lexington battle. Then there
was General Gates, who afterward gained great renown at Saratoga, and lost it again at Camden. General Greene, of Rhode Island, was likewise at the
council. Washington soon discovered him to be one
of the best officers in the army."

When the generals were all assembled, Washington
consulted them about a plan for storming the English
batteries. But it was their unanimous opinion that
so perilous an enterprise ought not to be attempted.
The army, therefore, continued to besiege Boston, preventing the enemy from obtaining supplies of provisions, but without taking any immediate measures to
get possession of the town. In this manner the summer, autumn, and winter passed away.

"Many a night, doubtless," said Grandfather,
" after Washington had been all day on horseback,
galloping from one post of the army to another, he

used to sit in our great chair, rapt in earnest thought. Had you seen him, you might have supposed that his whole mind was fixed on the blue china tiles which adorned the old-fashioned fireplace. But, in reality, he was meditating how to capture the British army, or drive it out of Boston. Once, when there was a hard frost, he formed a scheme to cross the Charles River on the ice. But the other generals could not be persuaded that there was any prospect of success."

" What were the British doing all this time ? " inquired Charley.

" They lay idle in the town," replied Grandfather. " General Gage had been recalled to England, and was succeeded by Sir William Howe. The British army and the inhabitants of Boston were now in great distress. Being shut up in the town so long, they had consumed almost all their provisions and burned up all their fuel. The soldiers tore down the Old North Church, and used its rotten boards and timbers for firewood. To heighten their distress, the small-pox broke out. They probably lost far more men by cold, hunger, and sickness than had been slain at Lexington and Bunker Hill."

" What a dismal time for the poor women and children ! " exclaimed Clara.

" At length," continued Grandfather, " in March, 1776, General Washington, who had now a good supply of powder, began a terrible cannonade and bombardment from Dorchester Heights. One of the cannon-balls which he fired into the town struck the tower of the Brattle Street Church, where it may still be seen. Sir William Howe made preparations to cross over in boats and drive the Americans from their batteries, but was prevented by a violent gale and storm.

General Washington next erected a battery on Nook's Hill, so near the enemy that it was impossible for them to remain in Boston any longer."

"Hurrah! Hurrah!" cried Charley, clapping his hands triumphantly. "I wish I had been there to see how sheepish the Englishmen looked."

And as Grandfather thought that Boston had never witnessed a more interesting period than this, when the royal power was in its death agony, he determined to take a peep into the town and imagine the feelings of those who were quitting it forever.

CHAPTER IX.

"ALAS for the poor tories!" said Grandfather. "Until the very last morning after Washington's troops had shown themselves on Nook's Hill, these unfortunate persons could not believe that the audacious rebels, as they called the Americans, would ever prevail against King George's army. But when they saw the British soldiers preparing to embark on board of the ships of war, then they knew that they had lost their country. Could the patriots have known how bitter were their regrets, they would have forgiven them all their evil deeds, and sent a blessing after them as they sailed away from their native shore."

In order to make the children sensible of the pitiable condition of these men, Grandfather singled out Peter Oliver, chief justice of Massachusetts under the crown, and imagined him walking through the streets of Boston on the morning before he left it forever.

This effort of Grandfather's fancy may be called

THE TORY'S FAREWELL.

Old Chief Justice Oliver threw on his red cloak, and placed his three-cornered hat on the top of his white wig. In this garb he intended to go forth and take a parting look at objects that had been familiar to him from his youth. Accordingly, he began his walk in the north part of the town, and soon came to Faneuil Hall. This edifice, the cradle of liberty, had been used by the British officers as a playhouse.

"Would that I could see its walls crumble to dust!" thought the chief justice; and, in the bitterness of his heart, he shook his fist at the famous hall. "There began the mischief which now threatens to rend asunder the British empire. The seditious harangues of demagogues in Faneuil Hall have made rebels of a loyal people and deprived me of my country."

He then passed through a narrow avenue and found himself in King Street, almost on the very spot which, six years before, had been reddened by the blood of the Boston massacre. The chief justice stepped cautiously, and shuddered, as if he were afraid that, even now, the gore of his slaughtered countrymen might stain his feet.

Before him rose the Town House, on the front of which were still displayed the royal arms. Within that edifice he had dispensed justice to the people in the days when his name was never mentioned without honor. There, too, was the balcony whence the trumpet had been sounded and the proclamation read to an assembled multitude, whenever a new king of England ascended the throne.

"I remember — I remember," said Chief Justice Oliver to himself, "when his present most sacred Majesty was proclaimed. Then how the people shouted! Each man would have poured out his life-blood to keep a hair of King George's head from harm. But now there is scarcely a tongue in all New England that does not imprecate curses on his name. It is ruin and disgrace to love him. Can it be possible that a few fleeting years have wrought such a change?"

It did not occur to the chief justice that nothing but the most grievous tyranny could so soon have changed the people's hearts. Hurrying from the spot, he

entered Cornhill, as the lower part of Washington
Street was then called. Opposite to the Town House
was the waste foundation of the Old North Church.
The sacrilegious hands of the British solders had torn
it down, and kindled their barrack fires with the fragments.

Farther on he passed beneath the tower of the Old
South. The threshold of this sacred edifice was worn
by the iron tramp of horses' feet; for the interior had
been used as a riding-school and rendezvous for a regiment of dragoons. As the chief justice lingered an instant at the door a trumpet sounded within, and the
regiment came clattering forth and galloped down the
street. They were proceeding to the place of embar-
kation.

" Let them go! " thought the chief justice, with
somewhat of an old Puritan feeling in his breast.
" No good can come of men who desecrate the house
of God."

He went on a few steps farther, and paused before
the Province House. No range of brick stores had
then sprung up to hide the mansion of the royal governors from public view. It had a spacious court-
yard, bordered with trees, and enclosed with a wrought-
iron fence. On the cupola that surmounted the edifice was the gilded figure of an Indian chief, ready to
let fly an arrow from his bow. Over the wide front
door was a balcony, in which the chief justice had
often stood when the governor and high officers of the
province showed themselves to the people.

While Chief Justice Oliver gazed sadly at the Province House, before which a sentinel was pacing, the
double leaves of the door were thrown open, and Sir
William Howe made his appearance. Behind him

came a throng of officers, whose steel scabbards clattered against the stones as they hastened down the court-yard. Sir William Howe was a dark-complexioned man, stern and haughty in his deportment. He stepped as proudly in that hour of defeat as if he were going to receive the submission of the rebel general.

The chief justice bowed and accosted him.

"This is a grievous hour for both of us, Sir William," said he.

"Forward! gentlemen," said Sir William Howe to the officers who attended him; "we have no time to hear lamentations now."

And, coldly bowing, he departed. Thus the chief justice had a foretaste of the mortifications which the exiled New-Englanders afterwards suffered from the haughty Britons. They were despised even by that country which they had served more faithfully than their own.

A still heavier trial awaited Chief Justice Oliver, as he passed onward from the Province House. He was recognized by the people in the street. They had long known him as the descendant of an ancient and honorable family. They had seen him sitting in his scarlet robes upon the judgment-seat. All his life long, either for the sake of his ancestors or on account of his own dignified station and unspotted character, he had been held in high respect. The old gentry of the province were looked upon almost as noblemen while Massachusetts was under royal government.

But now all hereditary reverence for birth and rank was gone. The inhabitants shouted in derision when they saw the venerable form of the old chief justice. They laid the wrongs of the country and their own sufferings during the siege — their hunger, cold, and sickness — partly to his charge and to that of his brother Andrew and his kinsman Hutchinson. It was by their advice that the king had acted in all the colonial troubles. But the day of recompense was come.

"See the old tory!" cried the people, with bitter laughter. "He is taking his last look at us. Let him show his white wig among us an hour hence, and we'll give him a coat of tar and feathers!"

The chief justice, however, knew that he need fear no violence so long as the British troops were in possession of the town. But, alas! it was a bitter thought that he should leave no loving memory behind him. His forefathers, long after their spirits left the earth, had been honored in the affectionate remembrance of the people. But he, who would henceforth be dead to his native land, would have no epitaph save scornful and vindictive words. The old man wept.

"They curse me, they invoke all kinds of evil on my head!" thought he, in the midst of his tears. "But, if they could read my heart, they would know that I love New England well. Heaven bless her, and bring her again under the rule of our gracious king! A blessing, too, on these poor, misguided people!"

The chief justice flung out his hands with a gesture, as if he were bestowing a parting benediction on his countrymen. He had now reached the southern portion of the town, and was far within the range of cannon-shot from the American batteries. Close beside him was the broad stump of a tree, which appeared to have been recently cut down. Being weary and heavy at heart, he was about to sit down upon the stump.

Suddenly it flashed upon his recollection that this

was the stump of Liberty Tree! The British soldiers had cut it down, vainly boasting that they could as easily overthrow the liberties of America. Under its shadowy branches, ten years before, the brother of Chief Justice Oliver had been compelled to acknowledge the supremacy of the people by taking the oath which they prescribed. This tree was connected with all the events that had severed America from England.

"Accursed tree!" cried the chief justice, gnashing his teeth; for anger overcame his sorrow. "Would that thou hadst been left standing till Hancock, Adams, and every other traitor, were hanged upon thy branches! Then fitly mightest thou have been hewn down and cast into the flames."

He turned back, hurried to Long Wharf without looking behind him, embarked with the British troops for Halifax, and never saw his country more. Throughout the remainder of his days Chief Justice Oliver was agitated with those same conflicting emotions that had tortured him while taking his farewell walk through the streets of Boston. Deep love and fierce resentment burned in one flame within his breast. Anathemas struggled with benedictions. He felt as if one breath of his native air would renew his life, yet would have died rather than breathe the same air with rebels. And such likewise were the feelings of the other exiles, a thousand in number, who departed with the British army. Were they not the most unfortunate of men?

"The misfortunes of those exiled tories," observed Laurence, "must have made them think of the poor exiles of Acadia."

" They had a sad time of it, I suppose," said Charley. " But I choose to rejoice with the patriots, rather than be sorrowful with the tories. Grandfather, what did General Washington do now? "

" As the rear of the British army embarked from the wharf," replied Grandfather, " General Washington's troops marched over the Neck, through the fortification gates, and entered Boston in triumph. And now, for the first time since the Pilgrims landed, Massachusetts was free from the dominion of England. May she never again be subjected to foreign rule, — never again feel the rod of oppression! "

" Dear Grandfather," asked little Alice, " did General Washington bring our chair back to Boston? "

" I know not how long the chair remained at Cambridge," said Grandfather. " Had it stayed there till this time, it could not have found a better or more appropriate shelter. The mansion which General Washington occupied is still standing, and his apartments have since been tenanted by several eminent men. Governor Everett, while a professor in the University, resided there. So at an after period did Mr. Sparks, whose invaluable labors have connected his name with the immortality of Washington. And at this very time a venerable friend and contemporary of your Grandfather, after long pilgrimages beyond the sea, has set up his staff of rest at Washington's headquarters."

" You mean Professor Longfellow, Grandfather," said Laurence. "Oh, how I should love to see the author of those beautiful VOICES OF THE NIGHT! "

" We will visit him next summer," answered Grandfather, " and take Clara and little Alice with us, — and Charley, too, if he will be quiet."

CHAPTER X.

WHEN Grandfather resumed his narrative the next evening, he told the children that he had some difficulty in tracing the movements of the chair during a short period after General Washington's departure from Cambridge.

Within a few months, however, it made its appearance at a shop in Boston, before the door of which was seen a striped pole. In the interior was displayed a stuffed alligator, a rattlesnake's skin, a bundle of Indian arrows, an old-fashioned matchlock gun, a walking-stick of Governor Winthrop's, a wig of old Cotton Mather's, and a colored print of the Boston massacre. In short, it was a barber's shop, kept by a Mr. Pierce, who prided himself on having shaved General Washington, Old Put, and many other famous persons.

"This was not a very dignified situation for our venerable chair," continued Grandfather; "but, you know, there is no better place for news than a barber's shop. All the events of the Revolutionary War were heard of there sooner than anywhere else. People used to sit in the chair, reading the newspaper, or talking, and waiting to be shaved, while Mr. Pierce, with his scissors and razor, was at work upon the heads or chins of his other customers."

"I am sorry the chair could not betake itself to some more suitable place of refuge," said Laurence. "It was old now, and must have longed for quiet. Besides, after it had held Washington in its arms, it ought not to have been compelled to receive all the world. It should have been put into the pulpit of the Old South Church, or some other consecrated place."

"Perhaps so," answered Grandfather. "But the chair, in the course of its varied existence, had grown so accustomed to general intercourse with society, that I doubt whether it would have contented itself in the pulpit of the Old South. There it would have stood solitary, or with no livelier companion than the silent organ, in the opposite gallery, six days out of seven. I incline to think that it had seldom been situated more to its mind than on the sanded floor of the snug little barber's shop."

Then Grandfather amused his children and himself with fancying all the different sorts of people who had occupied our chair while they awaited the leisure of the barber.

There was the old clergyman, such as Dr. Chauncey, wearing a white wig, which the barber took from his head and placed upon a wig-block. Half an hour, perhaps, was spent in combing and powdering this reverend appendage to a clerical skull. There, too, were officers of the continental army, who required their hair to be pomatumed and plastered, so as to give them a bold and martial aspect. There, once in a while, was seen the thin, care-worn, melancholy visage of an old tory, with a wig that, in times long past, had perhaps figured at a Province House ball. And there, not unfrequently, sat the rough captain of a privateer, just returned from a successful cruise, in which he had captured half a dozen richly laden vessels belonging to King George's subjects. And sometimes a rosy little school-boy climbed into our chair, and sat staring, with wide-open eyes, at the alligator, the rattlesnake, and the other curiosities of the barber's shop. His mother had sent him, with sixpence in his hand, to get his glossy curls cropped off. The incidents of the Revolution plentifully supplied the barber's customers with topics of conversation. They talked sorrowfully of the death of General Montgomery and the failure of our troops to take Quebec; for the New-Englanders were now as anxious to get Canada from the English as they had formerly been to conquer it from the French.

"But very soon," said Grandfather, "came news from Philadelphia, the most important that America had ever heard of. On the 4th of July, 1776, Congress had signed the Declaration of Independence. The thirteen colonies were now free and independent States. Dark as our prospects were, the inhabitants welcomed these glorious tidings, and resolved to perish rather than again bear the yoke of England."

"And I would perish, too!" cried Charley.

"It was a great day, — a glorious deed!" said Laurence, coloring high with enthusiasm. "And, Grandfather, I love to think that the sages in Congress showed themselves as bold and true as the soldiers in the field; for it must have required more courage to sign the Declaration of Independence than to fight the enemy in battle."

Grandfather acquiesced in Laurence's view of the matter. He then touched briefly and hastily upon the prominent events of the Revolution. The thunderstorm of war had now rolled southward, and did not again burst upon Massachusetts, where its first fury had been felt. But she contributed her full share to the success of the contest. Wherever a battle was fought, — whether at Long Island, White Plains, Trenton, Princeton, Brandywine, or Germantown, — some of her brave sons were found slain upon the field.

In October, 1777, General Burgoyne surrendered his army, at Saratoga, to the American general, Gates. The captured troops were sent to Massachusetts. Not long afterwards Dr. Franklin and other American commissioners made a treaty at Paris, by which France bound herself to assist our countrymen. The gallant Lafayette was already fighting for our freedom by the side of Washington. In 1778 a French fleet, commanded by Count d'Estaing, spent a considerable time in Boston Harbor. It marks the vicissitudes of human affairs, that the French, our ancient enemies, should come hither as comrades and brethren, and that kindred England should be our foe.

"While the war was raging in the Middle and Southern States," proceeded Grandfather, "Massachusetts had leisure to settle a new constitution of government instead of the royal charter. This was done in 1780. In the same year John Hancock, who had been president of Congress, was chosen governor of the State. He was the first whom the people had elected since the days of old Simon Bradstreet."

"But, Grandfather, who had been governor since the British were driven away?" inquired Laurence. "General Gage and Sir William Howe were the last whom you have told us of."

"There had been no governor for the last four years," replied Grandfather. "Massachusetts had been ruled by the Legislature, to whom the people paid obedience of their own accord. It is one of the most remarkable circumstances in our history, that, when the charter government was overthrown by the war, no anarchy nor the slightest confusion ensued.

This was a great honor to the people. But now Hancock was proclaimed governor by sound of trumpet; and there was again a settled government."

Grandfather again adverted to the progress of the war. In 1781 General Greene drove the British from the Southern States. In October of the same year General Washington compelled Lord Cornwallis to surrender his army, at Yorktown, in Virginia. This was the last great event of the Revolutionary contest. King George and his ministers perceived that all the might of England could not compel America to renew her allegiance to the crown. After a great deal of discussion, a treaty of peace was signed in September, 1783.

"Now, at last," said Grandfather, "after weary years of war, the regiments of Massachusetts returned in peace to their families. Now the stately and dignified leaders, such as General Lincoln and General Knox, with their powdered hair and their uniforms of blue and buff, were seen moving about the streets."

"And little boys ran after them, I suppose," remarked Charley; "and the grown people bowed respectfully."

"They deserved respect; for they were good men as well as brave," answered Grandfather. "Now, too, the inferior officers and privates came home to seek some peaceful occupation. Their friends remembered them as slender and smooth-cheeked young men; but they returned with the erect and rigid mien of disciplined soldiers. Some hobbled on crutches and wooden legs; others had received wounds, which were still rankling in their breasts. Many, alas! had fallen in battle, and perhaps were left unburied on the bloody field."

" The country must have been sick of war," observed Laurence.

"One would have thought so," said Grandfather. "Yet only two or three years elapsed before the folly of some misguided men caused another mustering of soldiers. This affair was called Shays's war, because a Captain Shays was the chief leader of the insurgents."

" O Grandfather, don't let there be another war ! " cried little Alice, piteously.

Grandfather comforted his dear little girl by assuring her that there was no great mischief done. Shays's war happened in the latter part of 1786 and the beginning of the following year. Its principal cause was the badness of times. The State of Massachusetts, in its public capacity, was very much in debt. So likewise were many of the people. An insurrection took place, the object of which seems to have been to interrupt the course of law and get rid of debts and taxes.

James Bowdoin, a good and able man, was now governor of Massachusetts. He sent General Lincoln, at the head of four thousand men, to put down the insurrection. This general, who had fought through several hard campaigns in the Revolution, managed matters like an old soldier, and totally defeated the rebels at the expense of very little blood.

" There is but one more public event to be recorded in the history of our chair," proceeded Grandfather. " In the year 1794 Samuel Adams was elected governor of Massachusetts. I have told you what a distinguished patriot he was, and how much he resembled the stern old Puritans. Could the ancient freemen of Massachusetts who lived in the days of the first charter have arisen from their graves, they would probably have voted for Samuel Adams to be governor."

" Well, Grandfather, I hope he sat in our chair," said Clara.

" He did," replied Grandfather. " He had long been in the habit of visiting the barber's shop, where our venerable chair, philosophically forgetful of its former dignities, had now spent nearly eighteen not uncomfortable years. Such a remarkable piece of furniture, so evidently a relic of long-departed times, could not escape the notice of Samuel Adams. He made minute researches into its history, and ascertained what a succession of excellent and famous people had occupied it."

" How did he find it out?" asked Charley; "for I suppose the chair could not tell its own history."

" There used to be a vast collection of ancient letters and other documents in the tower of the Old South Church," answered Grandfather. " Perhaps the history of our chair was contained among these. At all events, Samuel Adams appears to have been well acquainted with it. When he became governor, he felt that he could have no more honorable seat than that which had been the ancient chair of state. He therefore purchased it for a trifle, and filled it worthily for three years as governor of Massachusetts."

" And what next?" asked Charley.

" That is all," said Grandfather, heaving a sigh; for he could not help being a little sad at the thought that his stories must close here. "Samuel Adams died in 1803, at the age of above threescore and ten. He was a great patriot, but a poor man. At his death he left scarcely property enough to pay the expenses of his funeral. This precious chair, among his other effects, was sold at auction; and your Grandfather, who was then in the strength of his years, became the purchaser."

Laurence, with a mind full of thoughts that struggled for expression but could find none, looked steadfastly at the chair.

He had now learned all its history, yet was not satisfied.

"Oh, how I wish that the chair could speak!" cried he. "After its long intercourse with mankind, — after looking upon the world for ages, — what lessons of golden wisdom it might utter! It might teach a private person how to lead a good and happy life, or a statesman how to make his country prosperous."

CHAPTER XI.

GRANDFATHER was struck by Laurence's idea that the historic chair should utter a voice, and thus pour forth the collected wisdom of two centuries. The old gentleman had once possessed no inconsiderable share of fancy; and even now its fading sunshine occasionally glimmered among his more sombre reflections.

As the history of his chair had exhausted all his facts, Grandfather determined to have recourse to fable. So, after warning the children that they must not mistake this story for a true one, he related what we shall call

GRANDFATHER'S DREAM.

Laurence and Clara, where were you last night? Where were you, Charley, and dear little Alice? You had all gone to rest, and left old Grandfather to meditate alone in his great chair. The lamp had grown so dim that its light hardly illuminated the alabaster shade. The wood-fire had crumbled into heavy embers, among which the little flames danced, and quivered, and sported about like fairies.

And here sat Grandfather all by himself. He knew that it was bedtime; yet he could not help longing to hear your merry voices, or to hold a comfortable chat with some old friend; because then his pillow would be visited by pleasant dreams. But, as neither children nor friends were at hand, Grandfather leaned back in the great chair and closed his eyes, for the sake of meditating more profoundly.

And, when Grandfather's meditations had grown very profound indeed, he fancied that he heard a sound over his head, as if somebody were preparing to speak.

"Hem!" it said, in a dry, husky tone. "H-e-m! Hem!"

As Grandfather did not know that any person was in the room, he started up in great surprise, and peeped hither and thither, behind the chair, and into the recess by the fireside, and at the dark nook yonder near the bookcase. Nobody could he see.

"Poh!" said Grandfather to himself, "I must have been dreaming."

But, just as he was going to resume his seat, Grandfather happened to look at the great chair. The rays of firelight were flickering upon it in such a manner that it really seemed as if its oaken frame were all alive. What! did it not move its elbow? There, too! It certainly lifted one of its ponderous fore legs, as if it had a notion of drawing itself a little nearer to the fire. Meanwhile the lion's head nodded at Grandfather with as polite and sociable a look as a lion's visage, carved in oak, could possibly be expected to assume. Well, this is strange!

"Good evening, my old friend," said the dry and husky voice, now a little clearer than before. "We have been intimately acquainted so long that I think it high time we have a chat together."

Grandfather was looking straight at the lion's head, and could not be mistaken in supposing that it moved its lips. So here the mystery was all explained.

"I was not aware," said Grandfather, with a civil salutation to his oaken companion, "that you possessed the faculty of speech. Otherwise I should often have been glad to converse with such a solid, useful, and substantial if not brilliant member of society."

"Oh!" replied the ancient chair, in a quiet and easy tone, for it had now cleared its throat of the dust of ages, "I am naturally a silent and incommunicative sort of character. Once or twice in the course of a century I unclose my lips. When the gentle Lady Arbella departed this life I uttered a groan. When the honest mint-master weighed his plump daughter against the pine-tree shillings I chuckled audibly at the joke. When old Simon Bradstreet took the place of the tyrant Andros I joined in the general huzza, and capered on my wooden legs for joy. To be sure, the by-standers were so fully occupied with their own feelings that my sympathy was quite unnoticed."

"And have you often held a private chat with your friends?" asked Grandfather.

"Not often," answered the chair. "I once talked with Sir William Phipps, and communicated my ideas about the witchcraft delusion. Cotton Mather had several conversations with me, and derived great benefit from my historical reminiscences. In the days of the Stamp Act I whispered in the ear of Hutchinson, bidding him to remember what stock his countrymen were descended of, and to think whether the spirit of their forefathers had utterly departed from them. The last man whom I favored with a colloquy was that stout old republican, Samuel Adams."

"And how happens it," inquired Grandfather, "that there is no record nor tradition of your conversational abilities? It is an uncommon thing to meet with a chair that can talk."

"Why, to tell you the truth," said the chair, giving itself a hitch nearer to the hearth, "I am not apt to

choose the most suitable moments for unclosing my
lips. Sometimes I have inconsiderately begun to speak,
when my occupant, lolling back in my arms, was inclined to take an after-dinner nap. Or perhaps the
impulse to talk may be felt at midnight, when the
lamp burns dim and the fire crumbles into decay, and
the studious or thoughtful man finds that his brain is
in a mist. Oftenest I have unwisely uttered my wisdom in the ears of sick persons, when the inquietude
of fever made them toss about upon my cushion. And
so it happens, that though my words make a pretty
strong impression at the moment, yet my auditors invariably remember them only as a dream. I should
not wonder if you, my excellent friend, were to do the
same to-morrow morning."

"Nor I either," thought Grandfather to himself.

However, he thanked this respectable old chair for beginning the conversation, and begged to know whether
it had anything particular to communicate.

"I have been listening attentively to your narrative
of my adventures," replied the chair; "and it must be
owned that your correctness entitles you to be held up
as a pattern to biographers. Nevertheless, there are
a few omissions which I should be glad to see supplied.
For instance, you make no mention of the good knight
Sir Richard Saltonstall, nor of the famous Hugh
Peters, nor of those old regicide judges, Whalley,
Goffe, and Dixwell. Yet I have borne the weight of
all those distinguished characters at one time or another."

Grandfather promised amendment if ever he should
have an opportunity to repeat his narrative. The good
old chair, which still seemed to retain a due regard for
outward appearance, then reminded him how long a

time had passed since it had been provided with a new cushion. It likewise expressed the opinion that the oaken figures on its back would show to much better advantage by the aid of a little varnish.

"And I have had a complaint in this joint," continued the chair, endeavoring to lift one of its legs, "ever since Charley trundled his wheelbarrow against me."

"It shall be attended to," said Grandfather. "And now, venerable chair, I have a favor to solicit. During an existence of more than two centuries you have had a familiar intercourse with men who were esteemed the wisest of their day. Doubtless, with your capacious understanding, you have treasured up many an invaluable lesson of wisdom. You certainly have had time enough to guess the riddle of life. Tell us, poor mortals, then, how we may be happy."

The lion's head fixed its eyes thoughtfully upon the fire, and the whole chair assumed an aspect of deep meditation. Finally it beckoned to Grandfather with its elbow, and made a step sideways towards him, as if it had a very important secret to communicate.

"As long as I have stood in the midst of human affairs," said the chair, with a very oracular enunciation, "I have constantly observed that JUSTICE, TRUTH, and LOVE are the chief ingredients of every happy life."

"Justice, Truth, and Love!" exclaimed Grandfather. "We need not exist two centuries to find out that these qualities are essential to our happiness. This is no secret. Every human being is born with the instinctive knowledge of it."

"Ah!" cried the chair, drawing back in surprise. "From what I have observed of the dealings of man with man, and nation with nation, I never should have suspected that they knew this all-important secret. And, with this eternal lesson written in your soul, do you ask me to sift new wisdom for you out of my petty existence of two or three centuries ? "

" But, my dear chair " — said Grandfather.

" Not a word more," interrupted the chair ; " here I close my lips for the next hundred years. At the end of that period, if I shall have discovered any new precepts of happiness better than what Heaven has already taught you, they shall assuredly be given to the world."

In the energy of its utterance the oaken chair seemed to stamp its foot, and trod (we hope unintentionally) upon Grandfather's toe. The old gentleman started, and found that he had been asleep in the great chair, and that his heavy walking-stick had fallen down across his foot.

" Grandfather," cried little Alice, clapping her hands, " you must dream a new dream every night about our chair ! "

Laurence, and Clara, and Charley said the same. But the good old gentleman shook his head, and declared that here ended the history, real or fabulous, of GRANDFATHER'S CHAIR.

𝕿𝖍𝖊 𝕽𝖎𝖛𝖊𝖗𝖘𝖎𝖉𝖊 𝕻𝖗𝖊𝖘𝖘

Electrotyped and printed by H. O. Houghton & Co.
Cambridge, Mass., U. S. A.